Christian Kaunert • Bhupinder Singh
Rhishikesh Dave • Sally Lukose • Anjali Raghav
Editors

Artificial Intelligence for Global Counter-Terrorism

Utilizing Deep Learning and Innovative Strategies

Springer

Editors
Christian Kaunert
School of Law and Government
Dublin City University
Dublin, Ireland

Rhishikesh Dave
Sharda University
Greater Noida, Uttar Pradesh, India

Anjali Raghav
Sharda University
Greater Noida, Uttar Pradesh, India

Bhupinder Singh
Sharda University
Greater Noida, Uttar Pradesh, India

Sally Lukose
Sharda University
Greater Noida, Uttar Pradesh, India

ISSN 2948-2283 ISSN 2948-2291 (electronic)
Contributions to Security and Defence Studies
ISBN 978-3-031-99234-6 ISBN 978-3-031-99235-3 (eBook)
https://doi.org/10.1007/978-3-031-99235-3

This Springer imprint is published by the registered company Springer Nature Switzerland AG
The registered company address is: Gewerbestrasse 11, 6330 Cham, Switzerland

Contributions to Security and Defence Studies

This book series offers an outlet for cutting-edge research on all areas of security and defence studies. Contributions to Security and Defence Studies (CSDS) welcomes theoretically sound and empirically robust monographs, edited volumes and handbooks from various disciplines and approaches on topics such as international security studies, securitization, proliferation and arms control, military studies, strategic studies, terrorism and counter-terrorism, defence and military economics, economic security, defence technologies, cyber-warfare, cyberdefence, military applications of artificial intelligence, security policies, policing and security, political violence, and crisis and disaster management.

All titles in this series are peer-reviewed.

Preface

The rapid pace of development of artificial intelligence is bringing about transformational changes in a range of fields and nowhere can its impact be felt more acutely and contentiously, than in the field of global counter-terrorism. This edited book "*Artificial Intelligence for Global Counter-Terrorism: Utilizing Deep Learning and Innovative Strategies*" is timely and provides value to academia by exploring the convergence of leading-edge technology innovation and the enduring and dynamic threat of terrorism in the Information Age. The book brings together a diverse group of experts from the fields of artificial intelligence, security studies, international law, ethics, and policy. The chapters evolve issues around the development of deep learning, natural language processing, computer vision, and predictive analytics for the purpose of identifying, disrupting, and preventing terrorist operations in physical and cyberspaces. Alongside the technological potential, the book provocatively explores legal, ethical, and operational challenges, highlighting instances in which AI systems deployed in sensitive national security contexts fall short of issues of privacy and civil liberties, discrimination and bias, and the potential impact on international norms.

The book contributes to the global efforts in solving the AI ethics and governance problem in counter-terrorism by equipping and enabling decision-makers, security practitioners, researchers, and technologists to build trust in the positive use of AI and to promote the use of AI techniques in counter-terrorism in a right-respecting and human rights supporting manner. The book tackles pressing questions related to cross-border data flows, automated surveillance, misinformation campaigns, and the place of AI in intelligence work and threat assessment. There is an urgent requirement for a technology-enabled framework that integrates the functionality of AI-based solutions focusing on an ethical-legislative perspective. We trust this book will spur a constructive conversation, an ethical response, and joint action on the way to enhancing global security in a manner that also respects democratic values and human rights. We thank all the contributors who have provided their experiences and knowledge and believe that readers will appreciate this collection as being insightful, practical, and visionary.

Greater Noida, India
11 May 2025

Bhupinder Singh

Contents

Artificial Intelligence and Drone Technology in Counterterrorism

Swapnil Shankhwar and Gopa Mahali

Abstract In this era of technologies like artificial intelligence (AI) and drone technology, where they both converge in counterterrorism (CT) and other industries, AI-enabled drones are assumed to be on the rise while being used heavily for different applications like counterterrorism, city planning, logistics and agriculture. The great thing about today's drones is the strong equipment of sensors, cameras and navigators that can perform tasks which could not be done before or proved difficult to achieve. Through the application of artificial intelligence, drones now can fly on their own, process huge amounts of data in real time and take intelligent decisions, thus making them much more powerful than they already were before. The ever-growing possibilities alongside the applicability present in today's world such as cloud computing, Internet of Things (IoT) and 5G connectivity allow for greater complexity in drones. AI-powered drones can be used in counterterrorism missions, providing faster reaction times, greater situational awareness and reduced risk to human soldiers. With accelerating growth in technology, in the near future artificial intelligence-led drones are going to attain significance in the growth of smart cities, optimisation of logistics and protection of the public. The deployment of advanced AI-enabled drones will, therefore, revolutionise counterterrorism by empowering security experts to deal effectively with emerging threats. To some extent, the combination of technology using artificial intelligence and drone technology is changing paradigms in the way challenging tasks across most industries are being accomplished. Counterterrorism and other military operations involve a great level of input from AI-powered drones into various fields.

S. Shankhwar (✉)
Dr. Ram Manohar Lohiya National Law University, Lucknow, India

G. Mahali
West Bengal National University for Juridical Sciences, Kolkata, India

C. Kaunert et al. (eds.), *Artificial Intelligence for Global Counter-Terrorism*, Contributions to Security and Defence Studies,
https://doi.org/10.1007/978-3-031-99235-3_1

1 Introduction

Terrorist attacks have generally been based on weapons and materials that are readily available. In the United States, two of the biggest terrorist events in U.S. history, the 1995 Oklahoma City bombing and the September 11, 2001, attacks were carried out using materials obtained through legal channels for the most part. These attacks needed actual person, and personal menace, typically brought about their capture or fatalities. Yet drones entirely break that paradigm. Drones permit terrorists to assault without being themselves on the ground. This has decreased the chances of detection, increased anonymity and allowed the possibility to extend the geographical area of targets which may otherwise be far too difficult to operate [1].

One of the main aims of terrorism is to instil fear and insecurity in a population or government, probably in the expectation of political flexibility or to weaken institutions. Drones inherent in them is quite able to be tools for this goal. They also have standoff which allows operator to be at some distance from assault point. This gap provides for the assailant protection as well as prevention of tracking and arrest processes. Drones may be used with surveillance gear to gather intelligence or might be armed with explosives for precise assault. The ability for new tactics of swarming, deploying multiple drones doing all at the same time allows for swamping of government or emergency responders that goes much greater than attack [2].

Moreover, as the technology of the drones improves and becomes more prevalent, the qualification for flying them has died down. Many latest drones are equipped with autonomous flight routes, GPS navigation, remote control via cell phones, etc. This convenience enables terrorists a shorter training than needed and decreases the barrier to carrying complex operations. Psychological effect of the usage of drones is significant. The uncertainty, speed and range of drones can create a perpetual sense of unease in individuals and in officials of government. The mere fact of such a threat may be enough to give rise to fear and change public behaviour, which fits perfectly with the objectives of terrorists [3].

2 Past Development and Adaptation of Drones in Terrorism

The employment of drones, or unmanned aerial vehicles (UAVs), has evolved significantly over the years, from original military use to a versatile, more commercially available technology for private, commercial and unfortunately also for terrorist purposes. Drones were initially created with the purpose of military use and its first application was in the hands of professional military forces during World War II. When it came to serving as armament weapons in this era, their effectiveness was insignificant but their aptitude in aerial surveillance and intelligence gathering became apparent as the Korean War escalated. In the next decades, like in several military developments, the capabilities of drones would gradually move into the civilian arena. Advances in technology, in particular with battery energy capacity, motor propulsion and power density, have facilitated that man (and company) now can avail upon demand, upon order "Blue Drones" [4].

In the first decade of these two millennia, the use of drones experienced a change. Improvement in energy storage and propulsion allowed for the creation of even smaller, more agile and cheaper drones. Many professional drones were under two feet broad, therefore portable, discreet and feasible for mass creation at a low cost. These advances made it more user-friendly for civilian use in photography, agriculture, surveying and leisure. In addition, the attributes that render drones appealing to consumers also make them attractive to terrorist organisations, which have identified their supplementary value as platforms for intelligence gathering, delivery of weaponry, and the execution of coordinated attacks [5].

Over the period of 1994–2018 more than 14 instances of ordered or attempted terrorist acts employing aerial drones could be documented, meeting a changed pattern of strategies in asymmetric warfare employed by non-state actors. One amongst the initial recorded cases was once in 1994 the Japanese cult Aum Shinrikyo tried to use remotely managed helicopter to release sarin gas. Luckily, the mission was unsuccessful due to technical issue, and the helicopter crashed in the test. Although this experiment was a partial failure, it demonstrated an early recognition that UAVs could be applied for dissemination of chemical weapons [6].

By 2013, terrorist groups had progressed and used more sophisticated tactics. Al-Qaeda allegedly planned to carry out a strike with many drones in Pakistan. That campaign highlighted the soaring aims and a tactical lookahead of terrorist teams, despite regional law enforcement officials' intervention. In 2014, the Islamic State (ISIS) has extensively employed both standard and homemade drones in its military campaigns inside Iraq and Syria. These UAVs served not only for surveillance and combat controlling but for separate attacks, transporting and deployment of bombs on anti-locations. Use of drones by ISIS was one of the first large-scale utilisation for UAV technology by a terrorist organisation showing high efficacy in psychological, as well as, tactical warfare [7].

There were two notable events in 2018 in which drone-borne terrorist attacks reached new level of sophistication so far. In January a cluster of 13 pieces of art drone struck two Syrian military facilities run by the Russians. Although the attack caused little physical damage, it demonstrated the capacity of cheap, improvised UAVs to be employed against the target in superior numbers that overwhelm defence systems. In August of the same year, two GPS-equipped drones armed with explosives were employed in a foiled assassination attempt of Venezuelan President Nicolás Maduro while giving a public speech. The capture of the drones highlighted the capabilities of UAVs in carrying out targeted political attacks, even on the high-security lives of influential leaders [8].

The acts of the terrorist groups operating drones are very diverse, and complex. Drones have been employed not only for direct explosive attacks but for information collection as well, that is, as an aerial reconnaissance to observe enemy activities, and assess the establishment of the suspected targets. Some UAVs were modified to drop grenades or improvised explosive devices (IEDs), some other types act as impactors thereby turning the drones into aerial bombs. There have been experiments to mount rocket launchers or chemical dispersal devices on drones showing up a worrying incline by terrorist groups to resort to unconventional weaponry [9].

The rapid adoption and adaptation of drone technology by both non-state actors and mainstream society exemplifies the broader phenomenon of technological democratisation, in which functions once classified become accessible to anyone for the cost of modest capital investment and basic technical training. Drone-based terrorism, the way that 'Pandora's box' has opened has been seasoned with grave challenges in the ways of containment. Advances in drone technology have been quickly matched by malicious actors seeking to incorporate these developments into their arsenals. Drones give utility, stealth and cost-effectiveness distinguishing them from traditional weapon platforms that typically require extensive infrastructure or logistical support [10].

The global spread of drone-enabled terror is also very important. In many places including Africa, Middle East, Arabian Peninsula, South East Asia, Eastern Europe and South America various non-state actors have either employed or wish to employ drone capabilities. In many countries, a combination of unstable political circumstances, unresolved long-standing conflicts, and porous borders enables the operations and strategic testing of terrorist groups. Drone strikes can be carried out from long range; it is very difficult for the authorities to find out where these strikes emanated from, or to catch them ahead of time. Also, these drones usually resemble the commercially available drones that are used legally for personal or corporate use, thereby confusing regulation and enforcement [11].

Counter-drone technologies including jamming systems, net guns as well as radar-detection networks are being developed; however, most products tend to be reactive, not really routinely available cross country. In addition, there is an immediate requirement for a more relevant legislation to do with drone creation, advertising as well as operation primarily regarding GPS features, flying independence as well as payload limitations. Governments must engage closely and authentically with partners from the private sector, including the drone manufacturers and software developers, to ensure that safety measures and tracking systems are embodied into drones at the point of sale.

As we delve deeper into the age of intelligent machines, the field of counterterrorism (CT) is about to experience a sea change. By contrast, other methods are typically location- or threat-type-specific, such as a focus on counter-radicalisation in certain circumstances and violent interdiction in others, while artificial intelligence (AI)-based counterterrorism efforts offer immense flexibility. AI and machine learning (ML) can potentially improve every part of CT. For viable understanding, the point where AI is being utilised is through the examination of its utilisation in three specific tactical segments: counter-radicalisation, awareness gathering and direct action. These areas offer a favourable environment for employing AI techniques, particularly in a way that gains operationally significant effects. This talk does not pretend to be scouting ahead or telling people what's going to happen; rather, it laughs at some insights and bumps along the path of wishing that more people would go down the road examining the concatenation of AI and CT that seems to be forming [12].

At the centre of practically all terrorist activities is an ideology, which usually relates to the belief that violence can be a suitable way to achieve political or social change. This line of reasoning assumes that one of the best anti-terror methods is the prevention of the initial radicalisation of people. Nonetheless, the counter-radicalisation is very complicated. This encompasses not only the political views of an individual but also the potential willingness for violence and the passion for their ideologies. Here, these dimensions may intersect in complex and surpassing ways. This intricacy hinders counter-radicalisation efforts. The human mind has considerable capacity for protecting against disconfirmation of beliefs. Radicalised people usually devise reasons to reject or dismiss data that contradict their views. This means spreading fake news outlets and debasing factual reporting, or selectively talking to media that supports their views. Sometimes, radicalisation may result from genuine grievances such as exclusion or systemic inequality, which, if ignored, can develop into a pretext for at least militant activity. The Internet piles on another problem by enabling an unavailable platform, allowing rapid and comprehensive distribution of extremist material. This information is often ahead of the curve and any counter-narrative that the government formulates, and difficult to stay in sync [13].

In the present digital and decentralised world, AI technologies, especially large language models (LLMs), allow for the possibility of new counter-radicalisation initiatives. Large language models can be trained on extensive counter-radicalisation sources to determine cognitive interventions that may interrupt or reverse the radicalisation process. With this data, they could assess counter-extremist propaganda to look for the traces and openings in the language around it. They will consequently create particular counter-messages in mass, publishing them on numerous websites that carry jihadist material. This tactic, attractive as it might be, has a logic, but it stops there. A major challenge is the "uncanny valley" effect when AI responses appear almost human but fail, causing discomfort to users. This issue can be diminished either by boosting AI models to manifest more than a human-like intelligent model or by exploring how to explicitly structure them as artificial agents [14].

The existence of such AI systems constitutes a total weaponry for governments. Counter-messaging is especially important here due to the fact that radicals are often sceptical of government-run media and usually rely upon alternative media networks. Even if such initiatives deter just some individuals from violence, they would constitute a significant contribution in the overall context of counter-terrorism [15].

The speedy improvement in drone innovation, primarily driven by client demand and business applications, is making a world where drones will develop to become more intelligent, in addition to being presumably even more risky. Highlighting these improvements, they have included advancements in drone size, configuration, battery technology, propulsion, sensors and onboard computing elements. These upgrades individually enhance the range, lifting capability, speed and versatility of drones, enormously increasing the abilities of both the beneficial and the malevolent utilisation of drones. Drones are greatly employed in private uses for practices like thermal camera roof inspections, thermal surveys, extensive agriculture land mapping, chemical application, disaster response, goods delivery, photography, videography and drone racing. In the amateur/enthusiast segment, people without commercial backgrounds use drones just for their personal enjoyment and because they are creatively drawn to them. That being said, the exact technical properties that lead to drones being useful in these zones are exactly the same properties that can so easily be exploited by dangerous people wanting to do some harm [16].

First, drones were expensive, gasoline-powered, radio-controlled planes used mainly as a hobby. The arrival of small, high-density batteries, powerful, efficient electric motors and tiny electronics allowed for the shift to modern quadcopters. These small drones, generally smaller than two feet, have progressively transformed into bigger multi-rotor drones with eight motors, capable of lifting up to 500 pounds (227 kg), and able to reach speeds of over 80 mph (129 kph) or travel 10 miles (16 km). Nowadays, proponents are working on creating gas-powered jet engines for miniature drones, which can achieve speeds up to 600 mph (965 kph) and fly to heights of 30,000 ft (9144 m). Some of these drones are amphibious and are ready to land on the water, which adds to their use from practical to forbidden applications [17].

Smaller drones in professional racing leagues have a top speed of 80 mph over a period of up to 5 min, and their controllers are being used by the operators with first-person view (FPV) goggles. Drones on the micro scale, small enough to fit in the hand, have been around for some time, and many of them are equipped with cameras and can carry out missions over considerable distances, often hundreds of yards, either with autopilot or under human control. These $200 microdrones pose a different risk as such by being so cheap, highly affordable, compact, lightweight and stealthy [18].

In 2020, the US Federal Aviation Administration (FAA) lifted rules on flying drones beyond a pilot's visual range and paved the way for more commercial use of drones. This improves logistical and surveillance missions but makes the task of countering armed drones controlled remotely from hidden or safe locations even harder. Simultaneously, there are other advancements with hybrid drones that work well in many different situations. For example, a lot of different models will go from land-based wheeled systems to air-based systems, and others may change from aircraft to other modes of transportation. The ultimate growth of computing power and automation significantly improves the universality and efficiency of these drones, particularly in the waterborne division, in which preceding waterborne drones could function with only constrained signal and control stations [19].

Biomimicry is a fascinating field in the development of drone technology. Engineers are creating drones that mimic the movement of the animals—birds, sea creatures and mammals—in order for them to move quietly through any terrain, respectively, and never alert people or interfere with wildlife [20]. Some models imitate the flapping of bird wings or the swimming gestures of fish, while researchers are seeking the development of synthetic feathers that can replace the conventional materials, like carbon fibre, resulting in drones that weigh less, are stronger and more efficient in terms of energy [21]. All of these advancements enabled extended, steady flying in harsh weather, plus supposedly extended drone flight times from a few minutes to greater than half an hour [22].

With some recent improvements on drone control systems, drone control has become user-friendly and can operate considerably farther. Early versions required a line of sight and worked on single-direction radio frequencies. On the other hand, the modern-day drones operate between the range of 2.4 and 5 GHz and therefore enable the bidirectional communication between the drone and the operator. This enables real-time video link from onboard cameras, providing beyond line-of-sight operation and greater control. Drone altitude can now reach 1500 ft (457 m) and can go up to five miles (8 km) high. Autonomous features are becoming more mainstream, which include self-adaption of flight stability, real-time object tracking, GPS guiding and even autonomous return upon signal loss. These drones are able to navigate set paths and solo-explore difficult areas using advanced obstacle-avoidance algorithms [23].

Systems of the optical kind have analogously made huge progress. Drones now have a typical, routine case of high-definition 4 K video, infrared imaging, night vision and face recognition. When combined with object recognition and facial recognition technology, it allows drones to recognise, track and even pop man, significantly boosting their effectiveness in surveillance and potentially causing damage.

One of the technological breakthroughs in drone warfare is the emergence of drone swarms. A swarm operates as several drones operating together to achieve a common goal, such as disabling a defensive system. In 2018, a drone swarm, 13 fixed-wing, attacked Russian military facilities in Syria, showing the effectiveness of such tactics even based on very simple means. These drones accomplished dropping bombs from a distance of 30 miles (50 km) away. Advances in the area of swarm technology have yielded drones that enable the exchange of information between each other at low-power, ad hoc Bluetooth networks. The networks enable immediate communication and decision-making amongst drones, making their accomplishment of missions more efficient and resilient [24].

The consequences are multifarious. The easily available drone components, as well as open-source plans and Internet platforms, make way for people without money or technical expertise to build do-it-yourself drones for some applications, including attacks. The growth of the drone industry is anticipated to amplify it. Global drone sales grew to $14.1 billion in 2018, and were expected to grow to $43 billion by 2024. This rise necessitates companies to improve innovation and reduce cost, resulting in drones becoming more rapid, sensible and autonomous [25].

The development of drones poses a dual-use problem for regulators, law enforcers and security bodies. Indeed, drones have the ability to impact the way that community functions in several industries, including agriculture and rescue operations; however, they can also become new devices for people or entities with an ill intention. As the drone technology marches forward, countermeasures and legal frameworks need to be developed to combat the misuse, especially against terrorism. The future of drone warfare might belong not to big, big military things but little, fast and smart devices working together in an ever-changing battlefield that should draw equal attention from both politicians and engineers [26].

3 Detection System

The rise of the militarisation of commercial drones has caused massive concern across military and civilian spaces, and as a result, an acute need for the improvement of detection and countermeasure solutions. The Federal Aviation Administration (FAA) in the United States is noting an increasing number of drones being used commercially and personally; nonetheless, current systems are incapable of monitoring/controlling the airspace, which is of use to both manned/unmanned aircraft. The FAA has proposed regulations for forcing drones of a certain weight to be fitted with radio transponders for better tracking. However, transponders are amenable to tampering or disablement, hence reducing their utility in real-world scenarios, especially those with malicious or criminal aims [27].

Drones have to be automatically and easily identified for any interdiction program to be successful. Detection technologies will be categorised into four categories: radio frequency analysis, acoustic detectors, optical systems and radar. Each of these technologies has its own strengths and weaknesses, particularly in city or dense situations. Radio frequency (RF) analysis involves monitoring the radio spectrum to find out what controls drones. This technique is good for stopping hand-piloted drones right now, but not for discovering drones operating on their own or following a routine flight path. These autonomous drones do not send real-time control commands, making them almost invisible to RF-based systems. Also, heavily populated or highly frequented areas pose an even greater impediment for signals identified and source location, since the RF spectrum becomes jammed and unreliable [28].

Acoustic detection systems rely on microphones, which are often arranged in an array to detect the specific sounds produced by drone motors and rotor blades. This technology can be effective in a perfectly controlled or near-tranquil atmosphere, but may be limited in a noisy environment such as the urban setting, industrial district or entrance to any crowded venue. Range to them is often limited, usually below 500 m (about 1640 ft). This range limitation creates many difficulties regarding what speed drones may be allowed to operate at. A drone going at 80 miles per hour (129 km per hour), makes use of 100 m in like 3 s. However, a drone going 15 miles per hour (24 km per hour), takes 15 s to safeguard the very same range. Because of the small reaction interval, acoustic detection gives only limited effectiveness depending on a number of concrete terms.

Optical detection systems, a common method, utilise video cameras and image-processing algorithms to visually identify drones using the UK Drone Detection system. These technologies frequently use machine learning to locate drone structures and flight courses. Drones flying at high speeds or small drones with small reflective surfaces pose large detection woes. Reliability of such systems goes down when these systems are operating during nighttime or when drones hide behind a disguise or are equipped to look alike with their surroundings, thus making identification and tracking at times challenging [29].

Radar is still the primary means for the far-distance detection of drones. Conventional radar is able to locate drones at distances as far as 3 km (1.9 miles) provided there is a clear line-of-sight view [30]. Even if radar is able to effectively monitor low-flying and small drones, it struggles in cluttered environments such as cities with many buildings or natural terrain with dense foliage [31]. A major problem with radar is telling apart drones and birds, as both share similar radar tendencies. Most of the conventional radar systems are not accurate in distinguishing between the two [32]. Anyway, superior millimetre-wave radar technologies can effectively overcome this limitation [33]. These algorithms can recognise the unique rotational motion of drone rotor blade motion, a trait that differentiates them from birds that flap [34].

Despite these technical advancements, the increasing application of biomimicry in UAV development creates fresh obstacles to all detection methodologies. Biomimetic drones, which employ the behaviour and appearance of avians, insects or other fauna for greater stealth, are designed to evade traditional detection means [20]. Their flat materials and removal from stiff rotor housings render them not so noticeable to radar. Moreover, their natural behaviour and reduced decibel level make both optical and acoustic sensors ineffective. Some drones are being made of synthetic feathers and flying wings, thereby causing confusion when using traditional identification methods [35]. As these technologies continue to evolve, the identification of these drones will have to use more sophisticated and networked detection systems requiring multiple sensor types to provide an all-encompassing operational perspective [36].

The underwater drones, similarly, have their own kinds of challenges when it comes to their identification. Research in this field has mostly involved applying arrays of hydrophones and subaqueous microphones to locate sources of disturbance in marine ambient noise. An invading underwater drone can precipitate large behavioural effects in marine organisms, which is able to disrupt normal acoustic signatures and activate detection mechanisms of the drone. However, similar to their aerial counterparts, acoustic detection techniques of those kinds have problems in noisy underwater environments, such as, for example, busy harbours or shipping channels [36]. Background noise of vessel engines, industrial operations and other maritime usage periodically override weak acoustic signals that underwater drones make [37].

Biomimicry, increased autonomy, better energy retention and reduced forms continually move the advantage towards the man operating the drone, over the man on defence. As drones transmogrify themselves to rise quicker, softer and become more sophisticated in autonomous navigation, the traditional surveillance platform progressively proves redundant or slow in responding. This issue is particularly concerning in locations of high risk, like military sites, crucial infrastructure areas and special events, as in a matter of seconds, cheats could cause enormous damage or danger [38].

Drone innovation and attack-detection technology are getting into a better battle. Presently utilised detection solutions, such as RF investigation, acoustic sensors, optical systems and radar, imply a layered method to drone safety and security; however, each has natural obstacles. Technologies such as millimetre-wave radar, hybrid air surveillance systems pose possibilities, yet characteristics of drones, especially of advances in biomimicry, now compete with and outpace air detection. Drone security's future will heavily depend on the fusion of multiple sensor technologies, enforceable regulatory means and continuous innovation to stay ahead of threats that are evolving very rapidly [39].

A common method to counter drones is radio frequency (RF) "jamming" between the drone and its operator or the GPS signal. RF jamming units display many sizes and mobile capabilities, from handheld devices resembling rifles to multicarrier and conditioned systems set in buildings. These systems work by sending out signals that are far above those employed by drones to cause dozens of drones to activate their lost signal protocols, descending immediately or consequently returning to a predetermined location. Nevertheless, RF jamming has shown a few honourable outcomes because of the change in drone structure and users. Different drones have different frequencies, some of which can change the frequency while flying, so a one-size-fits-all jamming solution is impossible. Besides, line-of-sight may be required for portable jammers, and accurate alignment with a moving drone can be difficult in practice. Jammers of a vast range may generate all-around interference, but they carry with them a greater potential of interfering with near gear using identical frequencies, such as Wi-Fi networking links, car locking methods, house security methods and GPS-dependent programs. This unintended disturbance is most concerning in metropolitan areas. This, in turn, also leads to anti-jamming systems under development and patent cover; thus, for example, Amazon has submitted to protect an application to patent its own delivery drones [40].

In moving from RF jamming to kinetic countermeasures, the most popular tactic is the net. Nets are preferred over bullets or other impact-type tools because of the greater contact area, making seamless snaring and incapacitating the drone's propellers more likely. Net-launching devices come in several configurations. Special purpose shotgun ammo was produced to shoot a little rifle distance up to 50 m, a close alternative for law enforcement, for police forces' security [41].

Biological entities have been studied as possible countermeasures. Wild birds of prey were first tried out as a natural kinetic potential disruptor to destroy drones in flight. As a result, practical problems such as limited work hours, territorial approaches or tendencies and sensitivities to the disturbances, roughly took this approach off the books about most features. Research is also underway to use other bird species, like pigeons, that are being trained to respond to the movement and sound of drones, maybe as such providing a flock-based deterrent. For example, the US Navy has utilised trained marine animals like dolphins and sea lions in the past to find underwater mines and underwater intrusions. These creatures might have the ability to combat underwater drones; however, they have limitations on training, predictability and deployment logistics similar to birds [42].

Although there are a myriad of potential remedies, restrictions continue. RF illegal interception is established by its limited outreach and exposure for unintended interruption; it's not acceptable for significant or final utilisation. Physical interception has a problem, particularly with the altitude and the speed at which drones might operate. Most commercial drones can go up to 1500 ft elevation, far higher than what most counter-drone tools have as a maximum range, which is less than 200 m (656 ft) [43]. The height plus speed advantage gains a large edge in being able to neutralise most countermeasure systems prior to the drone finishing its mission. The idea of employing animals for drone capture has interesting potential, but is mostly still experimental and needs more research and refinement. The ever-changing features of drone technology combined with the existing flaws of current countermeasures specify the necessity for continuous reinforcement of innovation and the combination of several methods to effectively counter drone threats [44].

4 Conclusion

The employment of artificial intelligence (AI) and drone technologies for counter-terrorism purposes marks a significant shift in global security, offering transformational capabilities but also daunting ethical, legal and operational challenges. The world is grappling with the twin-use nature of innovative technologies, which can both safeguard and pose risks to societies, making it an acute need for a balanced, cooperative and ethically informed approach.

The progress of drone technology, evolving from straightforward military devices to sophisticated AI-boosted devices, has significantly affected the development of advanced counterterrorism systems. Drones with high-definition cameras, infrared imaging and auto-piloting are giving one real-time surveillance, accuracy, targeted operations and rapid operations in adversarial environments. Artificial intelligence is actually an extension of these skills, because it analyses large data sets in order to detect trends, predict problems and make choices, with a minimum human intervention. New advances featured in things as drone swarms and biomimicry improve their worth, with security types able to carry out large-scale operations, map the land and destroy threats efficiently than ever before. Innovative methods in countering radicalisation arise from generative AI models generating their own tailored counter-narratives to counteract aggressive sequences of extremist discourse and hamper the recruitment and radicalisation efforts.

The democratisation of drone technology poses a great danger. Commercially available drones have been used by non-state actors for surveillance, explosive-yielding purposes and for psychological warfare as demonstrated by ISIS's tactical use in Iraq and Syria and the assassination attempt of Venezuela's president. The existence of autonomous technologies, GPS navigation and swarm tactics decreases the thresholds to terrorists, making it open up for asymmetrical warfare that challenges conventional defensive tactics. Detection and mitigation face persistent issues: RF jamming is ineffective against frequency-hopping drones, acoustic sensors underperform in noise-heavy environments, and radars often mistake drones for biological targets such as birds. Biomimetic drones, designed to imitate living creatures, worsen what cuts the detection of those challenges, and show the necessity of diverse sorts of sensors and adaptable AI components.

Ethical problems are significant. The application of AI in counterterrorism stokes fears about algorithmic bias, privacy erosions and accountability in autonomous decision-making. Unbridled surveillance could curtail human liberties, and any unfair AI algorithms may result in inequality in marginalised communities, where a plethora of distrust will be ignited. In the absence of any international regulatory frameworks, these difficulties become worse, making it more difficult to avoid jurisdictional and policy gaps and inconsistencies. Moreover, the outrageous expense linked to contemporary drones and AI systems generates caricatures, making poor states attractive to both terrorists and technical issues.

Addressing these challenges needs a multifaceted effort. International cooperation is necessary to help set worldwide standards for the production, sale and usage of drone technology. Safeguards need to be set out in policies such as geofencing, transponders and payload limitations and also address security risks. Second, ahead of time investment in counter-drone technologies—much more AI-augmented detection techniques, directed-energy weapons and adaptive jamming—must be enhanced to satisfy the progressing threats. Third, ethical AI frameworks have to focus on transparency, reduce bias and provide human oversight in order to show responsibility. Public-private partnerships may make technological access more democratic, foster innovation and help bridge security gaps around the globe.

Looking ahead, emerging technologies like 5G, edge computing and quantum AI are set to strengthen drone capabilities, empowering faster data processing and decentralised decision-making. However, these enhancements also carry the risk of escalating an autonomous weapons arms race. In the future, counterterrorism efforts will need to strike a fine balance between using AI and drones to safeguard countries and adhering to ethical guidelines and human rights. As new technologies reshape security domains, forward-thinking approaches, continuous innovation and open talk will be key in dealing with the challenges of this new world. The goal should be to harness AI and drones as a force for better global security and justice, not just a tool for deterrence.

References

1. Terrorism, I. of M. (US) C. on R. to the P. C. of, Butler, A. S., Panzer, A. M., & Goldfrank, L. R. (2003). *Understanding the psychological consequences of traumatic events, disasters, and terrorism*. https://www.ncbi.nlm.nih.gov/books/NBK221638/.
2. Binder, J. F., & Kenyon, J. (2022). Terrorism and the internet: How dangerous is online radicalization? *Frontiers in Psychology, 13*. https://doi.org/10.3389/FPSYG.2022.997390/FULL
3. Definition of Terrorism—Social and Political Effects—JMVH. (n.d.). Retrieved April 15, 2025, from https://jmvh.org/article/definitionof-terrorism-social-and-political-effects/.

4. Drones and Terrorism: UAVs in Modern Conflicts. (n.d.). Retrieved April 15, 2025, from https://orionpolicy.org/terrorist-use-of-drones/
5. Unmanned Aerial Vehicles & AI: Policy measures & challenges. (n.d.). Retrieved April 15, 2025, from https://www.visionofhumanity.org/preventing-terrorists-from-using-emerging-technologies/
6. On the Horizon: The Ukraine War and the Evolving Threat of Drone Terrorism—Combating Terrorism Center at West Point. (n.d.). Retrieved April 15, 2025, from https://ctc.westpoint.edu/on-the-horizon-the-ukraine-war-and-the-evolving-threat-of-drone-terrorism/.
7. The Role of Drones in Future Terrorist Attacks | AUSA. (n.d.). Retrieved April 15, 2025, from https://www.ausa.org/publications/role-drones-future-terrorist-attacks.
8. Mutschler, M., Bales, M., & Meininghaus, E. (2024). The impact of precision strike technology on the warfare of non-state armed groups: Case studies on Daesh and the Houthis. *Small Wars & Insurgencies.* https://doi.org/10.1080/09592318.2024.2319216
9. Bultmann, D. (2018). The social structure of armed groups. Reproduction and change during and after conflict. *Small Wars and Insurgencies, 29*(4), 607–628. https://doi.org/10.1080/09592318.2018.1488402
10. Kidd, C. V. (1992). The evolution of sustainability. *Journal of Agricultural and Environmental Ethics, 5*(1), 1–26. https://doi.org/10.1007/BF01965413
11. Brander, J. A. (2007). Viewpoint: Sustainability: Malthus revisited? *Canadian Journal of Economics, 40*(1), 1–38. https://doi.org/10.1111/J.1365-2966.2007.00398.X
12. Hariram, N. P., Mekha, K. B., Suganthan, V., & Sudhakar, K. (2023). Sustainalism: An integrated socio-economic-environmental model to address sustainable development and sustainability. *Sustainability, 15*(13), 10682. https://doi.org/10.3390/SU151310682
13. Boyer, R. H. W., Peterson, N. D., Arora, P., & Caldwell, K. (2016). Five approaches to social sustainability and an integrated way forward. *Sustainability, 8*(9). https://doi.org/10.3390/SU8090878
14. Wall, C. (2025). The ghost in the machine: Counterterrorism in the age of artificial intelligence. *Studies in Conflict & Terrorism*, 1–27. https://doi.org/10.1080/1057610X.2025.2475850
15. Diel, A., & Lewis, M. (2024). Deviation from typical organic voices best explains a vocal uncanny valley. *Computers in Human Behavior Reports, 14.* https://doi.org/10.1016/J.CHBR.2024.100430
16. Bures, O. (2025). The new EU Authority for anti-money laundering and countering the financing of terrorism: A paradigm shift in EU efforts to combat terrorist financing? *Studies in Conflict & Terrorism*, 1–31. https://doi.org/10.1080/1057610X.2025.2460594
17. Gierulski, M. P., & Khandelwal, B. (2021). Electric-powered aircraft. In *Aviation fuels* (pp. 271–296). Elsevier. https://doi.org/10.1016/B978-0-12-818314-4.00009-1
18. Racing Drones. (n.d.). Retrieved April 15, 2025, from https://www.smithsonianmag.com/air-space-magazine/racing-drones-180960969/.
19. Drone Racing League's new drone will go 0-80 MPH in under a second | TechCrunch. (n.d.). Retrieved April 15, 2025, from https://techcrunch.com/2017/04/06/drone-racing-leagues-new-drone-will-go-0-80-mph-in-under-a-second/.
20. Tanaka, S., Asignacion, A., Nakata, T., Suzuki, S., & Liu, H. (2022). Review of biomimetic approaches for Drones. *Drones, 6*(11), 320. https://doi.org/10.3390/DRONES6110320
21. Biomimicry and Birds – Chirp Nature Center. (n.d.). Retrieved April 17, 2025, from https://chirpforbirds.com/nature-advocacy/biomimicry-and-birds/?srsltid=AfmBOoo-yWAfzhwbIM9HXhudHZ8zKnYZj2N6oj9xVssjaJOaVuLPurRz.
22. Abeginners'guidetounderstandingDrones|bySukantKhurana|Medium.(n.d.).RetrievedApril15, 2025,fromhttps://medium.com/@sukantkhurana/a-beginners-guide-to-drones-38d215701c4e.
23. Qasim, N. H., & Jawad, A. M. (2024). 5G-enabled UAVs for energy-efficient opportunistic networking. *Heliyon, 10*(12), e32660. https://doi.org/10.1016/J.HELIYON.2024.E32660
24. Kim, S.-W., Jung, S.-W., Seo, M.-W., Park, H.-Y., & Song, J.-K. (2019). Effects of bone-specific physical activity on body composition, bone mineral density, and health-related

physical fitness in middle-aged women. *Journal of Exercise Nutrition & Biochemistry, 23*(4), 36–42. https://doi.org/10.20463/JENB.2019.0030

25. Zhou, W., Qi, J., Li, Y., & Jiang, T. (2022). A low coupling broadband MIMO Antenna for 5G using meta-surface decoupling structure. *2022 IEEE international symposium on Antennas and propagation and USNC-URSI radio science meeting, AP-S/URSI 2022—proceedings*, 1784–1785. 10.1109/AP-S/USNC-URSI47032.2022.9886406.
26. Qasim, N. H., Abu-Alshaeer, A. M. J., Jawad, H. M., Khlaponin, Y., & Nikitchyn, O. (2022). Devising a traffic control method for unmanned aerial vehicles with the use of GNB-IOT in 5G. *Eastern-European Journal of Enterprise Technologies, 3*(9–117), 53–59. https://doi.org/10.15587/1729-4061.2022.260084
27. FAA Drone Detection Testing | Federal Aviation Administration. (n.d.). Retrieved April 15, 2025, from https://www.faa.gov/newsroom/faa-drone-detection-testing.
28. Comprehensive Guide to Counter-Drone Mitigation Technologies. (n.d.). Retrieved April 15, 2025, from https://d-fendsolutions.com/cuas-mitigation/.
29. Seidaliyeva, U., Ilipbayeva, L., Taissariyeva, K., Smailov, N., & Matson, E. T. (2023). Advances and challenges in drone detection and classification techniques: A state-of-the-art review. *Sensors, 24*(1), 125. https://doi.org/10.3390/S24010125
30. Sabins, F. F. (2004). Remote sensing for energy resources. In *Encyclopedia of energy* (pp. 291–300). Elsevier. https://doi.org/10.1016/B0-12-176480-X/00272-2
31. Goodman, R., & Carrara, W. (2005). Synthetic aperture radar algorithms. In *Handbook of image and video processing* (2nd ed., pp. 1131–1153). https://doi.org/10.1016/B978-012119792-6/50127-3
32. Bole, A., Wall, A., & Norris, A. (2014). Target detection. In *Radar and ARPA manual* (pp. 139–213). https://doi.org/10.1016/B978-0-08-097752-2.00003-9
33. Coluccia, A., Parisi, G., & Fascista, A. (2020). Detection and classification of multirotor drones in radar sensor networks: A review. *Sensors, 20*(15), 1–22. https://doi.org/10.3390/S20154172
34. Uddin, Z., Altaf, M., Bilal, M., Nkenyereye, L., & Bashir, A. K. (2020). Amateur Drones detection: A machine learning approach utilizing the acoustic signals in the presence of strong interference. *Computer Communications, 154*, 236–245. https://doi.org/10.1016/j.comcom.2020.02.065
35. ICNS | Underwater Acoustic Drone Detection via Neuromorphic Models of Marine Mammal Audition. (n.d.). Retrieved April 17, 2025, from https://www.westernsydney.edu.au/icns/research_projects/open_phd_projects/underwater_acoustic_drone_detection_via_neuromorphic_models_of_marine_mammal_audition.
36. Railey, K., DiBiaso, D., & Schmidt, H. (2020). An acoustic remote sensing method for high-precision propeller rotation and speed estimation of unmanned underwater vehicles. *The Journal of the Acoustical Society of America, 148*(6), 3942–3950. https://doi.org/10.1121/10.0002954
37. McGeady, R., Runya, R. M., Dooley, J. S. G., Howe, J. A., Fox, C. J., Wheeler, A. J., Summers, G., Callaway, A., Beck, S., Brown, L. S., Dooly, G., & McGonigle, C. (2023). A review of new and existing non-extractive techniques for monitoring marine protected areas. *Frontiers in Marine Science, 10*, 1126301. https://doi.org/10.3389/FMARS.2023.1126301/XML/NLM
38. Svanström, F., Alonso-Fernandez, F., & Englund, C. (2022). Drone detection and tracking in real-time by fusion of different sensing modalities, *6*(11), 317. https://doi.org/10.3390/DRONES6110317
39. Nair, M. M., Sriraman, H., Sai, G. H., & Pattabiraman, V. (2024). DroneSilient (drone + resilient): an anti-drone system. *Journal of Big Data, 11*(1), 1–15. https://doi.org/10.1186/S40537-024-01004-6/TABLES/2
40. Shi, X., Yang, C., Xie, W., Liang, C., Shi, Z., & Chen, J. (2018). Anti-drone system with multiple surveillance technologies: Architecture, implementation, and challenges. *IEEE Communications Magazine, 56*(4), 68–74. https://doi.org/10.1109/mcom.2018.1700430
41. Park, S., Kim, H. T., Lee, S., Joo, H., & Kim, H. (2021). Survey on anti-drone systems: Components, designs, and challenges. *IEEE Access, 9*, 42635–42659. https://doi.org/10.1109/access.2021.3065926

42. Entries on Transitional Justice Debates, Controversies, and Key Questions. (2023). *Encyclopedia of transitional justice*. (pp. 159–403). https://doi.org/10.1017/9781108678537.004.
43. From Conflict to Co-operation in International Water Resources Management: Challenges and Opportunities; proceedings—UNESCO Digital Library. (n.d.). Retrieved April 15, 2025, from https://unesdoc.unesco.org/ark:/48223/pf0000135494.
44. Offe, C. (1992). Coming to terms with past injustices. An introduction to legal strategies available in post-communist societies. *Archives Européennes de Sociologie, 33*(1), 195–201. https://doi.org/10.1017/s000397560000641x

AI Applications in Global Counterterrorism Efforts: Challenges, Compliance, and Regulatory Gaps

Shashwata Sahu and Saurabh Chandra

Abstract Artificial intelligence has infused various attempts at counterterrorism with technologies such as facial recognition, drone surveillance, and predictive analytics, accelerating and accurately justice security efforts. But this sudden embracement has taken a toll over regulation, and there are simply grave issues around privacy, due process, and human rights. The UN High Commissioner for Human Rights 2023 report shows how serious the wrecking effects on civil liberties of untrammelled AI surveillance are, particularly where jurisdiction falls short on openness and accountability. This chapter summarizes the regulatory aspect of the application of AI in security functions in terms of cross-referencing global and national rules. Speaking of doctrinal legal analysis, the research examines key devices, such as International Covenant on Civil and Political Rights (ICCPR), General Data Protection Regulation (GDPR), Digital Personal Data Protection (DPDP) Act of India, 2023, and Information Technology (IT) Rules, 2021, establishment reports, and court judgments, in comparison Comparative examination are EU's, US's, and India's best practices and enforcement gaps. The results indicate patchwork prevailing frameworks, with failing oversight mechanisms and minimal transparency. There are such progressive models as the EU AI Act, but their enforcement has been patchy. The chapter suggests enforceable safeguards, autonomous monitoring agencies, and algorithm audits to ensure that artificial intelligence operates in line with democratic values rather than against them.

S. Sahu (✉)
School of Law, KIIT-DU, Bhubaneswar, India

S. Chandra
School of Law, Bennett University, Greater Noida, India
e-mail: saurabh.chandra@bennett.edu.in

C. Kaunert et al. (eds.), *Artificial Intelligence for Global Counter-Terrorism*, Contributions to Security and Defence Studies,
https://doi.org/10.1007/978-3-031-99235-3_2

1 Introduction

Artificial intelligence (AI) has changed the world security architecture in recent years and is at the centre of a country's defence and counterterrorism strategy. Sophisticated AI technologies like facial recognition, predictive analytics, drone intelligence, and natural language processing have already been increasingly and extensively employed by governments in security-related operations to detect, measure, and dismantle threats entering a country faster and with an accuracy never before seen. The 2022 Global AI Index compiled by Tortoise Media found that over 70 countries have escalated interest in AI for national security use, calling it strategic for avoiding violence, online interaction monitoring and border defence. However, this rapid technology adoption also involves profound legal and ethical concerns. While AI can be optimized and streamlined, it poses grave threats, mainly when used in high-stakes surveillance and policing. Its capacity to enable mass data harvesting, computational targeting, and automated decision-making raises profound concerns about individual privacy, due process, and the reach of state power [1]. The 2023 report from the UN Office of the High Commissioner for Human Rights warns that unregulated use of AI surveillance technology threatens to create systematic abuses of rights, particularly in situations with no transparency, legal safeguards, and independent monitoring.

That's why using AI to manage terrorism globally has put civil liberties in the spotlight. Across a continuum ranging from democratic liberalism to state dictatorship, AI technologies are most rampantly deployed to surveil, profile, and screen citizens under increasingly amorphous framings of "national security" and "extremism." Such uses disproportionately damage already marginalized populations, political dissidents, and journalists—with core issues of accountability and the rule of law of a democracy. Many areas of the law relevant to AI are outdated or lack the depth required to navigate the complicated ethical issues presented by autonomous technology in police work and intelligence.

The chapter discusses such tensions in the context of rights by exploring the implications of the use of AI in security operations. It assesses how existing laws, domestic and international, may regulate the use of AI in counterterrorism. The current study's importance lies in the requirement to bridge technological innovation and legal accountability in proposing an approach for a governance system that is sensitive to human rights but is cognizant of legitimate security interests in the era of the Internet.

1.1 Research Objectives and Methodology of the Chapter

This chapter critically examines the existing legal regimes for using AI in security operations both globally and within individual nation states. It attempts to identify the most pertinent compliance issues for states in balancing the imperative of national security over the obligation to ensure meagre human rights, including the right to privacy, prohibition from discrimination, and due process. The chapter explores critical legal gaps in algorithmic accountability, data privacy, and access to meaningful redress for those negatively impacted by AI-mediated surveillance or enforcement actions. Finally, the chapter will construct a model of rights-based governance that can help ensure that the use of AI in counterterrorism contexts occurs in a way that is aligned with democratic values, legal accountability, and the rule of law [2].

The chapter adheres to a doctrinal approach to legal research, citing key legal documents such as the International Covenant on Civil and Political Rights (ICCPR), EU General Data Protection Regulation (GDPR), and national laws such as India's Digital Personal Data Protection (DPDP) Act, 2023, and the Information Technology (IT) Rules, 2021. It also analyses policy documents of institutions like the Council of Europe, Electronic Privacy Information Center (EPIC), and OECD, as well as relevant academic literature and jurisprudence. Comparative legal analysis highlights best practices and pitfalls in AI regulation across jurisdictions.

2 Conceptual and Theoretical Framework

The use of AI in security operations is a paradigm shift in how contemporary states conceptualize, manoeuvre, and react to perceived threats. For this paper, AI in security operations is defined as using computational networks with the ability to execute activities traditionally involving human intelligence, such as facial recognition, natural language processing, behavioural analysis, and predictive modelling. They become more entrenched in law enforcement, border management, intelligence collection, and counterterrorism systems. Its application has accelerated the spread of algorithmic decision-making in areas with direct and often troubling human rights and civil liberties implications (Fig. 1).

The most controversial element of AI in security is how it adapts to Shoshana Zuboff's notion of "surveillance capitalism," a mechanism where data about individuals are gathered, decoded, and sold, sometimes without their immediate knowledge. In national security, surveillance capitalism turns into state-directed surveillance, where data about individuals are gathered not for profit but to anticipate control. Through predictive policing algorithms, agencies attempt to foresee future crime or focus on at-risk offenders based on past histories, social links, or conduct patterns. Even as these applications vow to optimize resource allocation and reduce crime, they have the potential to reaffirm institutional racism and criminalize systemically over-watched and under-resourced communities [3].

The rule of law is at the centre of this inquiry, which requires that publicly accepted, legally enforceable standards bind every exercise of public authority. Unchecked AI in the security domain undermines this norm by facilitating decisions that will likely be black boxes, unreviewable, and without individualized suspicion. Where algorithmic forecasting is employed to automatically determine policing or surveillance targeting without the due process that a democratic country cannot do, state action's legality is at stake. The World Justice Project (2022) demonstrates how the rule of law indices fell worldwide, especially where governments employ

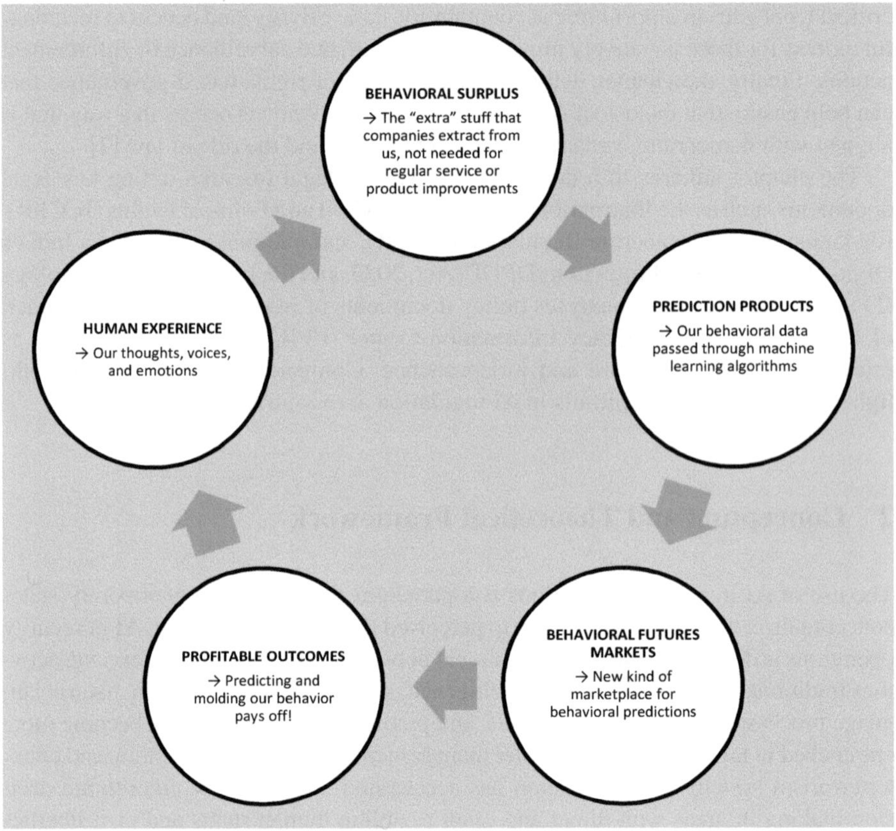

Fig. 1 Cycle of surveillance capitalism

emergency powers and untransparent technology without supportive accountability mechanisms. Therefore, a general theoretical interest is how AI can erode legal safeguards meant to shield citizens from arbitrary incursions by the state.

The chapter draws its premise from the human rights perspective, specifically regarding privacy, dignity, equality, and non-discrimination rights. Integrating AI into security operations leads to disproportionate monitoring of minority groups, activists, and politically dissenting individuals. The privacy right protected by Article 17 of the ICCPR is often at risk from surveillance methods based on data that gather, store, and analyse people's information without consent or oversight. Algorithmic profiling also endangers non-discrimination standards where decision-making occurs based on discriminatory information or training data that spans historical wrongs. Characterizing the relations between technology and law is often described as a dichotomy between technological determinism and digital constitutionalism. Technological determinism is the idea that technological development is driven by an unstoppable outside force penetrating society and law as a causal side effect of innovation. Legal orders, by this premise, lag behind the pace of technosphere evolution and respond late. Digital constitutionalism, by contrast, argues for integrating constitutional principles including transparency, accountability, and rights to be heard or participate into the digital use case from the outset. This aligns with the active regulation view, which does not understand AI as a tool for efficiency or a method but as a social institution that can be subjected to normative action.

When AI is implemented to ensure safety, it cannot simply be bad or good; it could only serve as an extension of our law enforcement system to either realize existing norms or challenge existing legal standards. AI makes it more efficient, in a sense, to prevent crime and gather intelligence. AI helps police agencies sift through vast data to spot threats faster than a human officer could. By contrast, AI gains entry into legal systems through inscrutable probabilistic decision-making models, normally with no democratic consent or legislative oversight of their application. AI-driven flagging or predictive surveillance erases notions of culpability, proportionality, and procedural justice, the very notions that for so long have undergirded notions of legitimacy in state coercion. Moreover, legal concepts that arise from stable categories like "suspect," "reasonable suspicion," or "national threat" tend to face challenges from AI systems that create categorizations by way of fluid patterns and correlations rather than facts. This comes at the cost of epistemic assurance and legal intelligibility, both necessary elements to support rightful rule.

The chapter draws from critical legal theory and ethics of novel technologies for addressing those questions at serious scales. The necessary legal theory challenges the neutrality of law and reveals how legal orders typically reproduce and legitimate, established power relations. Because AI systems are launched unaccountably in policing or surveillance, they can further entrench already at-risk communities to systemic oppression. Likewise, new technology ethics emphasizes design justice, algorithmic transparency, and public engagement [4]. Ethical AI development must pay attention to innovation and efficiency and the socio-legal context in which technologies are deployed. As Virginia Eubanks and Safiya Noble have demonstrated, unregulated automation in government and security will most certainly produce discriminatory, exclusionary, and unfair outcomes.

3 Legal and Regulatory Frameworks

As AI becomes an integral part of national security infrastructure, its implementation must be analysed within the constraints of current legal frameworks. Regulation of AI use in security activities overlaps with an extensive range of international, regional, and national legal instruments. These instruments are, however, quite different from each other in terms of their scope, enforceability, and flexibility to adapt to AI-enabled technologies [5]. This section defines the major global and regional laws that regulate the intersection of AI with human rights and security and then provides a comparative tabular regulation analysis of AI-related laws of India, the United States, and the European Union (EU). It ends by highlighting some of the multiple common regulatory overlaps, inconsistencies, and legislative reform gaps in tandem.

3.1 A. International and Regional Legal Frameworks

Some international legal instruments offer guidance in this respect, such as the ICCPR, signed in 1966 and ratified by 173 states, which includes a range of core civil and political rights directly affected by AI surveillance technologies. Article 17 protects against arbitrary or unlawful interference with privacy, family, or correspondence. The Human Rights Committee has established that state surveillance must be lawful, necessary, and proportionate. In the paradigm of AI, those standards are constantly violated when automated decision-making technologies are applied outside the judiciary's purview or in defence of transparency. There is also a violation of Article 14 on the right to a fair trial when AI products are used as evidence or as profiling instruments without procedural protection.

Universal Declaration of Human Rights (UDHR), 1948, is not legally binding but is still the basis of all international human rights discourse. Article 12 confirms protection from privacy; Articles 6 and 7 both state being of legal status and equality before the law. For instance, the racially biased error rates of facial recognition technology threaten to undermine the equality provisions and dignity guarantees in the UDHR. States' deployment of AI surveillance without democratic oversight can also violate the spirit of Article 21 concerning public affairs participation.

The UN Guiding Principles on Business and Human Rights (UNGPs) define the international standard for the business responsibility to respect human rights. In the context of security and AI, those principles are particularly significant in the context of the growing role of private contractors in providing surveillance technology to states [6]. We may need to conduct due diligence, recognize and avoid complicity as per UNGPs, and provide remedies. However, in most countries, procurement contracts for AI-related technology do not include human rights risk assessments or binding provisions for compliance. The GDPR, in effect from 2018 onwards, remains the world's most far-reaching and deepest data protection law.

Despite the exemption of part-national security activity, some of its core principles remain preponderant. Article 22 limits decisions based only on automated processing with a significant legal impact, except insofar as they are supplemented by human material control. This is particular to predictive policing, algorithmic profiling, and AI risk assessment in security applications. Recital 71 also addresses transparency, equity, and the right to review automated decisions often absent in national security technologies founded on AI. The Council of Europe's Convention 108+, a legally binding agreement among EU and non-EU member states, provides an international standard of transnational data protection.

In contrast to GDPR, it does not only target the EU and is, hence, a more general world rule. Article 10 of Convention 108+ focuses on automated decision-making and obliges people to be notified about the logic of processing and have the opportunity to object. It advocates for data minimization, limitation of purpose, and lawfulness of processing, and as such, it is especially pertinent to AI use in state security. The EU AI Act, which was presented in 2021, takes a risk-based approach to regulating AI.

Security-oriented applications like biometric monitoring and pre-crime policing fall under the "high-risk" system category. These should face conformity assessment, have transparency requirements, and maintain human control. Although still pending negotiation, the Act has promised to establish an international benchmark in regulating AI technology in ethics and rights-based terms. If enacted in its currently defined form, the AI Act will also be the first regional legislative tool to address AI's civilian and security aspects [7].

3.2 National Legal Frameworks

The following is a comparative summary of national policy and law in India, the United States, and the European Union regarding AI deployment in security operations (Table 1).

Although tremendous progress has been made in recognizing the necessity for regulation, legal instruments are marred by inconsistencies and overlaps. In India, for example, the DPDP Act allows exempting agencies from compliance "in the interest of sovereignty," creating a giant loophole for surveillance. The IT Act and Telegraph Act are old and mum on algorithmic decision-making, placing policing with AI in a legal limbo. In the United States, conflicting authorities between federal and state agencies leave it in the dark. The lack of a federal AI law results in agencies using (Foreign Intelligence Surveillance Act) FISA and executive orders widely, typically at the cost of transparency. Moreover, as seen in the United States and India, private sector engagement in AI surveillance raises accountability concerns when private enterprises are not held to the same rights-based responsibilities as public agencies [8]. The EU has sought to construct a more harmonized approach. However, enforcement across member states is not uniform, and the AI Act's future-oriented nature leaves some domains like surveillance-grade military uses and facial recognition without clearly established regulation boundaries.

4 Compliance and Enforcement Challenges

As AI technologies are increasingly embedded within national security policy, the absence of practical legal, institutional, and procedural structures to enforce adherence to human rights norms constitutes a structural governance problem. Unfortunately, the reality of regulation and enforcement on the ground, where AI-security is supposed to work, speaks to a profound structural failure, one where the efficiency and pre-emptive qualities of AI-security are as much its power as its vulnerability. From indeterminate regulatory guardrails to potential institutional

Table 1 National legal approaches to AI in security operations

Jurisdiction	Relevant laws/policies	Scope & key features	Gaps/challenges
India	– DPDP Act, 2023 – IT Act, 2000 & IT Rules, 2021 – Indian Telegraph Act, 1885	– Introduces basic data protection rights – Regulates digital platforms and intermediaries – Authorizes government surveillance on national security grounds	– No specific AI legislation – Overbroad national security exemptions – Weak judicial oversight and redress mechanisms
United States	– Executive Orders on AI (e.g., EO 13960) – Foreign Intelligence Surveillance Act (FISA) – National Security Commission on Artificial Intelligence (NSCAI) Reports	– Encourages innovation in AI for national defense – Legalizes warrantless surveillance under FISA Section 702 – Strategic guidance via NSCAI (2021)	– No comprehensive AI or data protection law – Minimal algorithmic transparency – Civil liberties concerns over mass surveillance
European Union	– GDPR – EU AI Act (proposed) – Law Enforcement Directive (LED)	– Strong data protection regime – Risk-based classification of AI systems – Explicit restrictions on biometric surveillance	– Fragmentation across member states – AI Act still pending final adoption – Limited coverage of privately procured AI systems

capture and unregulated collusion with private actors, the enforcement context is rife with blind spots. This section outlines four key compliance and enforcement issues: uncertainty of law, overly broad national security exceptions, institutional and procedural weakness, and the emergence of low-accountability private vendors.

4.1 Legal Opacity and Under Regulation of AI in Security

Cross-cutting among these questions is one of the most urgent challenges in using artificial intelligence for national defence. The lack of a well-defined legal framework governing its use as most legal regimes including existing laws were created before AI was developed and are unprepared to handle algorithmic decisions, biometric scrutiny, or predictive analysis. The application of AI in intelligence or law enforcement is omitted or only tangentially addressed, even where data protection regimes are put in place [9]. In India, for instance, although the DPDP Act, 2023, establishes basic safeguards for personal data, it allows extensive exceptions for government departments under the guise of promoting public order, sovereignty, or national security. Likewise, the IT Act of 2000 and the rules framed thereunder were enacted to control Internet content and cybersecurity well before the introduction of machine learning-based advanced surveillance systems (facial recognition etc.). The use of AI in security, thus, remains in a regulatory grey zone, with enforceability being variable and human rights endangered. According to the World Economic Forum, Global AI Action Alliance, 2022, a lack of regulation appropriate to the most critical industries, such as national security, inhibits innovation and trust. Without borders set by the legislature, AI technologies can be implemented in legally grey areas where accountability is distorted or bypassed by misinterpretations of legal loopholes.

4.2 Overbroad National Security Exemptions

A further major obstacle to enforcement stems from overly broad national security provisions in the statute. These exceptions are generally invoked as a blanket argument for avoiding human rights protection, including privacy, information, and access to court rights. States certainly require latitude in responding to changing threats, but the vagueness of setting out what qualifies as a "security threat" leaves the way open for abusive and excessive surveillance. For example, in India's DPDP Act, the central government, under Section 17, may exempt any agency of the central government from complying if it feels that such an exemption will be in the spirit of sovereignty, public order, or friendly relations with foreign states. Such a provision permits the near-complete evading of data protection regulations by agencies involved with AI-based surveillance [10]. In the United States, FISA Section 702 authorizes warrantless foreign non-citizen surveillance beyond US borders but has also been misused in a manner that impacts domestic citizens. In 2021, the Office of the Director of National Intelligence released declassified reports admitting to abuse of these surveillance authorities, such as improper querying of US citizen data. Excessive use or abuse of national security exceptions effectively paralyses otherwise sturdy data and rights frameworks, degrading public confidence. As the UN Special Rapporteur on the Right to Privacy has described, exceptions to human rights principles should be narrowly conceived, time-limited, and amenable to scrutiny by a judicial body—a call hardly met under the AI security paradigm.

4.3 Institutional and Procedural Gaps

The most essential elements of effective compliance is having institutions with the mandate to supervise, investigate, and enforce right-violating practices. Most countries lack specialized regulatory agencies with technical expertise to audit AI systems, especially in closed security environments. To begin with, there are no algorithmic audit requirements. AI systems deployed in counterterrorism or policing are rarely subjected to independent impact assessments. Where audits exist, they are typically internal or by the operating or procuring agencies themselves, thus introducing a built-in conflict of interest. In contrast, the EU's AI Act draft requires third-party conformity assessment of high-risk AI systems, such as law enforcement—a requirement other jurisdictions have not yet adopted. Two, mechanisms for redress of grievances are inchoate or inaccessible. People flagged or impacted by AI-based security choices may not even know they have been tracked, profiled, or blocked. Even when they are aware, the black-box nature of AI systems and the lack of transparency requirements prevent them from appealing decisions or demanding compensation. Third, judicial oversight is absent. Courts are hardly empowered or well-equipped to scrutinize algorithmic systems. Surveillance claims are often rejected on standing or national security privilege grounds. The effect is a procedural lacuna, where citizens and judges cannot reasonably challenge or review the lawfulness of AI application by government surveillance [11]. Very few nations maintain open registers containing information about AI systems applied in law enforcement or security institutions, curtailing democratic checks, the Access Now report in 2022 indicates. Without transparency at the institutional level, room for productive enforcement is narrow.

4.4 Private Vendor Involvement and Lack of Accountability

The most structurally under-resourced problem is the increasing involvement of private technology companies in developing, marketing, and even running AI systems employed by governments for surveillance and counterterrorism. The public-private character of AI procurement produces a diffusion of responsibility, with neither party fully taking responsibility for rights abuses. There have been some controversies in the United States regarding facial recognition firms like Clearview AI that scraped billions of web photographs to create facial recognition repositories without permission. Faced with resistance from civil society, police forces in most countries, including Australia and India, have partnered with Clearview AI or comparable suppliers. The issue is aggravated when procurement agreements do not contain clear human rights clauses, risk assessments, or audit standards [12]. Most government tenders prefer functionality and price over ethical protection, leading to the unregulated installation of invasive systems. Intellectual property rights and trade secrets also typically deny public access to such systems' source code or design logic, thereby constraining judicial scrutiny and public auditability. Even when the rights have been violated, the victims find themselves in a position of jurisdictional vacuum—they cannot decide whether or not the violation arose out of the exercise of the state or from the configuration of the vendor. The UN Guiding Principles on Business and Human Rights demand states and corporations to step up equally and avoid harm to human rights, even in joint ventures involving state-corporation arrangements. However, their implementation is still voluntary, and the extension of AI in national security is still on the drawing board.

5 Case Studies and Comparative Analysis

While the international security apparatus continues to embrace AI as a tool for surveillance, policing, and counterterrorism, the cross-border institutional and legal reactions range from form, priority, and impact. The following section compares three significant regions—the EU, the United States, and India—to set the scope of responses in balancing innovation and human rights. Through seminal cases and policy models, it looks at public accountability frameworks, transparency requirements, state surveillance regimes, and oversight challenges. While these jurisdictions vary in governance model and technology maturity, each has piercing insights into the continued evolution of AI regulation in national security [13].

5.1 European Union: Public Accountability and Mandatory Impact Assessments

The EU has continued to hold a leadership position in the ethical regulation of AI. While never centrally controlling security, the European Union has given a regulatory baseline in general data protection and digital rights that well informs AI applications to security domains. A salient feature of the EU model is mandatory impact assessments for risky AI systems, as in the proposed EU AI Act, 2021. Algorithmic transparency, data quality, and risk mitigation must be addressed before deployment. Article 29 of the Bill defines AI used in law enforcement and surveillance as "high-risk," subject to stringent testing relative to the severity of risk, human oversight mechanisms, and registration in an open database. The Bill is in its discussion phases, but it is a move in the right direction to mainstream public accountability. The European Union's GDPR also claimed the EU's front-runner status for rights-based governance. GDPR Article 35 necessitates DPIAs, where technologies like AI or biometric tools significantly impact the individual's rights. Self-regulatory authorities like France's Commission Nationale de l'Informatique et des Libertés (CNIL) and Germany's Federal Commissioner for Data Protection have proactively enforced provisions by investigating the use of AI systems in law enforcement, border control, and public surveillance. Challenges remain, though. Member states can still be responsible for their own national security and defence policies, which can create inconsistencies. For instance, even with the GDPR's robust protections, certain member states have implemented facial recognition in public areas without adequate legal support, a field the new AI Act will seek to harmonize.

5.2 United States: Surveillance-Heavy Approach and Civil Liberty Trade-Offs

The United States functions on a decentralized, tech-facilitated model under one overarching top-most policy priority: preserving national security. AI generally extends to policing and intelligence activity based on in-depth federal spending and collaboration with outside non-government tech companies [14]. That national security angle has, for the most part, substituted civil liberties and public disclosure for its gain. Perhaps the most significant example is the PRISM program, which was revealed by whistleblower Edward Snowden in 2013. Administered by the National Security Agency (NSA), PRISM gave access to communications data from major technology firms such as Google, Apple, and Microsoft. PRISM was conducted under the FISA, specifically Section 702, allowing foreign intelligence collection without a warrant. Although the program was aimed at foreigners, it inadvertently collected enormous amounts of data related to American citizens and hence faced severe criticism for privacy invasion. In response to the people's outrage, some alteration was brought about like the USA FREEDOM Act (2015), which restricted the bulk metadata program. However, recent audits of Privacy and Civil Liberties Oversight Board (PCLOB) indicate ongoing compliance issues such as unwarranted Section 702 searches into American citizens' information. It only exacerbates it without a federal data protection act and close to zero transparency around algorithms. Although the National Security Commission on Artificial Intelligence (NSCAI) produced ethics standards recommendations and public-private partnership proposals around AI, none are binding. Directing mechanisms like congressional hearings or in-house agency audits have limited leverage in constricting the operational flexibility of intelligence agencies. In contrast to the EU, the US machinery emphasizes security effectiveness more, frequently overriding procedural and rights-based protections essential in a democratic world.

5.3 Comparative Insights: Convergence and Divergence

The comparative landscape discloses both convergence and significant divergence in the legal reaction to AI for national security. Convergence occurs in the international acknowledgement of the dual-use potential of AI technologies both as instruments of public security and as possible infringers of fundamental rights. All three jurisdictions acknowledge the necessity of some regulation, and public discourse increasingly focuses on the dangers of unregulated surveillance. Private contracting for AI deployment is a common denominator for all three regions, each struggling with accountability to public-private partnerships. The disparity lies in institutional and normative responses. The EU is ahead of the rest of the world in a vigorous rights-oriented concept of the rule of law, which engages public accountability through mandatory impact assessment and independent inspection [15]. The technologically advanced United States is also sacrificing citizen rights and procedure protection with its relentless pursuit of national security and innovation. India highlights the risks of a slowly digitizing state with an underdeveloped legal architecture in which prerogatives in security always triumph over privacy and due process. But most of all, where the EU confidently marches with legally binding means to protect citizens in the GEPR and the AI Act, both the United States and India follow towards executive discretion and patchwork regulation which de facto send AI surveillance products on the fast track as unmonitored. There is no judicial oversight on these fronts, especially on national security issues, where the courts almost always bow to executive privilege.

6 Key Legal and Ethical Issues

The national security use of AI is remaking the regime of rights, obligations, and rules. This means that AI, in addition to existing methods, is at hand to enlarge the state's capacity to identify and preclude threats. Still, it also engenders complex legal and ethical problems. From opaque algorithmic processes and biased outcomes to violations of due process and erosion of civil liberties, these problems are not theoretical or one-off.

6.1 Algorithmic Opacity and Discrimination Risks

The most urgent legal concern in the use of AI is algorithmic transparency, more commonly referred to as the "black box" problem. Most AI systems—especially deep-learning systems—make decisions based on layers of neural networks piled on top of each other so high that their creators can no longer read them. The transparency problem is most pernicious where decisions have real-world consequences, such as surveillance prioritization, predictive policing, or risk assessment in immigration and border control. They are trained on skewed data or generated with minimal awareness of the social context, and they deliver uneven results. A 2020 report by the US National Institute of Standards and Technology (NIST) published the results that face recognition software was systematically much more likely to yield false positives for darker-skinned individuals, women, and older adults. These mistakes already resulted in wrongful arrests in cities such as Detroit and New Jersey, where Black males were mistakenly matched as suspects through defective AI connections. In national defence, where ethnic or racial profiling has always been the hot issue, an algorithmic bias repeats the existing ones. Minority populations already disproportionately victimized by too much policing will be disproportionately tagged by AI-reliant mechanisms by patterns of conduct or territorial studies [16]. The threat is twofold here: not just are these systems a reflection of the existing bias of society. Still, they accomplish that with the added cover of an appearance of objective mathematical certainty whose judgements grow harder to refute and challenge.

6.2 Due Process Violations and the "Black Box" Challenge

Legal systems are founded on the due process doctrine, which affords one a right to a fair hearing, a presumption of innocence, and the ability to deny unfavourable action. AI systems tend to undermine these ideals by creating or making decisions in impenetrable and unreviewable forms. The "black box" aspect of AI systems means that people cannot know how or why they were determined to be dangerous or to have their privileges removed. In predictive policing programs, for example, people can end up on watchlists based on trends in their social network or prior associations even though they've committed no crime. Generally, there is no notice, evidence disclosure, and no appeal process, essentially stripping the injured of their right to an explanation and compensation.

In judicial systems in which secrecy can be justified in the name of national security, the problem is even worse. Agencies cite "classified operations" as the excuse to conceal the functioning of AI systems or the nature of the data on which they are operated. As such, AI-based security controls function outside the courts' view, insulating themselves from judicial review or public oversight.

6.3 Impact on Freedom of Expression, Protest, and Movement

AI-driven surveillance technology has a chilling influence on human rights, especially the right to movement, assembly, and expression. Technology that surveils people in public places, including facial recognition technology and gait analysis, is used to monitor people in public areas for the most part, especially during demonstrations or politically charged assemblies. In Hong Kong, as documented, AI-driven surveillance cameras tracked protesters during the 2019–2020 pro-democracy protests. The same fears were also present in India during farmer protests and Citizenship Amendment Act (CAA) protests, when police used facial recognition software in protest areas without notice to the public or legal protection [17].

The UN Human Rights Council has warned that such tools if used indiscriminately, have the potential to stifle dissent and violate the right of peaceful assembly under international human rights law. Moreover, AI sentiment or behaviour analysis technology can classify online speech as extremist based on ambiguous standards. Social media monitoring technologies employing natural language processing have been applied to track political, satire, or religious speech—sometimes without court warrants or public sensitization [18]. This induces self-censorship, dismantling the democratic nature of open debate and discussion. Freedom of movement is also eroded when AI is employed to impose blanket automatic travel bans, deny entry at borders, or track migrant populations. Decisions based on impenetrable threat scores or machine-generated risk assessments are made without sufficient human review or judicial review, contrary to international refugee law and domestic constitutional protections.

6.4 *Ethical Accountability in Semi-autonomous Threat Detection*

There goes a strong ethical challenge with more dependence on autonomous or semi-autonomous threat detection technologies, those that can detect, evaluate, and, in some cases, react to perceived threats with little human control. Some examples include autonomous surveillance drones, public transit anomaly detection software, and AI weapons of war. As the technologies become more responsive and scalable, they threaten to offload moral responsibility. If a semi-autonomous system erred, who is responsible? The designer, the operator, or the purchasing organization? Such ambiguity makes legal litigation more difficult and disconnects moral responsibility. Moreover, public procurement guidelines for security technologies still do not embrace moral design practices like human-in-the-loop control, fairness by design, and explainability. A 2022 audit by AlgorithmWatch showed that less than 15% of AI used in European public administration possesses a minimum ethical level of transparency. This figure is lower in national security because of confidentiality safeguards and exemption clauses. Where ethics are not applied to design and deployment, normalization of surveillance practices, which are neither rights-based nor democratically tested, occurs. Ethical systems must not be idealistic; they must be provided with legal enforcement systems, mandatory ethical impact assessments, and web surveillance [19].

7 Recommendations

To cope with AI's complex legal, ethical, and governance dimensions in national security, there must be an emergency rights-based and holistic regulatory framework. The mosaic of regulation and oversight mechanisms in jurisdictions to date has been insufficient to ensure transparency, accountability, and protection of human rights in the face of AI capabilities rushing ahead at a breakneck speed. This chapter offers a set of practical and normative recommendations to guide policymakers, legislators, and regulators on how best to craft a robust and equitable AI governance framework, particularly regarding security operations.

7.1 Institutionalize Rights-Based AI Governance

This involves applying principles of legality, necessity, proportionality, and accountability standards at all stages of the deployment of AI systems' design; acquisition and deployment; and oversight. Rights-based governance requires that states make clear, precise boundaries on the use of AI in the security sphere, narrow the broad national security exemptions that currently apply, and guarantee meaningful public consultation in decision-making. The UN High Commissioner for Human Rights (OHCHR), in its 2021 report on human rights and AI, urged states to adopt legislation ensuring fairness, transparency, and remedy in all contexts of automated decision-making. Governments must enshrine these values in statutory law so that AI-based technologies provide privacy, dignity, and equality before the law.

7.2 Enforceable Algorithmic Audit Mandates

One of the significant reforms of the laws is mandatory auditing of AI technologies used in national defence and law enforcement. The auditing must verify technical competence and performance, ethical issues, data representativeness, and potential discriminatory bias. These kinds of audits must be performed by external, independent third parties, not by vendor self-certification or internal agency review. They must be periodic, risk-based, and publicly reported, especially for high-risk applications like facial recognition, predictive policing, or social media surveillance. Canada and the Netherlands have already tested algorithmic impact assessments (AIAs) for government AI deployment offering templates for institutionalizing such practice. Secondly, audit conclusions must be traceable to ensure follow-up corrective measures, for example, the ability to suspend or mothball systems that fail the legal or ethical test. If audits are not enforceable, they will be a paper ritual and not an instrument of accountability.

7.3 Ethics-by-Design in Public Procurement Policies

Governments are required to adopt ethics-by-design approaches in the procurement of public AI technology. This includes incorporating ethical requirements like transparency, fairness, and explainability in procurement contracts and vendor evaluation processes. Public purchasers must require rights-based principle conformity demonstrations by AI vendors and submission of end-to-end documentation of training data, algorithmic logic, and risk-mitigation procedures. The 2022 OECD Guidelines for AI Procurement propose that government contracts for AI systems should be drafted to include data governance, auditability, and user training provisions. National procuring entities must localize and translate guidelines so that public money is not wasted on black box or harmful technologies. Procurement should further entail "red lines" explicit prohibitions on some uses of AI, such as real-time public biometric surveillance or religion, race, or political opinion profiling.

7.4 *Create Independent Oversight and Redress Mechanisms*

Good governance requires impartial oversight bodies to monitor, research, and discipline the abuse of AI in security operations. Such bodies should be able to conduct surprise audits, screen procurement processes, and inspect deployment for legality. Equally important, the victims of AI treatment deserve open and simple mechanisms of redress. These include a right to be told whether one is profiled or surveilled through AI, the right to explanations, and the right to appeal and remedial relief in case of harmful decisions [20]. They should be within reach, with a time-bound limit, and based on rules of procedural fairness. Data Protection Authorities (DPAs) in the EU have a central role in regulating algorithmic systems. A similar multi-stakeholder process can be repeated elsewhere, too, involving technologists, legal professionals, civil society, and user representatives.

7.5 *Promote Global Cooperation and Standard-Setting*

Because digital surveillance and AI development are transnational, no individual state can solve them unilaterally. International coordination is needed to develop shared norms, interoperability standards, and responsibility mechanisms. Groups like the Organization for Economic Co-operation and Development (OECD), Council of Europe, and UNESCO are already leading the discussion regarding AI ethics but need to become legally binding global standards. A multilateral agreement on operations, similar to how the Budapest Convention on Cybercrime, could set minimum global standards in transparency, impact assessments, and data protection needs. Also, Global South nations should be represented in such exercises lest they practice technological neocolonialism and make global standards culturally rich and balanced [21].

8 Conclusion

This chapter critically assessed the AI deployment's ethical and legal implications for national security missions. Using doctrinal and comparative analysis exposes some critical issues nebulous in algorithmic secrecy, data-based discrimination, procedural bias, and institutional vulnerabilities to a lack of legal accountability. In courts worldwide, from the European Union to the United States and India, the results show a frightening disconnect between technological progress and legal readiness. While a few countries have moved towards regulation, like the EU's proposed AI Act and Canada's algorithmic impact assessments, most remain in a regulatory void, particularly where AI is employed in the quest for national security.

The risk of unfettered surveillance practices, particularly by private contractors and opaque procurement practices, emanates from the failure to harmonize and legalize protection. In a world where machine decision-making can establish the boundaries of individual liberty, fundamental rights such as privacy, freedom of speech, and due process are increasingly under threat. Legal harmonization across borders and sectors is more important now than ever as AI technology becomes increasingly autonomous and ubiquitous.

The need to put national and international legal standards that look to the future, not by stifling innovation but by an in-the-wild sprinkling of democratic accountability, human rights principles and ethics-by-design into the AI lifecycle, is pressing and evident now. This needs strong algorithmic audits, transparent public procurement, and the establishment of independent oversight bodies. As the global security environment continues to evolve, it is no longer enough to speculate as to whether or not AI can be applied to the war against terrorism, we must now question how it must be governed in both a legal, ethical, and inclusive manner. It is only by doing so that AI can be an agent of public security without compromising the democratic ideals it is intended to serve.

References

1. Martini, A. (2024). AI, counter-terrorism and global governance: State of the art. *Revista de Paz y Conflictos, 17.*
2. Montasari, R. (2024). Addressing ethical, legal, technical, and operational challenges in counterterrorism with machine learning: Recommendations and strategies. In *Cyberspace, cyberterrorism and the international security in the fourth industrial revolution: Threats, assessment and responses* (pp. 199–226). Springer.
3. Chinagorom, A. E., Alpheaus Chika, J., & Charity, N. (2025). Artificial intelligence and counter-terrorism in Nigeria: Prospects, pitfalls, and the future of security strategy. *Jalingo Journal of Social and Management Sciences, 6*(3), 154–165.
4. Khan, F. A., Li, G., Khan, A. N., Khan, Q. W., Hadjouni, M., & Elmannai, H. (2023). AI-driven counter-terrorism: Enhancing global security through advanced predictive analytics. *IEEE Access, 11*, 135864–135879.
5. Singh, C., & Lin, W. (2021). Can artificial intelligence, RegTech and CharityTech provide effective solutions for anti-money laundering and counter-terror financing initiatives in charitable fundraising. *Journal of Money Laundering Control, 24*(3), 464–482.
6. Wall, C. (2025). The ghost in the machine: Counterterrorism in the age of artificial intelligence. *Studies in Conflict & Terrorism*, 1–27.
7. Rahman, A. A. S., Kaur, A., & Saroj, P. (2024). Artificial intelligence and international crimes against humanity: Challenges and solutions. In *2024 International conference on advances in computing research on science engineering and technology (ACROSET)* (pp. 1–5). IEEE.

8. Rassler, D. (2021). Commentary: Data, AI, and the future of US counterterrorism: Building an action plan. *CTC Sentinel*, 31–40.
9. Maniszewska, K. (2024). Countering terrorism: Key challenges and proposed solutions. In *Towards a new definition of terrorism: Challenges and perspectives in a shifting paradigm* (pp. 65–82). Cham.
10. Black, M., Obradovic, L., & House, D. (2024). Behind the curve: Technology challenges facing the homeland intelligence and counterterrorism workforce. *Journal of Cybersecurity, 10*(1), tyae002.
11. Ayorinde, R. (2024). Legal appraisal of the role of artificial intelligence in combatting global terrorism. Available at SSRN 4986676.
12. Bahriansyah, I. M., Supriyadi, A. A., & Nurisnaeny, P. S. (2024). Anticipating the impact of artificial intelligence to increase national vigilance against terrorism attacks in Indonesia. *Remote Sensing Technology in Defense and Environment, 1*(2), 86–97.
13. Josyula, H. P. (2024). Enhancing security and compliance. In *Redefining cross-border financial flows: Transforming remittances with AI and other technologies* (pp. 49–64). Apress.
14. Riaz, M. (2024). The legality of targeted killings in counterterrorism operations: A human rights perspective. Available at SSRN 4888073.
15. Sukabdi, Z. A. (2021). Bridging the gap: Contributions of academics and national security practitioners to counterterrorism in Indonesia. *International Journal of Law, Crime and Justice, 65*, 100467.
16. Ganor, B. (2021). Artificial or human: A new era of counterterrorism intelligence? *Studies in Conflict & Terrorism, 44*(7), 605–624.
17. Khan, A. (2024). Artificial intelligence in National Security: Opportunities and risks. *Fari Journal of Global Affairs and Security Studies, 1*(02), 101–121.
18. Marsili, M. (2023). Military emerging disruptive technologies: Compliance with international law and ethical standards. *BRILL eBooks*, 25–50.
19. Jha, A., Bahuguna, R., Kathuria, S., Sunil, G., Gupta, M., & Pachouri, V. (2023). Role of AI in combating cyber terrorism. In *2023 4th international conference on smart electronics and communication (ICOSEC)* (pp. 1156–1160). IEEE.
20. Bimantara, A., & Supriyadi, A. A. (2024). Counterterrorism prevention concept to support government policy in Indonesia. *Green Governance: Exploring Politics, Social Justice, and the Environment, 1*(2), 89–102.
21. Sholeh, M. B., & Iswanti, A. (2024). Countering cyberterrorism: The confluence of artificial intelligence, cyber forensics and digital policing in US and UK national cybersecurity: By Reza Montasari, United Kingdom, Springer, 2023, xv+ 164 pp., £ 139.99 (hardback), ISBN 9783031219191.

Ethical Considerations in AI-Driven Counterterrorism

Ashima Jain and Laeeq R. Janjua

Abstract Artificial intelligence (AI) has entered a new generation that focuses on counterterrorism strategies, thereby altering the processes of detection, prevention, and response to terrorist threats as followed by the governments and security interfacing agencies. With AI-powered technologies like machine learning, predictive analytics, and excellent surveillance systems, there is the added capability of dealing with vast amounts of data in near real time. This, in turn, identifies the potential threats and detection of suspicious activity patterns and facilitates the governments in timely and accurate analysis. AI-enabled instruments, such as unmanned aerial vehicles (UAVs), facial recognition biometrics programs, and data-mining applications, add to the effectiveness in the realms of intelligence acquisition, targeting of suspects, and operational efficacy in counterterrorism. The related issue of algorithmic bias presents ethical quandaries. AI systems are only as trustworthy as the data they are trained on, and any biases present in such datasets, be they on the basis of race, religion, or socio-economic background, can lead to disproportionate targeting of specific communities. Intentionally or unintentionally, these biases can also strengthen existing prejudices, aggravate social divides, and contribute to wrongful actions against the counterterrorism enforcement. On a parallel, AI-specific mass surveillance tools trigger the privacy versus civil liberties argument. The more mass data subjected to collection and scrutiny, the greater the potential infringement on individual freedoms and the greater the concern, particularly with the use of coercive means lacking in law. This great concern applies particularly to already marginalised communities that could be disproportionately impacted by AI-empowered surveillance systems and data-monitoring systems.

A. Jain (✉)
School of Law, Manipal University, Jaipur, India

L. R. Janjua
WSB University, Dąbrowa Górnicza, Poland
e-mail: laeeq.janjua@wsb.edu.pl

C. Kaunert et al. (eds.), *Artificial Intelligence for Global Counter-Terrorism*, Contributions to Security and Defence Studies,
https://doi.org/10.1007/978-3-031-99235-3_3

1 Introduction: Autonomy and Accountability in AI Systems

The introduction of artificial intelligence (AI) into counterterrorism has brought about a significant leap in the efficiency and accuracy of counterterrorism operations and further stirred raging ethical and legal controversies as to the actual level of autonomy afforded AI systems in making high-stakes decisions. For example, AI autonomy in counterterrorism refers to the capability of the machine to autonomously analyse data and identify possible threats to execute actions without human involvement. The primary ethical issues entailed with such autonomous AI in counterterrorism are regarding the fact that decisions may be wrong due to the fact that a particular system cannot deviate from such pre-programming and machine learning systems. An AI system functions based on a massive collection of data but fails to adopt the in-depth view that humans have towards judgement, especially in an unpredictable and complex battlefield. Without the guidance of a human, there will be some misinterpretations of the data that might lead to unforeseen results due to ill targeting of the wrong individual or perhaps civilian casualties [1]. The very application of AI in counter-terrorist operations raises moral, legal, and human rights problems. The question of how autonomously AI-driven systems might operate in situations involving life-and-death decisions becomes a prime fear. Also vexed are issues of how much AI would independently assess and identify targets or even execute pre-emptive strikes while leaving human accountability less than absolute. To reduce dangers associated with unregulated AI decision-making, human judgement must remain the foundation of such operations. Given the immense consideration humanitarian principles and accuracy have demanded from counterterrorism operations, greater emphasis is placed on finding the value of using AI but at the same time irrevocably leaving important decisions in human hands. One of the many major issues related to ethical considerations, accountability also remains one of the highest among the current trends questioning AI autonomy in security and military operations. If AI-driven systems take life-and-death decisions, complex questions of law will arise concerning who shall be held responsible for any errors or damage that may result. If an AI system incorrectly labels a civilian as an enemy and takes lethal action against that civilian, that throws up the question of whether the engineers who built the algorithm, the military personnel that deployed it, or the government authorities who consented to such deployment should be held responsible. Due to the lack of mechanisms for accountability, the case will end up in a legal grey area, which disappointingly will serve to erode the public trust in the application of AI for national security purposes. This legal dimension needs to be addressed in a way that will see the legal framework adapt and advance to draw clear lines on accountability, oversight mechanisms, and avenues through which redress for wrongful harm might be achieved.

The utilisation of AI in counterterrorism raises legal concerns on several fronts, including international law and national sovereignty in internal matters. It is said that some states have deployed AI-equipped military interventions or cross-border counterterrorism measures, thereby directly or indirectly raising a range of questions regarding the legality of AI intervention, compliance with existing international human rights law standards, and state sovereignty in the territories where interventions are undertaken. There is an additional issue of governance of AI concerning operations on security-level questions or debates over transparency and the integrity of the AI-generated data. At the same time, misuse will be from the manipulation of the AI data or by its happening in the unforeseen error. This underlines the importance of developing regulatory frameworks that will ensure accountability and ethical use of AI technologies.

In light of such concerns, a careful equilibrium should be struck between the utility that AI can provide for better security in tandem with ethical and legal principles. Governments and international bodies should work together and formulate clear guidelines that can be applied for the responsible use of AI in counterterrorism activities while focusing on human rights, accountability, and transparency. Thus, a very well-regulated model will ensure that AI serves as a tool for security without undermining fundamental freedoms or negatively impacting vulnerable populations.

It has also become really critical about human participation in AI-generated counterterrorism interventions. AI will be able to provide operational effectiveness, but appropriate levels of autonomy attached to the systems remain debatable. Experts warn against complete autonomy of the decision-making process when entailing lethal force, with strong justification that AI systems operate without contextual cognisance or ethical and legal understanding of their actions. Human involvement becomes critical in such operations, as Droni termed them, so that it subscribes to international principles on distinction, proportionality, and necessity, as set forth in the laws of armed conflict [2].

The amount considered as necessary supervision would depend on the types and complexities of operations, but by and large, the growing consensus would be that human presence finally determines all situations involving force use. That way, no unintended intervention is done, reducing the possibility of errors, as well as strengthening accountability for actions taken by AI-enabled systems. As revolutionary as AI could be in counterterrorism operations, its extent of autonomy should be regulated tightly to prevent ethical and legal dilemmas. For responsible use of AI in national security, there is a need for a well-defined framework that provides human oversight and accountability within transparent decision-making processes.

2 Bias and Fairness in AI Decision-Making

The employment of artificial intelligence in counterterrorism raises multiple questions from an ethical and legal perspective—whose prejudices and whose notions of fairness enter into decision-making processes? An AI system is trained over myriad centuries of existing data—historical data at that. They tend to inherit and perpetuate the existing prejudices enacted against individuals, whether in the history of intelligence collection, law enforcement, or military practices. Such discrimination targets particular ethnic, religious, or political groups that may become falsely identified and wrongfully acted against. The stakes are so high in counterterrorism projects that the consequences of bias could be calamitous to the point of wrongfully profiling and persecuting innocent persons or communities at large [3].

Left unchecked, such AI systems are today entry-point systems for widespread, systematic discrimination and further entrenchment of already existing inequalities, further delegitimising counterterrorism efforts. Such ethical necessity for prevention of injustice by global screams must be complemented by extensive oversight, legal protection, and public reporting regarding deployment of AI. It requires strict regulatory mechanisms to lessen biases and thus ensure that AI systems usurp the name of justice and human principles.

Conducting periodic scrutiny and evaluation to identify and correct discrimination patterns in AI decision-making would constitute other strategies to address these concerns. Furthermore, representative and exhaustive datasets that capture the phenomenon are intrinsic to training an AI model. Transparency in AI algorithms and decision-making processes is critical; that is what guarantees accountability and prevents these technologies from being weaponised against particular groups of people. Without those safeguards, however, counterterrorism AI will be no more than an instrument of oppression—hewing to incursions against victims but not actually providing protection [4].

A glaringly precise and deeply concerning example of AI misuse in counterterrorism is the deployment of the AI systems 'Lavender' and 'Where's Daddy?' by Israel in military operations against Palestine. Reports allege that these programs were used by AI to create target lists for bombings, procuring mass killing of persons even allegedly even in the slightest sense connected to Hamas. The most devastating consequence of these arbitrary, automated decisions has been the unfortunate loss of civilian life on thousands of occasions in the early days of the airstrikes. These included thousands of Palestinian women, children, and non-combatants. An AI-autonomous system biased by the military forces can certainly give rise to more violence against terror groups and further violations of basic human rights.

This case exemplifies the magnitude of danger and exposure when AI decisions are not void of bias in counterterrorism. Unfortunately, AI is reduced to an instrument of destruction when it is not enshrined with values of fairness, transparency, and ethical oversight. Any use of AI for military or security applications should be subject to the most rigorous ethical considerations to ensure that it does not operate in any way in contradiction to principles related to justice, equal dignity, and respect. The international community must, therefore, urgently engage in scrutinising, monitoring, and regulating the use of AI in counterterrorism because neglecting to address those ethical concerns will only expedite legitimising war crimes under the guise of technological progress [5].

3 Privacy and Civil Liberties

The integration of artificial intelligence (AI) in counterterrorism operations gives rise to immeasurably complex ethical and legal problems, mostly covering privacy and civil liberties. AI technology is by its very nature based on obtrusive mass collection, analysis, and interpretation of personal information—communications, movement, and lifestyle patterns of individual persons. On one side, intelligence is compulsory to avoid security threats; on the other side, it makes the scope to violate personal privacy broader. AI surveillance tools could amass unbelievable volumes of data, hardly watched or made accessible, which is problematic in an extreme manner when considering the invasion of even the most fundamental privacy rights. Therefore, the next significant challenge is to guarantee that the scope of surveillance must be limited, proportionate against a given threat, and supported legally to prevent governmental trespass at the same time as well as illegal execution. Apart from such direct threats to privacy, we have civil liberties on a more ambitious scale, which is another problem as significant as AI's integration into counterterrorism platforms. Such ramifications will be acute if AI algorithms are used with what may be suspected to be biased datasets and which result in disparate enforcement practices which disproportionately harm marginalised or minority groups. Such algorithmic bias will help overturn other basic rights, whether it be the freedom from arbitrary interference; freedom of speech as well as the right of assembly or due process [6]. If we allow AI-mediated monitoring and predictive analytics, we risk having a surveillance society arise, in which the citizens will live under continued surveillance, thus denying their autonomy and undermining the very ideas of democracy aimed at their protection. Without robust legal frameworks and proper accountability, counterterrorism action through AI may work to curtail civil liberties in the name of national security. Those ways are by subjecting the artificial intelligence systems processing personal data for its purposes to specific and stringent regulations in the General Data Protection Regulation (GDPR) ratified by the European Union on the requirement for transparency, consent, and rights of individuals in data protection. This brings in one of its most significant provisions, namely the right to explanation: the ability of individuals to seek justification for decisions that are made solely by automated processing, including profiling by AI, as enshrined under Article 22 of the GDPR. This right was established to safeguard individuals from significant decisions made without the intervention of their own minds. Its effectiveness, however, remains questionable in relation to counterterrorism activities. The principles of national security tend to be strong enough grounds for most governments to seek exceptions or overrides to privacy protections, limiting the ability of persons to contest the decisions made by an automated AI system. On the other hand, the GDPR generally offers a strong legal framework within which data are protected. However, in the context of counterterrorism, it may not be sufficient to completely ensure individuals' rights from potential abuses by AI surveillance systems [7].

At the heart of it, the balancing act between national security interests and the privacy and civil liberties demands requires a multifaceted approach. Strong regulatory mechanisms, ethical governance of AI, judicial oversight, and citizen accountability will need to work together to ensure that AI applications in counterterrorism remain lawful and justifiable. Countries must work towards transparent policies that prevent abuses of power and enhance democratic values through the promotion of rights against unnecessary surveillance and discrimination.

4 International Law and Sovereignty

Worldwide challenges and confrontations in counterterrorism operations add to complex problems under international law towards the sovereignty of the states. Mostly, the very AI technologies line up for application in surveillance systems, intelligence-gathering machines, and cyber operations, or enable the use of autonomous weapons—for example, drone strikes—which can reach much farther beyond the borders of any sovereign country. And it creates considerable legal and ethical dilemmas because such actions can amount to sovereignty infringement or, arguably, a violation of the right to self-determination of nations. Cross-border counterterrorism operations using AI should be construed within international law to ascertain that it does not amount to unauthorised encroachment into the affairs of sovereign states [8].

Another of the great legal considerations from that kind of operation was an adherence to international humanitarian law (IHL), the one which sets international standards for any use of force in armed conflict. Proportionality and distinction stipulate that AI warfare does not overly harm a civilian population or escalate a conflict between states. AI-directed targeted strikes conducted without an explicit agreement by the state in which they are occurring may be seen as an infringement of territorial integrity, thus leading to diplomatic tensions with possible retaliation. These aspects indicate the ongoing tension between a country's right to use self-defence against terrorism and its duty to respect the sovereignty of another country.

The international system makes concerns of accountability and regulatory concerns even more complex. Armies of AI systems in this field are created and utilised in many types of collaboration between such a number of different governments, private defence contractors, and multinational corporations. Due to the spread of responsibility, it is problematic to introduce any legal standard or even make one subject responsible for violation of international law. Lack of universally derived laws regulating extraterritoriality in the deployment of AI to military and security purposes sees legal ambiguities being created; every state can have its interpretation on the issue of sovereignty of force [9]. Such legal loopholes can lead to circumstances of one-action instances, whereby nations can justify their own construction of counterterrorism responsibility measures with the use of AI technology with little serious concern for the present international law demand.

Multilateral collaboration in the construction of such agreements to define locations where AI can be implemented, accountability measures and mechanisms that can ensure that AI is not misused is paramount. Without such legal clarity, the lack of clarity in AI use could lead to uneasiness in counterterrorism and cases that set deadly precedents, leaving the world incurably unstable and nations not trusting each other. The resolution of such concerns by way of such internationally accepted legal instruments shall be used to create a balance between the appetite for national security and that overall sense of the need to establish a just and lawful international order.

5 Impact on Human Rights

While AI-enabled techno-systems can detect and respond to threat types much better, the unrestricted spread of such technology into surveillance, profiling, and decision-making brings ethical and legal issues into sharp focus. How states utilise AI for counterterrorism activities will, consequently, shape how freedoms that citizens enjoy, including privacy, freedom of movement, and access to justice, will be restricted.

Out of the many human rights violations that could arise due to AI in counterterrorism, the most significant is the accumulation of massive data facilitated by modern surveillance technologies. These systems of mass surveillance by means of AI ingest and sometimes analyse a huge amount of someone's private information and thus can easily violate the right to privacy when they extend their scope beyond real national security interests. Without adequate supervision, such tools may end up indiscriminately spying on civilians while innocently being part of security databases [10]. Facial recognition and predictive algorithms do contribute enormous pressures to these problems. Such technology usually results in biased policing practices. Usually, marginalised or minority communities face more scrutiny because of how algorithmic profiling is done. Hence, AI is a tool that ends up inciting racial or religious profiling in figuring out potential security threats, thereby violating the rights to equality and non-discrimination, which international human rights law confers.

Another cause for great concern is the opacity and fallibility associated with AI-based decision-making in counterterrorism. AI models are rapidly becoming more commonly introduced in security risk assessment, monitoring and tracking of individuals, and even providing possible suggestions for pre-emptive actions like arrest or drone strike. However, such decisions are made mostly by opaque systems without adequate judicial review. Therefore, the risk of mistargeting and punishment of a wrongly identified innocent human being increases greatly, especially when AI-influenced assessments drive actions in counterterrorism operations without human involvement. Algorithmic mispredictions come with severe consequences; they may include, but are not limited to, arbitrary detentions, travel restrictions, or even extrajudicial actions. Such practices infringe upon some of the core legal principles, like due process, the right to a fair trial, and access to justice. In addition, it is worsened by the absence of any accountability system, as it would become almost impossible for persons affected by the AI error to contest or correct their wrongful actions [11].

Civil liberties and democratic freedoms are finding their very distant frontiers beyond privacy violations and judicial concerns within the use of AI in counterterrorism. Enforced by AI, widespread surveillance will establish an aura of dread: to keep people from expressing freely, engaging in political activism, or assembling peacefully or avoid simply by being present. For those countries where governments have suppressed dissent on the premise of national security, artificial intelligence counterterrorism solutions will hardly add to public safety; they will be seen merely as political censorship programmes. Once one fears always watching, potentially punishing eyes, there is the danger that even the most careful reformers may begin self-censorship, slowly but surely undermining the key democratic principles of free speech and assembly, and dissent itself [12].

Ethical inclusion of AI in counterterrorism strategies should bring its usage under internationally recognised human rights standards. Comprehensive legal frameworks can proceed in clearly establishing limits for permissibly used action by AI-based surveillance and enforcement. Strong oversight mechanisms should be established by governments to prevent arbitrary intrusions into individual freedoms and ensure that AI systems in counterterrorism abide by principles such as necessity, proportionality, and accountability, among others. In addition to this, the development and deployment of AI technologies must adopt measures towards mitigating bias, improving algorithmic transparency, and offering avenues for redress to affected individuals.

While they shed light on some corporate responsibilities regarding the ethical deployment of AI, the UN Guiding Principles on Business and Human Rights are not extensive as to the general implications of using AI for impeding counterterrorism operations. Global governance frames comparing security needs to the need to observe human rights are pressingly required due to the heavy reliance upon AI in national security strategies. International cooperativeness would ensure that AI counterterrorism measures are transparent, legal, and non-discriminatory, and, therefore, a person would always be protected either by national security or by essential freedoms [13].

6 Ethical Dilemmas in AI-Driven Surveillance

The moral dilemma arising from the interrelation between artificial surveillance and the respect for human rights in the context of counterterrorism is highly complicated. However, the very same technologies create very significant threats to civil liberties and personal privacy. The ethical quandary is with understanding of accepted boundaries of surveillance, particularly when mass surveillance is offended by masses or certain communities.

Most disturbing of all, however, are the disparities in more general use of AI-based surveillance affecting marginal groups and the vulnerable. In this respect, mass monitoring leaves the threats of racial, ethnic, or political profiling and systemic discrimination. Enabling unchecked and extremely biased AI algorithms to perform just makes these biases worse, as it places such groups on the radar to be watched against, putting others that it should not touch on the radar. The opacity of the AI's decision-making process only exacerbates cruelty observed in those processes because people under surveillance hardly ever get a chance to question or attempt to understand the grounds on which they are targeted. Without information on how AI assesses threats, one cannot help but view unjust profiling and wrongful identification as grave human rights issues [14].

Another major ethical matter involves problems of consent and infringements by surveillance states. The acts of AI-oriented surveillance are often performed without any explicit permission from those under surveillance. Citizens do not even have the slightest idea as to the nature of the data that are being collected, used, and preserved, therefore posing enormous questions about personal autonomy and privacy. Counterterrorism contexts intensify this problem to another level in which issues of national security predetermine discretion and public debate. The absence of providing permission harms individual freedoms but also promotes a culture of fear in society over possible government encroachment and state control.

This unregulated growth of AI surveillance can drain the public trust in government institutions. A society in which individuals feel constantly spied upon can breed fear and self-censorship—both enemies to democracy and the open expression of thought and feeling. The psychological effect of constant surveillance might change social behaviour in ways that stunt dissent and inhibit open discourse [15].

As AI technologies advance, and their integration into counterterrorism operations becomes much more ingenious, the need for standard ethical and legal safeguards will increasingly become urgent. Policymakers must seek that fine balance between national security and the protection of rights, ensuring that surveillance mechanisms do not lead to arbitrary or excessive state powers. In instituting robust accountability frameworks and effective redress for all, the argument against AI surveillance being cast as an instrument of oppression rather than security can be laid to rest. Strict ethical standards and legal regulations are implemented to engage a society which leaves no question for prospective advancement to ensure such advancements would deliver benefits in terms of human rights rather than diminishing them.

7 The Ethics of Pre-emptive and Predictive Action

Increasingly reliant on artificial intelligence for their working, predictive policing and pre-emptive counterterrorism strategies harness sophisticated algorithms to analyse vast volumes of data with the aim of identifying potential threats even before they start to materialise. With capabilities to anticipate patterns of terrorist activities and other security threats, such technologies promise to advance enhanced national security through the mitigation of dangers at their very beginning. However, this imposition of artificial intelligence in such matters raises haunting ethical and legal concerns of great extent with respect to accuracy, fairness, and accountability for these pre-emptive actions [16].

A basic problem concerning AI-supported prediction-and-control mechanisms for security thermostats concerns the presence of uncertainty in the analyses being done. For they do not imply intent; rather, AI models find correlations and probabilities. Thus, it sometimes can be wrong: the hitherto common scenario of false positives erupts, whereby some accused persons or groups, conversely, are not really a threat and may indeed be the unfair subject of targeting, detention, or even a pre-emptive strike. Such action constitutes a denial of due process and the presumption of innocence and thereby undermines the very idea of justice in that those who are punished never committed or planned the punishment-worthy act.

Concerns about accountability and transparency further complicate the ethical questions involved in an AI-based counterterrorism initiative. In instances where the AI is activated after determining a threat, especially one that induces pre-emptive action directly through the AI or on the basis of recommendations submitted through AI to human decision-makers, there arises a difficult problem of attribution. Damages for wrongful targeting may not be recoverable because accountability falls between the AI developers, government decision-makers, and security personnel. The very obscurity of AI decision-making processes only worsens the problem; these decision-making systems often function in a black-box manner that precludes scrutiny of their rationale or verification of the accuracy or impartiality of any data that served as their input [17].

The possibility of misusing or overreaching in AI-fuelled pre-emptive security preparations is also at risk. Such threats may lead governments or security agencies to use this technology for justifying any form of excess surveillance, assigning biased profiles, or oppressive forces under national security. Predictive AI could cause grievous violations of human rights without strict laws and oversight mechanisms at work, which will predominantly affect underprivileged communities and individuals that already bear the brunt of systemic biases in law enforcement.

To have AI counterterrorism activities match up with national security needs alongside fundamental human rights concerns, it should include clarifying legal and ethical guidelines controlling their use. Strong safeguards, such as human oversight, clear criteria in decision-making, and access to appeal and redress, should be there to prevent loss that is unjustified. It would also include the relevant international law and principles of proportionality as one of the cornerstones in the deployment of AI in secured contexts so that unintended reactions do not go even beyond the appropriate indication of any perceived hazard [18].

High-stakes situations must have a good balance between pre-emptive action and civil liberties with regard to critical security decisions based on AI-driven predictions. And while AI can make terrorism counteraction much better in the future, exercising caution with this technology must ensure that justice, equity, and basic human rights will not be sacrificed.

8 Ethical and Legal Challenges of AI in Post-Terrorism Recovery and Justice

Emerging from the advances in AI technology are the sets of applications that involve post-terror recovery processes. This has very high potential for victim support, improvement of investigative procedures by security agencies, and generalised efforts towards rebuilding the devastated communities. An AI-enabled application is an important partner to call on in analysing the bulky databank of humans' images, videos, and witness accounts of rights violations or war crimes. AI offers event reconstruction for complex events through detection of behavioural patterns and movement tracing associated with terrorists, which human investigators may find difficult to piece together. Moreover, AI can optimise humanitarian aid by predicting sites of need and developing models for efficient resource distribution in post-conflict contexts [19].

Such realities notwithstanding, it has ethical implications for all the uses of the technology in a post-terror-recovery context. Among the thorny issues is possible bias in AI systems for surveillance and monitoring of detailed locations. Such misuses lead to improper profiling of beings or communities. All about human suffering that terrorism brings cannot possibly be scaled out of marks of data and somehow can thus escape the lines of red predictably drawn around AIs. This tool cannot see or help shape the trauma as 'invisible' or define the psychological and social implications of the light it may cast through utilising AI's investigative and aid-distribution capacities.

The other major issue is the measures for securing and using ethically the data that would be captured within immediate recovery following terrorism. For this reason, systems of AI will require gargantuan amounts of data for them to work well; the majority of this data are necessarily sensitive, even with much personal data about the victims and the populations affected. Subsequently, if it does not happen along this path of transparency and proper data protection measures, then the information may well be misused to be beyond recovery and justice, such as through actions of intrusive surveillance and/or wrongful profiling. Such long-term implications would apply to especially vulnerable communities if post-intrusive sweeps applying to AI monitoring still continued after the immediate crisis because all such thresholds would have been breached [20].

Moreover, the infusion of AI into justice systems is fraught with difficult legal and moral conundrums. Though AI would help in the evaluation of material evidence, identification of risks, or easing the functioning of judicial processes, any role of AI in conclusively determining guilt or innocence, or victim compensation, must be carefully thought out. Automated decision-making would unregulate open systemic biases or fail to grasp any of the complex nuances of particular cases. It is important to maintain the principles of fairness, due process, and accountability through ensuring that AI becomes an adjunct to human judgement, rather than a substitute for it.

Beyond investigations and legal proceedings, AI's role in post-terrorism recovery needs to evolve, keeping the respective wider societal objectives for reconciliation and healing in the justice system: a humane version of technology that would work against driving deeper wedges between people. Any misapplication of AI-driven classification systems might potentially lead to stigmatising persons on the basis of previous affiliations or behaviours, which might hinder reintegration efforts and further widen societal rifts. AI, therefore, needs to be deployed in post-terrorism contexts in a manner that guarantees respect for human dignity, trust, and long-term reconciliation outcomes [21].

AI would provide excellent opportunities concerning post-terrorism recovery. However, its usage should follow ethical guidelines in a way to highlight fairness, empathy, and respect for human rights. It should be able to strike a balance between making full use of the capabilities of AI without restricting and maintaining human agency to ensure that justice is served and communities are rebuilt for lasting peace. AI should function as a supportive instrument that enhances rather than replaces human decision-making in addressing the complex challenges that arise in the aftermath of terrorism.

9 Scope for Future Work

Due to the rising complexity of cyber threats, the field of cybersecurity attracts rich attention. Human priority increases adversarial agents, such as viruses or worms, making them sophisticated in showing complex networked behaviour. This is pressing demand for intelligent cyber defence systems. This is an important task of training intelligent cyber-sensor agents or computer-generated forces for these problems, considering the vigour with which they should be capable of acquiring, processing, analysing, and reacting to cyber-attacks in real time and effective ways.

Using artificial intelligence (AI) in cybersecurity holds incredible promise, requiring careful design and extensive research to use that promise. A core issue in this field is the problem of knowledge management itself, particularly network-centric combat. The development of modular and hierarchical knowledge structures, which further enhance decision-making software, is an area for research for the future. Speed assessment of the scenario and decision dominance, possible only with automated knowledge-management systems, will be key for adopting AI successfully in cyber defence [22].

The ultimate objective of AI investigation, however, remains the ultimate form of intelligence greater than human strengths: artificial general intelligence (AGI). The appearance of an AGI may give rise to the singularity—the point of art where technology becomes intelligent but more intelligent than humans. As far as cyber defence is concerned, storage defence systems would require AI technologies that are more powerful than those used by cyber attackers. This guarantees that countermeasures with respect to computer networks always stay one step ahead of advancing attacks. This could prove particularly useful in the field of intelligent agent development to respond to the evolving interaction and situation of the dynamic nature of such cyberattacks [23].

This is a multifaceted and critical area of research in which the role of artificial intelligence (AI) becomes significant in combating cyber terrorism, and the future appears promising for progressive transformation. The advancement of AI models for prediction towards better identification and prevention of cyber acts associated with terrorism is, likewise, an impending focus of research. One could include a study into the design of more sophisticated algorithms and machine learning methods such that these systems would increase the proficiency of an AI towards identifying ad hoc dangers or serious threats. Furthermore, there is a growing deficit in research attempts to investigate how artificial intelligence may be integrated into cybersecurity architectures of governments, businesses and intelligence agencies. Such an investigation would focus on how AI technologies could improve existing defence mechanisms to meet the ever-evolving cyber threat of terrorists. Evaluating on-the-field deployment of AI-based cybersecurity solutions and the impact of these components would generate very useful insights for politicians and security practitioners.

Ethical and legal challenges surrounding AI applicability to counter cyber terrorism constitute a complex, multifaceted area in future work. Researchers in this area would be best advised to study how ethical norms and regulatory regimes evolved to limit application of AI for counterterrorism purposes, however. Hence, everyone now feels the necessity to know all such ethical matters and legal ramifications of these kinds of AI devices, as this information shall help to shape regulatory systems finding intermediate equilibria between the needs of security and the safeguarding of human privacy and human rights. For instance, with the introduction and advancement of AI technologies, it is very much possible to think about the investigation into properties of vulnerabilities that are inherent in AI systems. It is of immense importance to experience adversarial attacks on the algorithms of AI and develop techniques which shall improve the robustness of AI-based cybersecurity systems and therefore guarantee the reliability and validity of the systems in combating cyber terrorism [24].

A transdisciplinary approach to the study of socio-technical dimensions of AI with regard to cyberterrorism may open up quite promising avenues for future study. The human factor, for example, in terms of how humans will interact with AI-powered security systems and the social and political consequences of a much larger-scale application of AI in counterterrorism, can help paint a more holistic picture of AI's potential full impact on security practices.

There is a lot of scope and variety to research AI as an instrument against cyber terrorism. Researchers contribute to the technology and the development of applied innovations with their ethical and social consequences. Artificial intelligence must be used in the future because of increasing cyberattacks, which require continuous innovation to solve applied behaviour-based approaches in cyber terrorism in an ethical and feasible manner [25].

10 Recommendations

Such frameworks should prescribe norms on transparency in AI decision-making, create tangible boundaries for the gathering of data, and make them bear responsibility in counterterrorism arrangements in artificial intelligence.

In order to avoid potential maluses and ensure the basic rights, autonomous organisations, which would control, had to be instituted. With the right forms of oversight, such institutions will be able to moderate the risks associated with the use of the AI in the security of the surroundings [26].

Ethical use of AI for national security is influenced by public participation. This participative process will be a barrier that does not give technology a right to infringe on civil liberties or make the security measures unconstitutional.

It is also important to ensure human command over any operation related to counterterrorism in which the application of AI is used. There should be a very clear assignment of legal and ethical responsibility for AI-enabled choices to individuals or agencies to avoid responsibility by no one and to support the principle of human control of automated procedures. Fail-safe: there has to be an obligatory kill switch for all AI systems used in counterterrorism. This very mechanism would permit an immediate termination of an AI system in case of any kind of failure in the course of operational functioning which could potentially have unperceived effects. This check would see that decisions made by artificial intelligence would be followed by conscious human measures so as to minimise the risk of autonomous decision-making in high-stakes situations for security agencies. Such provisions would allow any government to strike a balance between pursuing national security initiatives and upholding the health of democracy, human rights, and ethical governance [27].

11 Conclusion

This research focuses on the outgrowing menace of cyber terrorism, laying emphasis on artificial intelligence (AI) as a technology in both preventing and responding to such terrorism. Given the fact that cyberspace is woven into the fabric of global economies, it sets national, international, political, and economic edges, and cultural and social security threats await cyber terrorism, providing some of the most significant threats in terms of national and international stability. Cyber terrorists deploy state-of-the-art technology to stage high-end attacks, which bring about interception of communication lines, encoding system exploitation, and cracking of cybersecurity. These attacks cannot be just on an individual level but on a wide level where thousands or even millions of devices become part of one large network. The large infiltration and execution speed enable criminal harm such as sabotage, terrorism, exploitation, and abuse.

Outlined Findings of the Research

1. Cyber terrorism: Cyber terrorism has become a series of systematic attacks, usually planned to accomplish some clearly defined political purposes. These attacks were targeted mainly to make the government bend to specific policies or disorient public endorsement. In their course of storytelling through fear acquisition, the perpetrators use the platform of digital media by threats or actual cyberattacks leading to the organising and destruction of merchandise.
2. Different Causes of Cyber Terrorism: The emergence and increase in cyber terrorism stem from several interrelated causes. Politically, it is linked to governmental restrictions on public participation, causing discontent and radicalisation. Economically, it is the social disparity and the high unemployment rates that give situations to individuals who are then vulnerable to the extremes of ideology. In technological terms, the digital networks, and most of them have intrinsic security vulnerabilities at the same time, expose terrorists and terrorist organisations to opportunities. With cyber terrorism becoming highly cost-effective and carrying very low risks, it has attracted many extremist organisations to the concept.
3. Using Digital Propaganda and Recruitment Approaches: Terrorists have used the Internet so much for their propaganda, recruitment, and even for coordinating their operational activities. The terrorist organisations manipulate the digital platforms in order to unduly access sensitive information and infiltrate websites. It is largely concerning their recruiting of the most vulnerable individuals, namely children, through deceptive means and psychological manipulation.
4. AI-Double-Edged Sword: Progress in AI has overhauled many sectors, including law enforcement, where security and surveillance operations become part of the implementation of its AI-driven tools. With crime detection, the possibility of improving intelligence gathering and real-time analysis of threats becomes considerable. But even though it bolsters the efficiency at which counterterrorism efforts can be made, it opens resistance completely. They can use this to create automated penetration techniques, sophisticated attack methods, and autonomous threats regarding terrorism.
5. AI Countermeasures, the Need: AI can also be applied for criminal purposes; thus, it has made the need for counter-AI threats more compelling. Law enforcement agencies should invest in an augmented collection of AI facilities to preemptively counter cyber threats. Strategies need to be put in place for predictive analysis, AI-based detection and monitoring of extremists over the Internet, and the construction of advanced defence systems against AI-enabled cyber terrorism.

Thus, while AI can turn into a magic wand for all transformative solutions related to enhancing security measures, its inherent dual-use nature calls for censorship through stringent regulations and technological interventions. The fight against cyber terrorism crossing geographical boundaries in the world must develop with AI, into which direct preventive measures evolve into the new threats.

References

1. Königstorfer, F., & Thalmann, S. (2022). Ai documentation: A path to accountability. *Journal of Responsible Technology, 11*, 100043. https://doi.org/10.1016/j.jrt.2022.100043
2. Bellaby, R. (2024). The ethical problems of 'intelligence–AI'. *International Affairs, 100*(6), 2525–2542. https://doi.org/10.1093/ia/iiae227
3. Singh, B., & Kaunert, C. (2024). Intelligent machine learning solutions for cybersecurity. In *Advances in computational intelligence and robotics* (pp. 359–386). https://doi.org/10.4018/979-8-3693-5380-6.ch014
4. Shafik, W. (2024). Toward a more ethical future of artificial intelligence and data science. In *The ethical Frontier of AI and data analysis* (pp. 362–388). IGI Global.
5. Bhardwaj, A. (2024). Secure framework against cyberattacks on cyber-physical robotic systems. In *Smart home and industrial IoT devices: Critical perspectives on cyberthreats, frameworks and protocols* (pp. 98–127). https://doi.org/10.2174/9789815256710124010006
6. Chithaluru, P., Al-Turjman, F., Kumar, M., & Stephan, T. (2023). Computational-intelligence-inspired adaptive opportunistic clustering approach for industrial IoT networks. *IEEE Internet of Things Journal, 10*(9), 7884–7892. https://doi.org/10.1109/jiot.2022.3231605
7. Wiafe, I., Koranteng, F. N., Obeng, E. N., Assyne, N., Wiafe, A., & Gulliver, S. R. (2020). Artificial intelligence for cybersecurity: A systematic mapping of literature. *IEEE Access, 8*, 146598–146612.
8. Zhang, Z., Ning, H., Shi, F., Farha, F., Xu, Y., Xu, J., Zhang, F., & Choo, K.-K. R. (2021). Artificial intelligence in cyber security: Research advances, challenges, and opportunities. *Artificial Intelligence Review, 55*(2), 1029–1053. https://doi.org/10.1007/s10462-021-09976-0
9. Promyslov, V. G., Semenkov, K. V., & Shumov, A. S. (2019). A clustering method of asset cybersecurity classification. *IFAC-PapersOnLine, 52*(13), 928–933. https://doi.org/10.1016/j.ifacol.2019.11.313
10. Millar, K., Cheng, A., Chew, H. G., & Lim, C. C. (2020, December). Operating system classification: A minimalist approach. In *2020 international conference on machine learning and cybernetics (ICMLC)* (pp. 143–150). IEEE.
11. Cvitić, I., Peraković, D., Periša, M., & Gupta, B. (2021). Ensemble machine learning approach for classification of IoT devices in smart home. *International Journal of Machine Learning and Cybernetics, 12*(11), 3179–3202.
12. Kure, H. I., Islam, S., Ghazanfar, M., Raza, A., & Pasha, M. (2021). Asset criticality and risk prediction for an effective cybersecurity risk management of cyber-physical system. *Neural Computing and Applications, 34*(1), 493–514. https://doi.org/10.1007/s00521-021-06400-0
13. Rivera, D., Monje, F., Villagrá, V. A., Vega-Barbas, M., Larriva-Novo, X., & Berrocal, J. (2019). Automatic translation and enforcement of cybersecurity policies using a high-level definition language. *Entropy, 21*(12), 1180. https://doi.org/10.3390/e21121180
14. Bringhenti, D., Marchetto, G., Sisto, R., Valenza, F., & Yusupov, J. (2019, October). Towards a fully automated and optimized network security functions orchestration. In *2019 4th international conference on computing, communications and security (ICCCS)* (pp. 1–7). IEEE.
15. Jazeera, A. (2023, January 31). Death toll from Pakistan mosque bombing rises to 100. Al Jazeera. https://www.aljazeera.com/news/2023/1/31/pakistan-rescue-operation-peshawar-mosque-suicide-bombing.
16. Amnesty International. (2022, August 8). Philippines: 'Battle of Marawi' leaves trail of death and destruction. https://www.amnesty.org/en/latest/press-release/2017/11/philippines-battle-of-marawi-leaves-trail-of-death-and-destruction/.
17. BBC News. (2018, July 16). Pakistan mourns 149 dead in country's second deadliest terror attack. https://www.bbc.com/news/world-asia-44847295.
18. Sen, N. J. (2021, December 12). The Big Read: Jemaah Islamiyah emerges from the shadows, playing the long game. CNA. https://www.channelnewsasia.com/singapore/jemaah-islamiyah-terrorist-group-indonesia-isd-20th-anniversary-2373556.

19. Ahmed, M., Moustafa, N., Barkat, A., & Haskell-Dowland, P. (2022). *Next-generation enterprise security and governance*. CRC Press eBooks. https://doi.org/10.1201/9781003121541
20. Davis, A. L. (2021). Artificial intelligence and the fight against international terrorism. *American Intelligence Journal, 38*(2), 63–73. https://www.jstor.org/stable/27168700
21. Möller, D. P. F. (2023). Cybersecurity in digital transformation. In *Advances in information security* (pp. 1–70). https://doi.org/10.1007/978-3-031-26845-8_1
22. Kaur, R., Gabrijelčič, D., & Klobučar, T. (2023). Artificial intelligence for cybersecurity: Literature review and future research directions. *Information Fusion, 97*, 101804. https://doi.org/10.1016/j.inffus.2023.101804
23. Dinu, A., Vasile, P. C., & Georgescu, A. (2024). AI-driven solutions for cybersecurity: Comparative analysis and ethical aspects. *Romanian Journal of Information Technology and Automatic Control, 34*(3), 35–48.
24. Habbal, A., Ali, M. K., & Abuzaraida, M. A. (2024). Artificial intelligence trust, risk and security management (AI trism): Frameworks, applications, challenges and future research directions. *Expert Systems with Applications, 240*, 122442. https://doi.org/10.1016/j.eswa.2023.122442
25. Rehan, H. (2024). AI-driven cloud security: The future of safeguarding sensitive data in the digital age. *Journal of Artificial Intelligence General Science (JAIGS)*: ISSN 3006-4023, *1*(1), 132–151.
26. Zhuwankinyu, E. K., Moyo, T. M., & Mupa, M. N. (2024). Leveraging generative AI for an ethical and adaptive cybersecurity framework in enterprise environments. *IRE Journals, 8*(6), 654–675.
27. Marsico, F., & Amigo, M. (2025). Ethical and security challenges in AI for forensic genetics: From bias to adversarial attacks. *Forensic Science International: Genetics, 76*, 103225. https://doi.org/10.1016/j.fsigen.2025.103225

[illegible]

Evolving Role of Autonomous Systems in Counter-Terrorism

Nituja Singh and Saquib Ahmed

Abstract The threat of terrorism demands a constant revaluation of security policy since it is of an unexpected nature and prone to constantly changing tactics. Autonomous systems (AS) which include, artificial intelligence, robots, and machine learning (ML) are increasingly being suggested as a revolutionary tool for counterterrorism (CT) operations. This chapter highlights the main operational, ethical, and legal issues while examining the different ways that AS may enhance capabilities, lower risks, and address current terrorist threats. AS is a paradigm change from conventional, human-centric CT techniques. It is characterised as systems that can operate and make decisions on their own within certain constraints. Its integration seeks to enhance human cefficiency and capacities in threat assessment, monitoring, reaction, and prevention to facilitate more successful and coordinated counterterrorism operations. The emergence of autonomous weapon systems challenge human understanding and ideas of autonomous combat and lethal force. Since artificial intelligence could someday be used for similar schemes against people and governments, terrorist organisations' use of technology could result in a deadly loop of technological improvement in the fight against terrorism. One of the main worries is how easily autonomous systems could be breached and used maliciously or against their operators. CT will be able to ensure security without compromising fundamental human values or international legal obligations by negotiating this difficult terrain and utilising the benefits of emerging technology while reducing their inherent risks.

N. Singh (✉)
Symbiosis Law School, Noida Campus, Faculty of Law, Symbiosis International (Deemed) University, Pune, India

S. Ahmed
School of Law, Sharda University, Greater Noida, India

C. Kaunert et al. (eds.), *Artificial Intelligence for Global Counter-Terrorism*, Contributions to Security and Defence Studies,
https://doi.org/10.1007/978-3-031-99235-3_4

1 Introduction

Essentially synonymous with the notion of advanced information technology solutions, AI refers to a variety of systems of different abstraction levels and computational intensity. At a basic level, it can refer to less advanced data-driven AI systems specifically designed to prevent or respond to terrorist attacks. More advanced systems leverage AI to synthesize a wider analytical base that is more comprehensive in generating observations. Ambitious attempts may be made in the future to replicate AI-driven theory of mind or value reasoning systems. It should also be noted that AI can be used by groups for malicious purposes as well. For this paper, the term will refer to human-based systems that accept different types of intelligence for counterterrorism [1].

The primary advantage of AS in CT is that it records tasks that need to be performed in settings that are considered too dangerous or stressful for human labour. By doing dangerous activities like bomb disposal, scouting in hostile environments, and neutralising active shooter situations, autonomous robots lower the risk to human life. Proactive CT measures and rapid response times would be improved by improving situational awareness through real-time data processing and threat assessment. AI-driven analytical tools may also search through massive datasets, including social media, communication networks, and open-source content, to identify possible terrorist threats, networks, and evolving patterns in order to give CT operations vital information. Data biases exercised in artificial intelligence systems may lead to biased or inaccurate CT applications that disproportionately impact specific demographics or individuals depending on protected qualities, like religion, colour, or another attribute. When autonomous decisions are made without human supervision, accountability, or oversight, there are major problems. When AS is allowed to use force, there are certain worries about the potential for unforeseen events, collateral damage, and violations of international humanitarian law. The comprehension of the reasoning behind self-governing decisions is also compromised by the 'black box' nature of some deep learning algorithms, which restricts transparency and the ability to rectify biases or errors.

AI systems are designed to automate or augment human intelligence activities as well as decision-making and assessment processes. Such systems could be used to filter, analyse, distribute, and archive intelligence. AI-aided systems are already used in detection and tracking systems for nuclear weapons, preventive data fusion mining tools for counterterrorism and urban warfare, and a system for detecting possible violations of international treaties. Some of the AI systems that are used in counterterrorism include predictive data mining for generating warnings about potential threats, risk assessment systems, identity recognition systems based on face biometrics, or general data mining tools applied to analyse resonance in social networks [2]. In other words, the progress in defence technology and the nature of future terrorist threats force decision-makers and experts involved in the counterterrorism debate to assess the available technical options and to steer away from the 'direct' military models based on military force or intervention only [3].

1.1 Definition and Scope of AI in Counterterrorism

'Artificial intelligence' (AI) is an umbrella term encompassing a large spectrum of data-driven technologies. This may include a variety of mathematical and statistical methods, algorithms, and data processing tools—and their hybrids. Such systems can be customized for manifold ends, including but not limited to advanced pattern recognition, cataloguing and linking archives and datasets, investigation and detection of anomalies, mapping of communication patterns, as well as the creation of predictive models. Accordingly, AI systems may form the core of a range of operative tools, for instance, in the form of decision support, as well as real-time or microsecond applications for flagged cases. The application of AI to counterterrorism is situated at the processing front end of security work, primarily to do the 'heavy lifting' of the massive accumulation of data and information in the twenty-first-century risk environment [4]. Although AI means different things in different organizational contexts and legal traditions, contemporary characterizations generally assume that data mining, processing, and analytics are all part of AI systems. Because it involves advanced computational capacity and massive amounts of data, AI may also necessarily involve some predictive capacities. At the same time, not all data analytics in counterterrorism is AI: many legacy systems, especially those designed to meet biometric and data exchange standards, operate according to algorithms that are not necessarily fully connected. Nor are they, in all cases, retrofitted to process advances in digital and communications technology [5].

1.2 Benefits of AI in Counterterrorism

The capability of using AI to enhance counterterrorism is closely linked to its potential in combating crime more generally. There are several key benefits to using AI with respect to terrorism:

1. Faster processing of large amounts of data: Through specific algorithms, AI systems can process huge quantities of data much faster than any human operator would be able to. This means more data on potential terrorists can be analysed with less lag, addressing the weaknesses of the current system.
2. The potential to predict from patterns: AI can also help security services predict terrorist behaviours based on patterns and behaviours of known terrorists. Systems have already been developed to predict behaviour in crime and abnormal behaviours more generally.
3. Automating routine procedures: AI can further be used to automate routine procedures for security staff, freeing their capacity for strategic decisions alongside improving efficiency.
4. Enhanced intelligence gathering and assessment: AI can be used to help security staff gather intelligence on potential terrorist threats and assess this more comprehensively and rapidly [6]. This sort of work is already being conducted in

areas such as border security. Numerous areas of security are using AI and machine learning to enhance their activities. At the most banal, federal intelligence services have talked openly about using AI algorithms to predict patterns of suspicious activity as part of their ongoing fight to stop individuals who have left the country to join extremist groups from re-entering and attending military facilities [7]. Finally, indeed, the government has been experimenting with machine learning systems when it comes to their threat analysis of extremism, as well as commercial companies that specialize in counterterrorism.

2 Ethical Frameworks and Principles in Artificial Intelligence

Understanding the ethical position of AI deployed in counterterrorism requires a solid foundation in ethical theory that establishes how such evaluation should be conducted. Recently, there has been interest in the development of ethical frameworks for AI that go beyond basic deontological considerations of 'non-maleficence,' 'autonomy,' 'beneficence,' and 'justice.' Several suggestions have been made for developing and intensifying an ethical AI project in counterterrorism. In order to add to the discussion on these key principles, this ethical section will critically assess these five different systems, stressing the importance of procedures as well as consequences. It puts together an account where different considerations are weighed against each other according to their potential to fulfil morality, which has particular implications for matters related to operational practice as well as law and policy [8].

Across accounts, a significant part of the reason why actions are performed, and an important function of how we appraise others' actions, is based on whether the consequences of these actions are beneficial or bring about better than bad. In the security and counterterrorism context, protecting the public stands by far as the most important good. So critical is the value of the greater good over subordinate good that, in deciding between deep dilemmas posed by such problems as collateral damage, decision-making personnel tend to prioritize the greater good generally. Hence, if confronted with exercising an operation that saves 10 people in Industrial Town and another military strike that could result in some civilian lives lost but prevents far greater deaths, the 'risk' would engage in the latter [9].

3 Challenges of Artificial Intelligence in Counterterrorism

There is an ongoing debate about the security implications of advancing AI for counterterrorism. To date, however, a scarce but growing body of literature has acknowledged the potential and severe risks and challenges of deploying AI in counterterrorism [10]. The first challenge is that AI-based threat assessment risks biases that are inherent to the algorithms used for detecting patterns and deviations from them. The use of AI in security screening is feared to lead to discriminatory practices and, hence, increase societal divisions. This is particularly concerning if suspected terrorists are already marginalized and discriminated against—an often-reproving recruitment factor of terrorist organizations [11]. A further challenge of AI-based counterterrorism is the potential lack of transparency in automated threat detections, warnings, and decision-making. An opaque, or 'black box,' decision-making process can dramatically reduce public trust in the state's security apparatus as it is likely to be perceived as arbitrary.

A third challenge is the question of accountability for automated decisions in AI systems. Unlike human radars and officers, AI-driven radars and security personnel cannot be held liable in court, nor can they voice the actual reasons for their decisions. Ethical and technical difficulties arise in ascribing legal responsibility to the programmer if the error cannot be traced back to one specific AI entity but is instead a consequence of a multitude of programming and data trade-offs that were made [12]. These concerns have manifold real-world implications. A critical analysis of the passport control systems at an airport showed that the AI-based algorithm deployed was significantly more successful in identifying 'terrorists' known and registered in the databases, while the human expert was more successful when it came to detecting those who were not yet known to the authorities.

3.1 Bias and Discrimination

Presumably, one of the most discussed issues in AI and big data applications in counterterrorism refers to bias and discrimination. This growing literature questions how AI applications could reproduce or create unfair targeting practices [13]. AI and big data technologies can capture and perpetuate existing discrimination in the AI training data because an AI-driven algorithm is only as good as the data that is fed into it. If the data includes biases, the algorithm replicates it, and the results are biased as well; i.e., its predictions tend to be unfair [14]. So far, the main concern related to biasness- in the counterterrorism literature is that algorithms produce predictions based on biased data and not that AI technologies could introduce or procure expressions of regulating agency. There are different ways in which using biased algorithms can generate biased results and perpetuate bias and discrimination in society. One well-known example of biased AI is the case of racial profiling. AI predictions in this respect tend to focus on people from racial or ethnic groups that are mostly represented in the training systems.

3.2 Transparency and Explainability

The last condition is how to create such systems that are technically explained, i.e., the considerations and decisions of such systems are transparent. The more the decisions of these types of systems are transparent, the more trust these systems can gain. One of the main requirements of standard ethical and philosophical practice in counterterrorism is that the outputs of any intuitive analysis are explained. Without an explanation, analyst decisions cannot be fully or effectively evaluated. Thus, intuitive decision support systems should be designed using approaches, techniques, and technologies that privilege transparency as the central motivation in the design of the system [15].

The importance of transparency for AI is an issue that has been highlighted in reports on this topic. The original panels on algorithmic transparency demonstrated how a lack of explainability increases scepticism and lack of trust in AI technologies. Understanding how an AI system 'arrives at its conclusions' can help ensure algorithms are transparent and subjected to robust design decisions, that they are accountable, and that users understand the decisions such systems make. Designers are not required to explain everything about how the systems operate (which can pose security vulnerabilities by revealing too much about how an algorithm operates) but are required to disambiguate and make expertise or evidence more understandable, rationalizing what the system shows the user [16]. A major concern in this area relates to 'black-box' algorithms, i.e., those that are inscrutable with respect to revealing their rationale or decision process. The implications of opaqueness for constitutional rights and individual freedoms are particularly evident in cases where data or algorithms employed by police and intelligence agencies are not clearly reported. Some AI systems can also process faulty data without knowing and, therefore, produce incorrect (and sometimes biased) results. When employed in criminal law or intelligence operations, the opaqueness of such systems can lead to wrongful accusations and misinformed operations. No hidden AI system can observe values or care about intuitions. Ethical implications: a lack of transparency can lead to ethical issues, particularly when people are implicated with contentious counterterrorism and security practices (specifically blocklisting, profiling, and biometric surveillance).

3.3 Accountability and Responsibility

Transferring accountability to an AI system complicates the question of who is responsible for decisions made by the AI and the rationality behind it. In cases of error, negligence can be difficult to determine when considering an AI, despite fault often being assigned to the operator by law. The wide implementation of AI decision-making systems could result in less responsibility and liability for errors and misconduct. In turn, this could create opacity and increase public suspicion concerning security agencies and other actors that utilize AI-driven systems [17]. Any serious negligence may result in damages or death, risking the reputation and legitimacy of AI-driven systems. However, as an entity, AI cannot be imprisoned or follow a court's authority, further complicating questions of legal responsibility. Where an individual cannot be determined, and the technological fault is established, or the results are too significant, the organization may be liable, further influencing accountability and the indictment of organizations for mistakes made in law enforcement and counterterrorism operations.

4 Case Studies and Examples

In this section, I first present case studies and examples to highlight how AI is used for counterterrorism. Second, I critically assess to what extent the implementation of AI yielded the desired results. At the same time, I also discuss pitfalls, such as the system's inaccuracy or bias, and the public discussions on this issue. While there has been substantial interest from academics in writing about threat detection, a critical analysis of existing counterterrorism practices is missing. Therefore, I discuss the four most prominent AI technologies: CI systems, NLP natural language processing is a sort of artificial intelligence. It enables AI to process, comprehend and decode human languages in any given context to find out a target result or outcome, network analysis, and tracking, and show how they are being used in practice [18]. Both AI scholars and practitioners agree that using these technologies can be problematic in the context of law enforcement as they lead to racial profiling and large numbers of false positives. It can be argued that the gathering, processing, and sharing of offline content and other information can be seen as the first step in operational prevention [19].

4.1 Predictive Policing

The deployment of AI in predicting where attacks will occur also raises the question of predictive policing and the vision underpinning these techniques. On one hand, AI-driven tools are said to help pinpoint where crime is likely to happen and dose the right locations and potential troublemakers with the necessary attention, potentially preventing a crime that would otherwise have occurred. On the other hand, the use of such techniques poses the risk of being perceived as legitimizing profiling on the basis of past data. These predictive techniques go one step beyond predictive policing into what has been called pre-policing, as the goal of identifying potential threats before they arise is not necessarily based on established criminal predictors [20].

Given the reticence towards targeted killing and rigid restrictions on its use, the risks of transfer to counterterrorism policy cannot be overstated. After all, if a suspect is monitored using some of these techniques and the risk of whether he will commit a crime is above a certain level, then a justification may suggest acting as a precautionary principle. In law enforcement, the doctrine of preventive interventionism is often linked to both reactive strategies that criminals are not able to deter and distinctive features in changing police priorities and strategies from a reactive approach to query shop work, in which criminal patterns are identified to facilitate the allocation of resources and prevention efforts. To begin with, predictive policing raises difficult ethical questions concerning surveillance, but it could also make it possible to adapt the strategies of law enforcement agents to the scale of the threat, massing them only where the risk of criminal activity is high and thus making society as a whole safer [21].

4.2 Surveillance Technologies

AI-based surveillance techniques, including facial recognition, are also utilized in an increasing number of countries as part of counterterrorism activities. Deployed mostly in urban environments, extensive monitoring of public spaces in several countries is aimed at identifying irregular behaviour and objects in order to deter or prevent attacks. Many of these technologies are aimed at real-time processing, for instance, to identify persons wanted by police who pass a network of cameras. Surveillance, in these cases, uses face recognition software that extracts a number of biometric features, making it possible to 'enrol' a person or to compare a picture with a whole set of random facial features in order to find if any other matches can be found. An algorithm looks for patterns in the biometric features [22].

5 Public Policy Perspectives on Counterterrorism

Counterterrorism policy formulation in terms of its complexity is the domain of political agents, institutions, and society. Counterterrorism studies, in contrast to terrorism studies, are theorized low relative to the number of theorized schemas. Policymakers work under a constraint of having very little information and as a result tend to make incremental rather than revolutionary changes [23].

Three primary factors i.e., ideas, interests, and institutions shape counterterrorism policies. Concepts refer to the cognitive and prescribing constructs of policies. Interests stem from cost benefit calculations and power relations, whereas institutions are formal rules and informal structures of governance, which restrain policymaking. The set of factors defines the counterterrorism strategy performance and its effectiveness [24].

6 Risk in Counterterrorism

Terrorism is one of the most serious problems facing international peace and security. Counterterrorism operations are no less complex, and there are masses of challenges that constrain counterterrorism effectiveness. This section delves into the specific challenges in counterterrorism [25].

6.1 *Technological Exploitation*

Terrorist organizations have increasingly exploited advancements in technology. The Fourth Industrial Revolution grants such organizations the chance to act with tools such as encryption, cyber applications, and drones, and operate thus in a more sophisticated and stealthy way [26]. Social media sites have also been exploited for many good purposes such as for recruitment, talent-hunts, social welfarism, etc. However; it is equally being misused as well; such as dissemination of propaganda, fake-information, and as a platform for inciting violence, deep- fake pornography, etc. which act as a virtual battlefield over social media platforms using different AI tools and it seems extremely hard to have a coherent effective control and monitoring such misuse of AI [27].

Anonymity in encrypted messaging software enhances the challenge to intelligence gathering, whereas the darknet is a hidden shop of illegal activities, such as weapons and national secret information. However, governments have made hardly any time to cope with these rapidly developing technologies that continue to change the terrain [28].

6.2 *Decentralized Networks*

Decentralized terrorist networks like the ones that emerged in recent years create unprecedented challenges for counterterrorism operations. These networks work in a non-hierarchical manner which makes them difficult to be observed and intervened by intelligence agencies. This decentralization enables small teams or even individuals to conduct attacks autonomously, often based on online radicalized content.

The geo dimension of the localized networks, the inseparability of time, reason, space, and human relationships at local, regional, and global levels is also useful as it involves in the morbidity concerns of each level and can be specialized for other sociopolitical issues. This plasticity nullifies conventional efforts at solving the issue of terrorism, as in [29].

6.3 Radicalization and Rehabilitation

Radicalization is a critical issue in counterterrorism. The adoption of extremist ideas in the personality is generally a sequential process of individual subjectivation shaped by the many socioeconomic and political factors. Counter-radicalisation interventions present practical difficulties in selectively identifying people to be at risk and in dealing with the antecedent precipitating factors that lead to frustration. Moreover, rehabilitation and reintegration of radicalized persons, especially foreign fighters returning from conflict areas, still is a costly issue [30].

6.4 Cyberterrorism

Cyberterrorism is a present danger, the computer network-based, politically motivated threat to threaten or to victimize. Terrorists are now also attacking critical infrastructures, as well as financial sectors and government networks. Due to the anonymity of cyberspace, attacks could be attributed and penalized very easily. Moreover, the rapid pace of technological advancements often outstrips the ability of regulatory frameworks to keep up, leaving gaps in cybersecurity measures [31].

6.5 Proxy Terrorism

The resurgence of proxy terrorism, in which states construct terrorist groups to destabilize adversaries, undermines the international antiterrorism campaign. These tasks are another challenge for attributions and the responsibility issues thereof which are not always easily resolved towards the root of terrorism.

Proxy groups are in their nature that which functions in dysfunctional states, attuning to and exploiting existing waves of violence and resentments that exist at the local level. Not only is this method destabilizing the targeted areas, but it also causes ongoing problems for the foreign peacekeeping and counterterrorism operations [32].

6.6 One-Size-Fits All Policies

Counterterrorism strategies based on AS often rely on the same algorithm same approach within the limitations of the data processed and its maximum permutation and combination in the given situations and therefore; it does not account for socio-political and cultural peculiarities of any particular region. Moreover; these individualised interventions are not provided, leading to poor results and sometimes cause the local groups to be alienated, thereby worsening the issue.

Areas with a variety of cultural and political environments require adaptation to the unique determinants of terrorism. Restricting oneself to these nuanced considerations could lead to oversimplifying of complex scenarios with undesirable consequences [33].

6.7 Financial and Resource Constraints

Counterterrorism efforts often face significant financial and resource constraints. Especially in the low- and middle-income countries, it is an absolute nightmare really to equitably be attending to so many resources' demand for counterterrorism while simultaneously addressing a host of other social and economic priorities. This scarcity of resource distribution provides opening for some gaps that can be exploited by terrorist organisations.

Coordinated international collaboration to share and develop resources is essential, but geopolitical paralysis repeatedly reflects that most of the times the objective is not achieved rather collaboration and coordination to counter terrorism is dicouraged. by not inducing robust equitable distribution of resources. Further; country relationship building is still one of the key challenges in the way of counterterrorism [34].

6.8 Balancing Security and Civil Liberties

Protective measures in order to safeguard national security and civil liberties are a constant struggle against terrorism. However, techniques such as mass surveillance and emergency powers usually conflict with democratic concepts and human rights. Getting that balance requires policy clarity, good management controls, and therefore, prevention from being a power-hungry person.

However, the image of public opinion for counterterrorism operations is also a factor to be considered. Unnecessary invasive interventions can create public alienation, undermine legitimacy of CT works, and incite opposition from enacting communities [35].

7 Role of Technology in Counterterrorism

Technology has provided an important resource for efforts to combat terrorism and has helped to establish the ability of agencies to predict, prevent, and respond to acts of terrorism. Due to scientific and technological developments, the context of national security has changed over the time and consequently the quality of the collection, analysis, and decision of data process has been enhanced. This section addresses the key roles that technology is assuming in the counterterrorism efforts, in particular information technology, surveillance, predictive modelling, and the strategic use of newly emerging technologies as an augmentation.

7.1 Public-Private Partnership in Counterterrorism

Public-private partnership (PPP) also has been the main accelerator of the war against antiterrorism and has covered its capacity shortcomings in terms of resource delivery from the government and in terms of its ability to function. Modern terrorism allows multidimensional threats which require original, interdisciplinary approaches. By leveraging public and private sector partnership, PPPs can serve as a viable framework to address the dynamic threat landscape [36].

7.2 Collaborative Mechanisms

Public-private partnerships (PPPs) are instrumental in fostering collaboration between public and private entities. This work has been designed in order to include joint risk estimations, standardization of protocols, and simulation sessions that lead to the improvement of the level of preparedness. These partnerships also help facilitate sharing of important messages and advice for optimal practices, so that a strong and unified response to new threats can be provided.

Confidence and mutual accommodation/partnership are dependents of PPPs. Achieving a 'common front' by the private organizations' voluntary efforts leading to a common front fostering common responsibility for achieving better results are not abandoned. However, the targets of some actors are contrary to national security goals; private sector actors can help create an efficient counterterrorism system [37].

7.3 Strategic Importance of PPPs

Deployment of PPPs is consistent with overall international counterterrorism efforts. Frameworks addressing actions of the United Nations Counterterrorism Strategy, for example, include the role of the private sector in protecting critical and vulnerable public and high technology infrastructure. These efforts by coalitions including the G8 even more underscore the role of such coalitions, as well as the continuing requirement for such structured activities and information sharing.

8 International Cooperation in Counterterrorism

International collaboration in antiterrorism is both urgent and a necessary issue. As complexity, advanced technology, and their national uses drive the evolution from layered interactions to networked collaborative interactions, the danger of terrorist threats will drive the way forward. Struggles to counter terrorism directly at the international level has however induced significant progress in this field including in the UN framework. The United Nations has established 13 conventions and 16 universal legal instruments covering terrorism as the whole. Among the main initiatives, the Counterterrorism Implementation Task Force (CTITF) established in 2005 coordinated numerous antiterrorism actions such as conflict prevention, terrorist financing, and human rights protection.

The 2006 adoption by the UN of the Global Counterterrorism Strategy as a blueprint for an international consensus on counterterrorism constituted a tipping point in the development of this shared set of cooperative norms. All 192 member states in 2008 pledged to increase their efforts to act in that regard by addressing the effective response to terrorist drivers more broadly, by strengthening the present capacity of member states, as well as to safeguard human rights [38].

International financial institutions also contribute significantly to counterterrorism efforts. Even institutes such as the World Bank, the International Monetary Fund (IMF), etc. render the same service, handing over to the nations a financial power so that they could not be captured by the terrorists' ill intent. Such efforts have boosted the global monitoring of payment transactions and improved the ability of national financial intelligence agencies to detect and address threats [39].

Capacity building is another critical area of international cooperation. Cooperation between countries on the more effective administration of aerospace and maritime security, the updating of customs laws, and the development of counterterrorism laws are of paramount importance. For instance, countries collected experience by organizing training workshops and conferences with the goal of improving the preparedness of their border security forces. Not only does this work answer the questions of their respective countries but it also gives a global response to terrorism targeting global security [40].

9 Future Directions in Counterterrorism

The global picture of countering terrorism will have to evolve with technological developments and blended tactics to cope with current manifestations of threats such as cyber-physical systems (CPS). CPS by an integration of physical and computation processes are being engineered to push the boundaries of security and surveillance in the city: real-time detection, forecasting, and automatic countermeasure against an attack [41].

The contribution of CPS technology as it is exemplified in smart surveillance, Internet of Things (IoT)-based sensors, and machine learning (ML) architectures can have good potential infighting against counterterrorism. These systems provide situational awareness through anomaly detection and threat warning in the street. For instance, intelligent video surveillance in integration with machine learning algorithms can be used to analyse crowd movements in real time and identify anomalies. The use of AI in these systems has in addition led to a major decrease in the levels of human error as well as in the functionality of the threat response systems [1].

There is a high research interest in the possibility of the counterterrorism future. Biometric-based identification systems, like face or gait recognition systems can be used to the highest security standard. These technologies can be applied for rapid tracking of persons in high risk zones, and can be combined with globally watch listed for promoting increased border security. Additionally, blockchain technology might be used as a tool for secure distribution of information and identity verification ultimately enabling the integrity of critical, confidential information by battling terrorism at an international level. Sensorics systems of high quality in aerial vehicles or drones are by far the newest technology and thus open the possibility of real-time remote aerial surveillance of events or monitoring of locations which would be inaccessible manually. Autonomous systems similar to this have potential in dense area patrol and surveillance [42].

Furthermore, intervention at the source of terrorism is a necessary component of antiterrorism policy. Socioeconomic inequalities and ideological extremism are if not kept under wraps almost inescapable catalysts for terrorist actions. An architecture, comprised of high tech and preventative measures, can result in an efficient counterterror system. This depends on the ability to foster cross-border work, intelligence sharing, and community-based prevention of radicalization.

10 Conclusion

The exploration of this chapter has shed light on the increasingly complex and diverse role that artificial intelligence plays in the international war on terrorism. We have seen how AI provides a potent toolkit to combat the changing dangers posed by terrorist groups because of its ability to process data quickly, recognise patterns, and do predictive analytics. AI's uses in counterterrorism have become increasingly complex and significant, ranging from spotting radicalised people online and upending terrorist finance networks to strengthening border security and anticipating possible attacks. However, this investigation has also highlighted how important it is to exercise prudence and take ethics into account. There are serious issues with privacy, bias, accountability, and the possibility of abuse when AI is used in such delicate situations. Careful examination and strong regulatory frameworks are necessary due to the possibility that algorithmic bias would reinforce current societal disparities, the degradation of civil liberties through invasive monitoring technologies, and the absence of distinct lines of accountability in AI-driven decision-making. It's still very difficult to strike a balance between protecting fundamental rights and using AI's potential to improve security.

Future developments in technology and the evolving character of terrorist threats will surely continue to influence the role of AI in counterterrorism. There are advantages and disadvantages to combining AI with other cutting-edge technologies like blockchain and the metaverse. The development of transparent, responsible, and morally sound AI systems that are adapted to the unique complexities of counterterrorism must be the main goal of future research and policy initiatives. To guarantee the ethical and efficient application of AI in this vital field, international cooperation and the creation of international standards are essential. The ultimate objective is to use AI's revolutionary potential to make societies safer while respecting the principles of justice, privacy, and human rights.

References

1. Martini, A. (2024). AI, counterterrorism and global governance: State of the art. *Revista de Paz y Conflictos*, 17.
2. Wall, C. (2025). The ghost in the machine: Counterterrorism in the age of artificial intelligence. *Studies in Conflict & Terrorism, 127.*
3. Montasari, R. (2024). Analysing ethical, legal, technical and operational challenges of the application of machine learning in countering cyber terrorism. In *Cyberspace, cyberterrorism and the international security in the fourth industrial revolution: Threats, assessment and responses* (p. 159197). Springer.
4. Bahriansyah, I. M., Supriyadi, A. A., & Nurisnaeny, P. S. (2024). Anticipating the impact of artificial intelligence to increase national vigilance against terrorism attacks in Indonesia. *Remote Sensing Technology in Defense and Environment, 1*(2), 8697.
5. Maniszewska, K. (2024). Countering terrorism: Key challenges and proposed solutions. In *Towards a new definition of terrorism: Challenges and perspectives in a shifting paradigm* (p. 6582). Springer Nature.
6. Montasari, R. (2024). Machine learning and deep learning techniques in countering cyberterrorism. In *Cyberspace, cyberterrorism and the international security in the fourth industrial revolution: Threats, assessment and responses* (p. 135158). Springer.
7. Alkaher, D., Yaakov, U. B., & Taylor, E. E. (2024). The dance of the scorpions: Leveraging Ai in deciphering geopolitical and CounterTerrorism complexities in the Middle East. *Journal on AI Policy and Complex Systems, 9*(1).
8. Martini, A. (2025). Developing CTS 4o: A CTS research agenda on AI, terrorism and counterterrorism. *Critical Studies on Terrorism, 124.*
9. Rickli, J. M., & Liang, C. (2024). New and emerging technologies for terrorists. *The Routledge Companion to Terrorism Studies*, 118126.
10. Aljohani, M., Mukkamalai, R., & Olariu, S. (2024). Autonomous strike uavs for counterterrorism missions: Challenges and preliminary solutions. *arXiv preprint arXiv:2403.01022.*
11. Warnes, R. (2024). *Human factors in effective counterterrorism: A comparative study.* Taylor & Francis.
12. Shi, M., He, X., Li, H., Zhang, H., Lu, P., Ma, J., et al. (2024, November). Research on the development status and future trends of foreign unmanned ground equipment. In *2024 4th international conference on industrial automation, robotics and control engineering (IARCE)* (p. 382387). IEEE.

13. Kim, J., & Joe, I. (2025). Deep LearningBased drone defense system for autonomous detection and mitigation of BalloonBorne threats. *Electronics, 14*(8), 1553.
14. Ayorinde, R. (2024). Legal appraisal of the role of artificial intelligence in combatting global terrorism. Available at SSRN 4986676.
15. Vepsäläinen, K. (2024). Cyber intelligence for antimoney laundering, counterterrorism financing and know your customer.
16. Zhuang, X., Li, D., Wang, Y., & Li, K. (2024). Military target detection method based on EfficientDet and generative adversarial network. *Engineering Applications of Artificial Intelligence, 132*, 107896.
17. Sakr, G., & Hakme, O. (2025). The impact of artificial intelligence on military and security in the MENA. In *AI in the Middle East for growth and business: A transformative force* (p. 363383). Springer Nature.
18. Demir, C. K. (2025). Counterterrorism in the age of hard power: Reassessing Turkey's policy against the PKK. *Southeast European and Black Sea Studies, 25*(1), 99120.
19. Papale, S. (2025). Changing course? The US Biden administration and the promotion of peace and counterterrorism in Africa. *International Peacekeeping, 126.*
20. Chitadze, N. (2025). Artificial intelligence, terrorism, and cyber security: Challenges and opportunities. *Machine Intelligence Applications in CyberRisk Management*, 87106.
21. Mahajan, N., Chauhan, A., & Kajal, M. (2024). An introduction to deep learning-based object recognition and tracking for enabling defense applications. *Advances in Aerial Sensing and Imaging*, 109127.
22. Bellander, S., Eriksson, M., Sundqvist, J., & Ghazinour, M. (2025). "A Gap Between Decision and Execution": An explorative study of the Swedish police's experiences in implementing the 2015 CounterTerrorism Strategy. *European Journal on Criminal Policy and Research*, 124.
23. Lee, B. T. F., Komšić, F., & Sims, J. P. Strategic pathways to minimal deterrence and counterterrorism: Enhancing Brunei's defense capabilities. *Journal of Terrorism Studies, 6*(1), 2.
24. Baig, M. A. A. (2024). Artificial intelligence, emerging technologies and National Security of Pakistan. *CISS Insight Journal, 12*(1), P90114.
25. Khattak, T., & Asghar, R. J. (2024). Strategic counter measures to terrorism and extremism in Pakistan and insights from home land security: A need for the enactment of Pakistan's National Counter Terrorism Department. *Inverge Journal of Social Sciences, 3*(1), 6174.
26. Weedon, M., Higgins, K. M., & Burke, C. (2024). CounterTerrorism measures in the classroom: The importance of professionalism, agency and autonomy when enacting the prevent duty. In *Critical perspectives on educational policies and professional identities: Lessons from doctoral studies* (p. 229246). Emerald Publishing Limited.
27. Chi, Z. (2024). The globalisation of China's counterterrorism efforts. *China: An International Journal, 22*(3), 5072.
28. Iqbal, K., Shoaib, M., & Bakhsh, S. (2024). Evolving dynamics of ChinaPakistan counterterrorism cooperation. *Journal of Policing, Intelligence and Counter Terrorism, 19*(3), 373389.
29. Samad, A. (2024). Regulating autonomous weapon systems: Challenges and future prospects. *Journal of Security and Strategic Analyses, 10*(2), 4158.
30. Stockhammer, N. Implications of the ukrainian war on world order and the future of counterterrorism. *The effects of the russiaukraine war on countering terrorism.* (p. 109).
31. Vladu, O. M. (2024). Nato's strategy for a changing world in 2024. The power of dialogue in a globalized world. (p. 85).
32. Velthuizen, A. (2025). Intelligence and the 'Heart'of the terrorist: Managing the system of systems to discover and respond to tactics of fear. *Journal of Policing, Intelligence and Counter Terrorism*, 118.
33. Song, L., Yang, P. A., Ding, Y., Mo, C., Yang, Y., Gui, Y., et al. (2024). Ultraflexible, high-stability woven yarn sensors with a wide detection range for enhanced human-machine interaction. *IEEE Sensors Journal.*
34. Schneider, J., & Macdonald, J. (2024). Looking back to look forward: Autonomous systems, military revolutions, and the importance of cost. *Journal of Strategic Studies, 47*(2), 162184.

35. Rassler, D., & VeilleuxLepage, Y. (2025). On the horizon: The Ukraine war and the evolving threat of drone terrorism.
36. Schlesinger, J. R. (2024). When enough is enough: Terrorism, counterterrorism, and public opinion. *Critical Studies on Terrorism, 17*(2), 376405.
37. Sandler, T. (2025). An economic perspective on terrorism and counterterrorism. *Terrorism and Political Violence, 37*(1), 5672.
38. Bimantara, A., & Supriyadi, A. A. (2024). Counterterrorism prevention concept to support government policy in Indonesia. *Green Governance: Exploring Politics, Social Justice, and the Environment, 1*(2), 89102.
39. Islam, M. D. (2024). Countering violent extremism in Bangladesh: How a norm receiver formulates CVE as public policy (Doctoral dissertation, University of Leeds).
40. Montasari, R. (2024). Addressing ethical, legal, technical, and operational challenges in counterterrorism with machine learning: Recommendations and strategies. In *Cyberspace, cyberterrorism and the international security in the fourth industrial revolution: Threats, assessment and responses* (p. 199226). Springer.
41. Kanellopoulos, A. N. (2024). Counterintelligence, artificial intelligence and National Security: Synergy and challenges. *Journal of Politics and Ethics in New Technologies and AI, 3*(1), e35617e35617.
42. Maguire, M., & Westbrook, D. A. Machine learning and artificial intelligence in counterterrorism. *States of Surveillance*, 164.

Impact Assessment of Artificial Intelligence (AI) on Human Rights and Privacy: Curbing Global Digital Terrorism with Legal Measures

Saurabh Chandra and Kittisak Wongmahesak

Abstract Human rights and privacy are increasingly at risk due to the rapid development of artificial intelligence (AI) that has revolutionized so many sectors. Surveillance, data gathering, and algorithmic decision-making with the help of AI raise red flags on possible mass surveillance and discrimination and breach data security. The lack of strong law aggravates the existing risk of privacy infringement and algorithmic bias. This chapter provides a critical analysis of the implications AI poses to fundamental rights and emphasizes the need for ethical AI governance and associated legal safeguards. By analyzing current policies and recommending regulatory measures, this research advocates a balanced approach to innovation that protects human dignity and individual freedoms. With autonomous operation and task performance on an exceedingly high level of efficiency when compared to human resourcefulness, it raises critical questions on the nature of fundamental rights and freedoms: Will AI be a support to human powers or will it gradually forsake AI powers and thereby lessen the role of human agents in processes of decision-making? Intrinsically in the same area of discussion is the consideration that in its various forms, AI may cause sundry encroachments upon some human rights protections quite inadvertently. This necessitates an understanding of assumptions about AI by which one may really interpret its functioning.

S. Chandra (✉)
School of Law, Bennett University, Greater Noida, India
e-mail: saurabh.chandra@bennett.edu.in

K. Wongmahesak
Faculty of Political Science, North Bangkok University, Bangkok, Thailand

Publication Research Institute and Community Service, Universitas Muhammadiyah Sidenreng Rappang, South Sulawesi, Indonesia

Faculty of Business and Management, Universiti Sultan Zainal Abidin, Kampung Gong Badak, Malaysia

Shinawatra University, Sam Khok, Thailand

C. Kaunert et al. (eds.), *Artificial Intelligence for Global Counter-Terrorism*, Contributions to Security and Defence Studies,
https://doi.org/10.1007/978-3-031-99235-3_5

1 Introduction

The generality and versatility of artificial intelligence (AI) make it indispensable for practically all areas of human existence. From the rapid changes that AI has been engineering upon the individual, it is going to greatly affect the interaction between man and his environment on a cultural and social basis down to that of technology. With these social and behavioral changes, AI's intellectual evolution is not just re-engineering how groups of people work anymore—it is impacting everything else from near necessities to concerns of the general socio-political and ethical nature. AI has remained extremely useful through time, deeply influential, and, with its powers being increasing day by day, has become relevant in guiding its own evolution. The applications of AI are now nearly present in every other human basic need, to name but a few, food production, clothing and fashion, housing and infrastructure, education, healthcare, and now even human rights. In the kind of society we live, the growing role of AI in these activities and the potential implications of an increasing dependence on the intelligent systems have become a real source of concern [1].

An enormous challenge exists on definitions of AI: they are widely used and accepted, yet a clear, strong meaning is difficult to formulate. For the first time, there was an accepted and valid definition of AI—challenged in many instances—through the work of John McCarthy and some others at Dartmouth College in 1956. They defined AI as a scheme that is able to accomplish actions that are considered intelligent if they are performed by a human. Basically, AI is a sort of designed technology that tries to mimic human capabilities and makes it possible for machines to carry out actions that hitherto could only be carried out by humans.

More recently, Stanford University states that AI is a scientific discipline covering computational technologies that, although inspired by human cognitive processes, are much distanced from them. In AI, of course, the basic processes are similar to those of human perception, learning, reasoning, and action achieved in dissimilar ways. Russell and Norvig also treat AI according to four different categories: (1) systems that think like humans; (2) systems that act like humans; (3) systems that think rationally; and (4) systems that act rationally. Although definitions may differ, one commonality remains: AI has been created primarily to help man work better and lighten the burden of difficult tasks. The other corollary engendered by the increasing importance of AI includes that such interactions with human beings will clearly try to interface with considerations of human rights since AI-powered systems can take decisions mimicking that of a human using near-perfect accuracy for their performance of different complicated tasks quite impersonally and may thus affect fundamental freedoms and ethical considerations in their endeavors. Even as it advances, scrutiny must be done on AI's divisible aspects of selection, enhancement, and omission for human aid and whether such applications become enablers or restrictions on the rights of privacy, autonomy, and equal opportunity. The related ethical and legal implications demand more detailed consideration for the balance to maintain progress in technology and fairness, justice, and accountability [2].

2 Conceptualizing Human Rights Under Relevant Domestic and International Laws

Human rights enjoy scrutiny and reasoned deliberation because of their intimate connection with human life beyond any particular geographical or socio-cultural setting. They belong to the set of inherent human entitlements within any given society, and these emanate from the very condition of being human. They are the irreducible minimum upon which a dignified and civilized existence stands.

In brief, human rights can be said to refer to basic concepts of equal treatment, fairness, freedom, and respect for all. Its supporters opine that it is an inherent right, one that was in existence before it had any formal legal recognition through institutions made for its codification [3]. In general, human rights include several freedoms, liberties, immunities, and benefits to which everyone is entitled on the ground of natural law, current human values, and international legal standards. These basic rights are required for a being's life, securing the respect and sustenance of an individual's dignity. Life would lose all significance and purpose without these rights. Thus, any derogation from human rights must be justified by weighty reasons.

The legal framework that recognizes and protects human rights is central to the nation's governance. Most legal systems accord some form of human rights provisions in their constitutions, providing for enforcement under domestic law. The 1999 Constitution of the Federal Republic of Nigeria (as amended), for example, enshrines fundamental human rights applicable in Nigeria and is the bedrock of all government policies. Nasir, P.C.A. in *Uzoukwu v. Ezeonu II* reiterated the importance of these rights, placing fundamental rights in a special category in domestic law, given their constitutional guarantee [4].

Human rights find explicit definition and concrete articulation in domestic legislation, especially in the country's Constitution and laws. Internationally, human rights have found expression in and enforcement through the various international legal instruments, many of which were already in existence prior to their domestic legal recognition and enactment into national law. Various international treaties and conventions were adopted to pave the way for unified protections for human rights across national boundaries. However, a number of these treaties are required to be ratified and domesticated before they attain the status of law in different jurisdictions. In Nigeria, this is expressly spelt out under Section 12(1) of the Constitution that international treaties shall not form part of the law of the land unless enacted by the National Assembly [5].

Another of the major human rights instruments is the African Charter on Human and Peoples' Rights (Banjul Charter), especially for African nations. Adopted on 27 June 1981 and in force since 21 October 1986, the Charter has almost been ratified and domesticated in all African states. The aim is to promote and protect human rights of individuals and communities on the African continent. Notable rights in the Charter include:

1. The right to freedom from discrimination (Articles 2 and 18(3)).
2. The right to equality ensures equal protection before the law for all persons (Article 3).
3. The right to life and to personal integrity (Article 4).
4. The right to dignity and protection from torture or degrading punishment (Article 5).
5. The right to religious freedom (Article 8).

The acceptance of human rights as a fundamental parameter of legal and social governance highlights their primacy in the welfare of domestic and international legal regimes. While law acts as a great vehicle in the expression and realization of these rights, human rights exist outside the bounds of law; they have existed ever since a time when such formal political and legal structures were yet to see the light of day. Nevertheless, the current challenges concerning human rights enforcement are right at the fore for responding effectively to maintain the dignity and existence of the rights of all [6].

Consequently, it should be an ongoing priority for every nation to safeguard and promote human rights and create an environment in which basic freedoms are respected so that people can lead lives of dignity and equality. This intertwining of both national and international human rights systems strengthens the collective fortress behind which governments and institutions stand in order to protect these indispensable liberties.

3 AI and Its Impact on Human Rights

With the advancement of AI, human rights, a very conception of human existence, are examined. A debate has ensued on whether AI promotes or violates human rights. While it is essential to acknowledge the fact that AI is a product of human invention, which aims at making things easy or efficient in various domains, the development of AI is not something that just happens in isolation. Its development and deployment are carried out with reference to the overlapping socio-political frameworks wherein human rights issues already exist. Various actors are using AI to automate decision-making processes within certain fields for objectives they consider of benefit. However, this automation has led to conflicting viewpoints as to whether AI is good for human rights or a bad thing that opposes their effective enjoyment.

It is clear that, wherever and whenever AI is applied, it manifests itself in the advancement of human society. The other very critical area in which AI is contributing is in monitoring and ensuring the respect of human rights. AI systems assist in the detection of possible incidences of human rights violations and in collecting and presenting evidence to support the legal process. Thus, making the case is now relatively easy, further reducing the burden of proof in the courtroom. The process of the digital age has, however, ushered in a pretty major era of pervasive surveillance, the actors being governments, corporations, and perhaps even non-state actors [7].

Human rights groups and investigators, as well as open-source research platforms like Bellingcat and the Syrian Archive, utilize vast quantities of publicly available digital information in order to bring about human rights violations. The advent of smartphones in conjunction with highly advanced imaging technologies like high-resolution satellite imagery has given rise to unprecedented levels of surveillance to ensure that an overwhelming majority of all events and incidents are being documented—aided by ground camera systems or satellite systems.

There are two sides to this AI-driven surveillance coin. The good side is that AI can help strengthen national security, assist in crime fighting, and even become a solid ally in the prosecution of human rights abuses. On the contrary, opposing arguments rest on the widespread potential misuse of AI in surveillance leading to privacy violations, state abuse of power, and civil rights infringements. One way or the other, it is going to be difficult to ensure that continued development of AI will protect human rights and inhibit its misuse. Not only should any future applications of AI be governed by ethical considerations and regulation, but full transparency should also characterize its deployment to ensure that it works as a means of upliftment rather than oppression. The degree to which society copes with these challenges, while preserving human rights, will determine the future of the chartered human rights course in AI times [8].

4 Artificial Intelligence and Right to Personal Liberty

Everyone, including you and me, is endowed with the right to personal liberty. This bestows on individuals the right to move freely within a certain defined geographical area, except under circumstances defined by law. While exercising this right is in principle universal, there are often exceptions established by legislation in the individual nations or jurisdictions. The presence of personal liberty is one of the basic characteristics of a democratic society: no one can be arbitrarily detained or arrested without due process to law. On the contrary, no government can justly deny this right; thus, protection and respect for this right are the hallmarks of human dignity and freedom. The significance of personal liberty is captured throughout the world in national constitutional organizations and international legal instruments. For example, the Constitution of Nigeria guarantees personal liberty, stating:

> Every person shall be entitled to his personal liberty, and no person shall be deprived of such liberty.

On the international level, there are a number of treaties and conventions that recognize and protect personal liberty. One of the most prominent instruments, the

International Covenant on Civil and Political Rights (ICCPR) rooted in the foundational principles of the Universal Declaration of Human Rights (UDHR) affirms:

> Everyone has the right to liberty and security of person. No one shall be subjected to arbitrary arrest or detention. No one shall be deprived of his liberty except on such grounds and in accordance with such procedure as are established by law [9].

4.1 The Role of Artificial Intelligence in Criminal Justice and Its Threat to Liberty

The unprecedented advancements made in the field of AI have severely impacted the administration of criminal justice systems across the globe. Criminal risk assessment and predictive policing are more and more relying on AI-based software applications as tools. Technologies like PredPol and HunchLab analyze crime trends and extrapolate the incidents of possible crimes so that law enforcement agencies are advised about the location of deployment of officers.

While these innovations promise a lot toward preventing crime, they are severely undermined by questions about personal liberty. Among them, the most hotly debated AI tools that come to mind are the risk assessment instruments (RAI), which assess an individual's likelihood of an action that would involve re-offending. Such assessments are frequently invoked in the judicial decision-making process regarding issues like bail, pretrial detention, and sentencing. This raises a whole range of critical legal and ethical dilemmas concerning the use of algorithmic predictions in the determination of vital legal matters [10].

Particularly alarming is the race-based AI risk scoring software that has made its road into the very veins of the American criminal-justice system. Black defendants are found to be loaded with discriminative implications as "high-risk," being imposed with restrictive bail conditions causing lengthy periods of pretrial detention, and the users of prison sentencing with discrimination pitfalls charging toward unfairness. Such inherent biases in AI-influenced judicial instruments have encouraged discrimination, further aggravating racial disparities in the justice system.

In addition, governments have left many predictive systems underregulated and arbitrarily bound on arbitrary inputs. As there is no explicit legal statement clarifying the methodologies employed, such inadmissible decisions could be declared unlawful or arbitrary under international law, thereby infringing upon the natural right of personal liberty.

Unlawful personal liberty is a cornerstone of human rights, with protection from both the constitutions and international treaties of nations worldwide. AI in the justice system is beneficial in some respects—it also greatly threatens this basic human right. Left unchecked, the use of AI risk assessments and predictive policing could result in outright miscarriages of justice, further marginalizing communities. Laws and regulations ought to be made to limit AI use in policing and law enforcement so that advances in technology are not in conflict with personal liberties and human rights [11].

5 Artificial Intelligence and Right to a Fair Trial

Hereby, the right for anyone, whether a citizen or not a citizen of the country in which the legal proceedings are held, to be granted a fair trial has been entrenched as one of those principles that guide the conduct of all legal processes. It is an essential tenet that also covers civil as well as criminal cases; it ensures not just that justice has generally been administered fairly but also that it has not been premised on bias. A fair trial is defined as one where a judging is free from bias; the proceedings are based on an established due process, and the legal rights of the accused have been preserved. A fair trial necessitates that judicial proceedings should be in a manner just, open, and totally in accord with procedural safeguards.

Generally, the fundamental rights to all these have been provided for by different legal systems. The right to fair hearing is clearly enshrined in the Nigerian Constitution: everyone with civil rights and obligations—including quarrels with the government—who must be thus adjudicated should be afforded a fair hearing in good time and by a competent statutory authority. The international human rights instrument Article 14(1) of the International Covenant on Civil and Political Rights (ICCPR) reemphasizes this right provision and states that due process shall always accompany legal proceedings within jurisdictions [12].

5.1 Artificial Intelligence and Its Influence on Judicial Proceedings

The rapid advancement of artificial intelligence (AI) has significantly affected every modality of the judicial system whereby they have converted existing decision-making processes and also the whole courtroom environment. AI has been introduced into legal systems in two predominant ways: integration of AI-based decision-making tools for judges or as so-called robot judges designed to totally eliminate human adjudicators.

The AI-based decision-making utilities for judges are what one would have as software applications supporting judges in their work by analyzing legal data, generating reports, and recommending actions on cases. They have been touted to facilitate performance improvement, reduction of the burden on judges, and enhancing minimization of human ignorance in making decisions. However, concerns have even begun to be raised about the overreliance on technology for determining the interpretation of legal principles that require human judgment, ethical reasoning, and contextual understanding [13].

Meanwhile, the most radical transformation in the field of law has involved the robot judges and virtual judges. The AI systems accomplish everything a civilian judge could do without the need for humans in the courtroom. While supporters argue that it would improve efficiency and return scheduled intervention of the system in dealing with cases, skeptics contend that replacing human judges with machines would create a major abolishment of core principles of the just existence such as fairness, impartiality, and the right to be heard.

5.2 *Concerns over AI-Induced Bias in Legal Decision-Making*

The embedded system bias as a coined term is going to cause riled debates on AIs in the judicial systems. AI decision-making systems include algorithms based on data, and they often inadvertently reflect and reproduce social biases endemic in the data they are trained on. A relatively clear-cut example of an issue with such bias was reported by a study in 2016 conducted by ProPublica regarding Correctional Offender Management Profiling for Alternative Sanctions. It determined that COMPAS software qualified black offenders as high-risk while wrongly representing white defendants as low-risk offenders, revealing racial bias issues within the system.

These disparities serve to underline the peril involving AI-derived outputs in the justice system when it fails to factor in deep-seated historical discrimination about crimes. Causes of bias include many things like discriminatory law enforcement practices, socio-economic disparity, and systemic biases percolated in the criminal justice system. Where a biased outcomes of AI-based tools are found, the question then becomes which of the three is wrong: the programming is flawed, biased training, or possibly one unintended but intrinsic limitation of the technology itself [14].

So even though AI is not designed in such a way to make decisions that are not fair, algorithms can often develop such inequalities because of the way they're set up and trained. Moreover, while race or gender is not mentioned explicitly in columns of a database, the AI still might be able to make inferences according to indirect factors and reinforce the intrusion of these biases. Such moral and legal issues are, indeed, germane to the judicious use of AI in their integration of judicial decision systems considering fundamental rights and freedoms of people.

5.3 *The Landmark Case of State v. Loomis and the Challenges of AI in Sentencing*

A key case amplifying these concerns was between *State v. Loomis* in a July 2016 decision by the Supreme Court of Wisconsin. Eric Loomis was convicted related to a drive-by shooting and sentenced to 6 years in prison. COMPAS heavily influenced his sentencing, defining him as having a "very high" risk of being a potential threat to society. While the Wisconsin Supreme Court upheld the use of AI-based risk assessment tools in sentencing decisions, the case offered ground for significant concerns regarding the reliability as well as transparency in usage of such technologies.

The problem taken in *State v. Loomis* related to the lack of accountability and interpretability of such AI-based risk assessment measures. In arguing against the software's assessment, the respondent noted that there is neither any understanding nor a method providing him with the chance to contest the results produced through the workings of this algorithm. The absence of such transparency violates the tenets of due process; defendants deserve to know the grounds on which their sentences are passed to fully challenge such factors that may have disproportionately affected the outcome of their case [15].

The case illustrates the general danger of integrating AI into the legal system without proper surveillance and ethical safeguards, as well as without mechanisms for ensuring fairness. AI risk assessment tools are likely to destroy public confidence in the justice system and mistrust in the judicial processes and ultimately may unfairly propagate injustice.

AI has potential in revolutionizing legal processes through increased efficiency and improvement of judicial tasks. However, its application in criminal justice needs caution. Courts have to ensure that AI-related instruments do not infringe on the most basic legal rights, namely, that of a fair trial. Policymakers, legal scholars, and technologists have to work together to develop ethical standards, transparency measures, and mechanisms for accountability in order to mitigate the risks of AI within the judiciary.

Ultimately, while AI could be a good tool in judicial administration, it cannot replace the nuanced judgment, ethical reasoning, and human empathy characteristic in justice delivery. This is what the legal system needs for true justice. It must, therefore, concern itself with fairness, due process, and human rights in order to solidify and advance the integrity of justice [16].

6 Artificial Intelligence and Right to Privacy

Privacy is a fundamental right recognized by many legal traditions, which serves to guard against governmental and private intrusion into the personal life of an individual. Broadly defined, this right is the right to be left alone and to be free from interference or intrusion, no matter how serious, or the right to be free from all surveillance. It implies the security of privacy of personal matters, the right to control their dissemination, and the right to dignity, independence, and personal integrity. Privacy also extends to anonymity or solitude and to keeping access to oneself limited.

At an international level, the right of privacy is recognized and upheld by international treaties such as the International Covenant on Civil and Political Rights

(ICCPR), which guarantees absence of arbitrary or unlawful interference with the privacy of individual, family, home, or correspondence. It guarantees further legal protection against unauthorized imposition or encroachment of the honor and reputation of a person. The Constitution of Nigeria, too, gives expression to the right of private life in it. It guarantees and preserves people's homes, correspondence, telephone conversations, and telegraphic communications.

However, much has been discussed in today's creation about the potential violation of privacy rights by the artificial intelligence (AI) and digital technology advances. These subsequent state-of-the-art surveillance tools include CCTVs, smartphones, and technologies for tracking data-movement to be used by governments and companies in tracking people's activities. In fact, modern tech-driven organizations like Amazon, Apple, Facebook, Google, and Yahoo have infiltrated people's lives to an extent that it just raises questions about where their data are stored or used without their authorization [17].

One of the finest examples that bring out the risks attached to the misuse of personal data is the Facebook-Cambridge Analytica scandal, where critical data about users were harvested and used for the purpose of psychographic profiling to influence electoral results. This controversy evinced the alarming depth to which data privacy can be violated in the digital age.

These advancements in artificial intelligence and innovative technology can benefit our security, business, healthcare, and many other fields, but they significantly threaten individuals' privacy. Data-based technologies are growing rapidly and will require stricter legislation, interpretation of the regulation, and introduction of ethics that safeguard above all technological advances against fundamental human rights. Greater efforts should be mounted by the world community in firm construction of data protection laws, building cybersecurity strength, and creating awareness for individuals regarding their entitlement to their private information. Only through this balanced approach can societies utilize the benefits of artificial intelligence while maintaining the sanctity of privacy.

7 Artificial Intelligence and Right Against Discrimination

Discrimination has always been regarded as a sensitive and complex subject as the issues that accompany it pertain to social, emotional, or ethical causes. It lies deep-rooted among norms and values in society, making it quite difficult and complex in discussion. From the legal angle, discrimination occurs when an individual is wrongfully disallowed from accessing human rights or other legal entitlements on an equal footing with others related to discriminatory policies, laws, or treatments. Many such practices have been forbidden through legal measures in domestic and international levels.

- Legal Provisions Against Discrimination
- "The foremost such instruments in international law, the International Covenant on Civil and Political Rights (ICCPR), explicitly prohibits discrimination in law and practice under a condition that one would be entitled to equal protection before the law and from arbitrary distinctions of basic rights and freedoms [18]."
- The Role of Artificial Intelligence in Arbitrary Arrests
- Arbitrary arrests occur when individuals are detained without legal grounds, without proper evidence, or without due process. These types of arrests violate the right to personal liberty and impair a person's freedom of movement without legal ground. The growing misuse of artificial intelligence online in law enforcement has inadvertently given way to arbitrary arrests. Most of the time, when these technologies misidentify an individual as a suspect, then that results in wrongful detention involving surveillance systems driven by AI, facial recognition technology, and predictive policing algorithms. Inherent algorithmic bias or systemic flaws in AI models are the culprits that contribute to such false identifications. Hence, these de facto contradictory indications will need strict scrutiny and regulation of AI in law enforcement.
- The Relation of Artificial Intelligence with Freedom of Expression
- Freedom of expression entails not being restrained from voicing thoughts, opinions, or beliefs; it is an inalienable right. Recognized as such in both international treaties, such as the ICCPR, and national constitutions, this right also protects individuals' liberties in expressing themselves by speaking, writing, artistic creation, and electronic communication.
- Artificial intelligence has enhanced the way in which communication and information are made available, creating newer pathways for freedom of expression through social media, digital platforms, and their automated content curation. However, it is another double-edged sword. AI content moderation systems that, on paper, are designed to filter out harmful or inappropriate content have come under fire for silencing dissenting views and perpetuating algorithmic biases. Furthermore, with regard to AI's role in the personalization of content, the possible creation of filter bubbles or echo chambers, in which individuals are inundated only with information that concurs with their pre-existing beliefs, becomes an impediment to the ability to engage in differing opinions. AI-enhanced social media then furthers already notoriously rejuvenated concerns such as cyberbullying, misinformation, online harassment, etc. Therefore, a sensible equilibrium should exist that allows for freedom of expression while limiting digital harms [19].
- The Impact of AI on Freedom of Assembly and Association
- The right to freedom of assembly and association is fundamental to democratic societies, permitting individuals to unite for common causes, express collective interests, and advocate for social and political change. The Internet, with its possibilities of connectivity and organizing, enabled by AI, has also posed challenges to the enjoyment of these freedoms. AI and surveillance mechanisms have been used to track the activities of activist groups, follow the movements of protests, and suppress dissent by governments and corporations alike. Very often, we have seen predictive policing technologies and AI monitoring tools being

used to disrupt nonviolent assemblies, raising questions about the erosion of democratic rights. Safeguarding these freedoms would require appropriate regulation that prevents AI misuse in surveillance and repression and allows for its responsible use in law enforcement and governance.

- Artificial Intelligence and Socio-Economic Rights
- Not limited to civil and political rights, it is socio-economic rights that are crucial to making a living dignified. Socio-economic rights involve access to healthcare, education, and employment, as well as social security and housing. Most significantly, the evolution of socio-economic rights has been progressive and selective in international human rights law. Perhaps, the importance given to socio-economic rights is well pronounced in the provisions of various international instruments, such as the Universal Declaration of Human Rights (UDHR) and the International Covenant on Economic, Social and Cultural Rights (ICESCR).
- AI has widely penetrated socio-economic rights, changing the carpet of labor enduring to education, healthcare, and social welfare. AI-driven automation has increased efficiency and innovation; at the same time, it has dismantled jobs and made widening socio-economic inequalities. There have also been concerns over algorithmic ways of deciding on discrimination with regard to hiring, while AI-enabled diagnosis in healthcare has improved medical outcome standards but brought ethical dilemmas involving accessibility and privacy. AI continues to shape the socio-economic status; meanwhile, policies must be taken to ensure equal access benefits and damages assessment [20].
- The Labour and Employment Right in AI Era
- The right to work involves not just getting employment but also fair remuneration, a healthy and safe working environment, and freedom from discrimination. The coming ages of AI and automation completely transformed the traditional nature of work-from-home jobs practical on to very efficient operational jobs, followed by major shifts into displaced old-time roles. It provided new job opportunities in tech-based activities; however, it also killed many jobs from the employment base that involved manual activity, including the outside industries.
- Reports of algorithmic recruitment biases have also been triggered by this development through its AI-based recruitment devices, which may favor or disfavor by causing biases within certain groups. In addition to these, the gig economy, in heavy reliance on AI, raises and is continuously being raised questions about job security, fair wages, and the rights of workers. In response to these challenges, governments and regulatory bodies should put in place frameworks that promote fair labor practices, upskilling opportunities, and equitable workplace policies in the AI-driven economy.
- AI and Little People's Rights
- Rights of Children are human rights that require special and extra protection. International legal instruments recognize children, such as the United Nations Convention on the Rights of the Child (CRC), with rights to education, healthcare,

and protection from all kinds of exploitation, as well as participation in societal affairs.

- AI has a multidimensional impact on children's rights. AI-enabled educational tools enhanced learning experiences by offering personal instructions that were supplemented with wider access to knowledge; on the other hand, AI-informed content recommendation systems, and social media algorithms have raised concerns on children being exposed to harmful content, data privacy threats, and digital addiction. More so, the expanding adoption of AI in children's welfare and predictive analytics has introduced ethical quandaries concerning privacy, surveillance, and possible discriminatory bias in decision-making. Given that children must be protected by strong regulations on the digital age to ensure responsible development and use of AI in educational and social settings, this will not be a very fruitful state of affairs.
- Artificial intelligence has indeed altered a lot of things in the human rights context, bringing more opportunities as well as challenges. Living with the blessings, one should be able to complain about the maledictions that arise from its use. Certain very significant concerns are raised such as discrimination and arbitrary arrests, the right to freedom of speech, labor rights and its implementation, and also the inequality in socio-economics. AI opens its wings, and with it, much law is also due for many legal frameworks and policies to be made in line with technological advancement so much that they rile up with human fundamental rights principles. A balanced approach is mainly needed to harness AI-oriented benefits to the dew side of mitigating the adverse risks that it could present [21].

8 The Impacts of AI on the "Rule of Law"

For any country wishing to grow or become something, the rule of law must be met as a basic prerequisite. The rule of law serves as the basis for international peace and security as well as for political stability. It fosters economic and social development and safeguards the rights and freedoms of individuals. In fact, the modern understanding of the rule of law was explicitly analyzed by a well-known constitutional theorist, A.V. Dicey.

Equality before the law creates an equality of subjection of all the individuals in society to the same law without respect to social or economic status. It emphasizes that no one, no matter how wealthy, powerful, or influential, is above the law. It is this that ensures all legal proceedings and judicial decisions are made without privilege or discrimination according to that person's position in society. Hence, whether a person is rich or poor, the law shall treat such a person equally, further reinforcing ideas of justice and fairness [22].

The principle of constitutional supremacy, another vital aspect of the rule of law, prescribes that the Constitution is the highest legal authority in the country. All organs of detention and application of law—the Executive, the Legislature, and the

Judiciary—derive legitimacy and powers from the Constitution. Therefore, their actions must conform to constitutional provisions, and any act in disregard of its injunctions is rendered innocent. This doctrine ensures that all laws and policies consonant with constitutional principles thereby contribute to the legitimacy of legal governance.

Besides the protection of basic human rights, this also constitutes an indispensable element of the rule of law. These rights belong with every human being and go beyond being simply international law enactment, thus remaining as something that preserves dignity and existence for humankind. Human rights could either be elaborated in legal documents or acknowledged as being natural, but they lay at the very heart of any just society. Therefore, enforcement of these rights constitutes a bulwark against oppression, an assurance of personal freedom, and a guarantee for the construction of an environment in which individuals, dignified and secure, get to live. To this end, the rule of law stands as an indispensable pillar for every just and progressive society. It ensures equality before the law through enforcement of constitutional supremacy; it provides for the protection of these fundamental human rights. Their application is necessary for the promotion of national stability, social harmony, and sustainable development [25].

9 AI's Impact on Human Rights, Democracy, and Law: Key Challenges

Artificial intelligence (AI) is an amazing field characterized by rapid growth and development across the sectors of government, business, and industry for technological advancement and efficiency in the modern world. Yet, for every good that comes out of it, AI poses the worst challenges—one of these relates to human rights, democracy, and the rule of law. These three are the essential building blocks of every legally governed political system.

Democracy is based on the people governing themselves in accordance with their will and wishes. The people's participation is predominant—the authority to govern derives from the consent of the governed. And along the same lines, the rule of law is one of the secret ingredients that ensure international peace, security, and political stability—by ensuring justice and promoting economic and social development while safeguarding the rights and freedoms of all [23]. It protects these rights from being infringed upon by various parties from discrimination and abuse by actors of the state and society.

The effect of AI on the established principles is both positive and negative. While AI is a vehicle for good governance, better decision-making, and access to justice, on the contrary, it raises issues regarding privacy, mass surveillance, biased decision-making, and the erosion of fundamental freedoms. Moreover, the uncontrolled deployment of AI-enabled technologies can lead to human rights violations, manipulation of democratic processes, and serious threats to the impartial application of the rule of law. This chapter will concentrate mainly on the negative effects of AI on human rights, democracy, and the rule of law. By conducting a careful examination on these issues, it becomes possible to consider the attendant ethical, legal, and regulatory concerns surrounding AI more broadly to prevent technological advancements from invading human fundamentals and principles [24].

10 Conclusion

The opportunities provided by AI for the good of civilization can be hampered on one hand by many challenges it generates that are hard to ignore. Mostly, these challenges tender moral dilemmas, draw ethical boundaries on what may be termed fairness, and accountabilities, and are perceived as phenomena antagonistic to basic human rights. Consequently, in some instances, it seems that AI and AI-powered systems amplify bias and unfairness in judicial decisions while silently snooping and threatening democratic processes. Meanwhile, horizontally spreading AI on the ground could lower or elevate socio-economic conditions for the individual, which sometimes aggravates inequality and affects an average citizen's living standards. While AI, in its peculiar way, is changing or has changed legal and democratic institutions with unprecedented speed and dexterity, these challenges should be addressed in a proactive manner so that technological advancement may serve justice, fairness, and human dignity.

References

1. Danks, D., London, A. J., & Carnegie Mellon University. (2017). Algorithmic bias in autonomous systems. In Proceedings of the 26th international joint conference on artificial intelligence (IJCAI 2017) [Conference-proceeding]. https://www.cmu.edu/dietrich/philosophy/docs/london/IJCAI17-AlgorithmicBias-Distrib.pdf.
2. Delcker, J. (2018, April 13). Europe divided over robot 'personhood' POLITICO. https://www.politico.eu/article/europe-divided-over-robot-ai-artificial-intelligence-personhood/.
3. Almada, M. (2018). Contesting automated decisions: Limits to the right to human intervention in automated decision-making. *SSRN Electronic Journal*. https://doi.org/10.2139/ssrn.3264189
4. Ananny, M., & Crawford, K. (2016). Seeing without knowing: Limitations of the transparency ideal and its application to algorithmic accountability. *New Media & Society, 20*(3), 973–989. https://doi.org/10.1177/1461444816676645
5. Beduschi, A. (2020). International migration management in the age of artificial intelligence. *Migration Studies, 9*(3), 576–596. https://doi.org/10.1093/migration/mnaa003
6. Berk, R., Department of Criminology, Department of Statistics, & University of Pennsylvania. (2017). Accuracy and fairness for Juvenile Justice Risks Assessments. https://crim.sas.upenn.edu/sites/default/files/Berk_FairJuvy_1.2.2018.pdf.
7. Courtland, R. (2018). Bias detectives: The researchers striving to make algorithms fair. *Nature, 558*(7710), 357–360. https://doi.org/10.1038/d41586-018-05469-3
8. Kongolo, T. (2024). Intellectual property and artificial intelligence. In *Routledge eBooks* (pp. 19–47). https://doi.org/10.4324/9781003309086-3

9. Arrieta, A. B., Díaz-Rodríguez, N., Del Ser, J., Bennetot, A., Tabik, S., Barbado, A., Garcia, S., Gil-Lopez, S., Molina, D., Benjamins, R., Chatila, R., & Herrera, F. (2019). Explainable artificial intelligence (XAI): Concepts, taxonomies, opportunities and challenges toward responsible AI. *Information Fusion, 58*, 82–115. https://doi.org/10.1016/j.inffus.2019.12.012
10. Access Now, & Andersen, L. (2021). Human Rights in the Age of Artificial Intelligence. In Access now. (pp. 6–8). https://www.accessnow.org/cms/assets/uploads/2018/11/AI-and-Human-Rights.pdf.
11. Burri, T. (2017). International law and artificial intelligence. *SSRN Electronic Journal*. https://doi.org/10.2139/ssrn.3060191
12. Chawla, R. N., & Goyal, P. (2021). Emerging trends in digital transformation: A bibliometric analysis. *Benchmarking an International Journal, 29*(4), 1069–1112. https://doi.org/10.1108/bij-01-2021-0009
13. Gans, J. (2024). Copyright policy options for generative artificial intelligence. *SSRN Electronic Journal*. https://doi.org/10.2139/ssrn.4716669
14. Marsico, F., & Amigo, M. (2025). Ethical and security challenges in AI for forensic genetics: From bias to adversarial attacks. *Forensic Science International: Genetics, 76*, 103225. https://doi.org/10.1016/j.fsigen.2025.103225
15. Shafik, W. (2024). Toward a more ethical future of artificial intelligence and data science. In *The ethical Frontier of AI and data analysis* (pp. 362–388). IGI Global.
16. Bhardwaj, A. (2024). Secure framework against cyberattacks on cyber-physical robotic systems. Smart home and industrial IoT devices: Critical perspectives on cyberthreats, frameworks and protocols. (pp. 98–127). https://doi.org/10.2174/9789815256710124010006.
17. Dzuranin, A. C., Jones, J. R., & Olvera, R. M. (2018). Infusing data analytics into the accounting curriculum: A framework and insights from faculty. *Journal of Accounting Education, 43*, 24–39. https://doi.org/10.1016/j.jaccedu.2018.03.004
18. Fagundes, D. (2025). Genetic property rhetoric and the public domain. *Texas A&M Journal of Property Law, 11*(1), 1–16. https://doi.org/10.37419/jpl.v11.i1.1
19. Hayes, C. M. (2023). Generative artificial intelligence and copyright: Both sides of the black box. *SSRN Electronic Journal*. https://doi.org/10.2139/ssrn.4517799
20. Hashmi, E., Yamin, M. M., & Yayilgan, S. Y. (2024). Securing tomorrow: A comprehensive survey on the synergy of artificial intelligence and information security. *AI and Ethics*, 1–19.
21. Bellaby, R. (2024). The ethical problems of 'intelligence–ai'. *International Affairs, 100*(6), 2525–2542. https://doi.org/10.1093/ia/iiae227
22. Singh, B., & Kaunert, C. (2024). Intelligent machine learning solutions for cybersecurity. Advances in computational intelligence and robotics. (pp. 359–386). https://doi.org/10.4018/979-8-3693-5380-6.ch014.
23. Mehan, J. (2024). Artificial intelligence: Ethical, social, and security impacts for the present and the future.
24. Rehan, H. (2024). AI-driven cloud security: The future of safeguarding sensitive data in the digital age. *Journal of Artificial Intelligence General Science (JAIGS)*: ISSN 3006-4023, *1*(1), 132–151.
25. Cath, C. (2018). Governing artificial intelligence: Ethical, legal and technical opportunities and challenges. *Philosophical Transactions of the Royal Society a Mathematical Physical and Engineering Sciences, 376*(2133), 20180080. https://doi.org/10.1098/rsta.2018.0080

Impact of AI on Human Rights and Privacy in Counterterrorism: Legal and Ethical Perspectives

Ismail Suardi Wekke and Shashwata Sahu

Abstract Counterterrorism training in artificial intelligence (AI) has turned international security layouts upside down. Such AI-oriented technologies are often motivated by state power through mechanisms like predictive policing systems, biometric surveillance systems, or even machine-augmented threat spotting. Yet, such services also pose grave threats to the essence of fundamental human rights, including privacy, due process, and nondiscrimination. A 2021 UN High Commissioner for Human Rights report is sounding the alarm about the violations perpetrated through AI's unlawful, unchecked applications in security operations. This article scrutinizes the law and ethics of AI for counterterrorism purposes in light of its implications for human rights and data protection. Using a doctrinal legal research lens, it conducts a comparative analysis between international mechanisms (ICCPR, UDHR), inter-regional treaties (GDPR, Convention 108+), and national legislations (India's IT Rules, 2021; DPDP Act, 2023), and secondary literature as well as reports on human rights. Its salient challenges relate to facial recognition of public places, predictive profiling, drone surveillance, and the use of "black-box" AI solutions with minimum transparency or oversight. The study concludes that most countries lack obligatory mechanisms to ensure accountability and compliance with human rights. It supports mandatory impact assessments, ethics-by-design approaches, and independent regulatory examination of AI in counterterrorism. Lastly, the chapter suggests that safeguarding human rights while adopting AI innovation is not only essential but a democratic necessity.

I. S. Wekke
The Academia of Papua, Papua, Indonesia

S. Sahu (✉)
School of Law, KIIT-DU, Bhubaneswar, India

C. Kaunert et al. (eds.), *Artificial Intelligence for Global Counter-Terrorism*, Contributions to Security and Defence Studies,
https://doi.org/10.1007/978-3-031-99235-3_6

1 Introduction

Artificial intelligence (AI) has become a cornerstone of modern counterterrorism policy in the age of algorithmic warfare and cyber-governance. Governments worldwide increasingly turn to AI-driven technologies to predict, detect, and eliminate security threats at lightning speed and with unprecedented precision. From facial recognition software and real-time monitoring cameras to predictive policing and autonomous drones, AI gives states a technology edge in monitoring patterns of radicalization, monitoring suspicious behavior, and addressing security threats to the nation [1]. In its 2022 report, the Brookings Institution discovered that over 60 countries have already integrated AI-based tools into their national security apparatus, often in partnership with private tech companies.

While these developments have strengthened the hands of state surveillance and allowed it to improve its effectiveness, they also provoke serious ethical and legal questions. AI-fueled systems enable the mass collection and analysis of people's data without their ordinary ignorance or knowledge and often without the knowledge and consent of the individuals concerned. Where surveillance technologies are intensively deployed against vulnerable sectors of society, such as minority groups, political activists, or human rights defenders, the blurring of civilian and national security has added to the more extensive scrutiny of government behavior. The global diffusion of AI in counterterrorism, therefore, highlights a longstanding tension between national security imperatives and civil liberties, one that may be exacerbated by the internationalization of counterterrorism practices all the same.

This chapter engages that tension by examining the intersection of fundamental human rights, namely, the equal right to privacy, data protection, and nondiscrimination with AI-enabled counterterrorism. Using doctrinal legal analysis, it considers whether existing international human rights regimes (detailed in the first article), specifically the International Covenant on Civil and Political Rights (ICCPR) and General Data Protection Regulation (GDPR), are adequate to regulate the use of AI for security purposes. It also examines legal and regulatory measures at the national level, including India's IT Rules, 2021, and the Digital Personal Data Protection (DPDP) Act, 2023, as case studies that showcase the dynamics of legal responses in emerging economies [2]. This chapter contributes to the intersection of law, ethics, and technology and focuses on an emerging model of governance that respects the need for innovations while also ensuring accountability, transparency, and democratic governance. In so doing, the article contributes to the global debate over the ethical deployment of AI in security operations and advocates for the establishment of safeguards to ensure technology serves humanity rather than the opposite.

1.1 *Objectives of This Chapter*

The goal of this chapter is to critically examine the intersection of artificial intelligence and counterterrorism from legal as well as ethical perspectives. This study aims to contribute to the conversation/debate on the degrees and forms of AI usage in counterterrorism across the world and also, more importantly, the implications that such technologies have on more basic rights that people are entitled to, such as privacy, freedom, and nondiscrimination. It can also explore how existing international law governs the use of AI for security operations, notably data protection law and human rights treaties. This chapter seeks to search for and put forward concrete legal and ethical principles, ensuring that AI instruments deployed in counterterrorism are created and used consistently with standards that protect rights and advance democratic ideals.

1.2 *Methodology for This Chapter*

This chapter views legal research through a doctrinal lens, which is based on analysis of primary law sources, as well as on authoritative documents. The key international treaties under consideration are the ICCPR and the Universal Declaration of Human Rights (UDHR), which place essential protections on personal liberties. Regional legislation such as the EU GDPR and the Council of Europe Convention 108+ is also examined for their relevance to the regulation of AI and data privacy. At the national level, the research compares India's IT Rules, 2021, and the DPDP Act, 2023. These are supplemented with secondary sources, including reports by organizations such as the United Nations, Electronic Frontier Foundation (EFF), Amnesty International, and academic literature on AI ethics, surveillance law, and national security [3].

2 Role of AI in Contemporary Counterterrorism

AI has quickly raised as the primary propellant of counterterrorism development initiatives around the globe. Modern threats from single-wolf operations to international networks of radicalized extremists are always posing new challenges that require an amount of speed, forethought, and processing of information that traditional types of intelligence have typically been built fail to provide. With its ability to automate and recognize patterns and conduct analysis in real time, AI is increasingly being harnessed in its application to, arguably, all levels of counterterrorism apparatus. Its footprint is most readily visible in areas like surveillance, facial recognition, predictive threat modeling, and drone-enhanced operations, all of which are rewriting the rules of engagement for security agencies across the globe (Fig. 1).

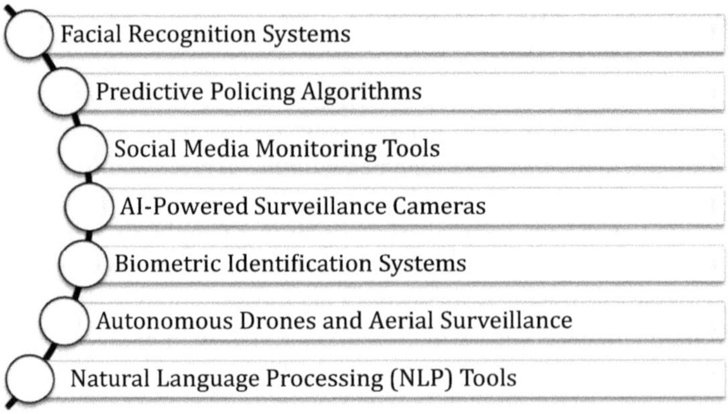

Fig. 1 Key AI tools in counterterrorism

2.1 Overview of AI Tools in Counterterrorism

Intelligent surveillance is one of the most broadly used AI technologies that have been applied to counterterrorism. They use computer vision and natural language processing (NLP) to observe not only physical space but also virtual space for various frequencies of atypical behavior or suspicious keywords. For example, AI-enabled CCTV systems can be employed to analyze and automate consideration of large volumes of video data to identify abnormalities such as planners of attack activity, unexplained luggage, or unusual crowd behavior. Facial recognition technology has also been used to compare live video feeds to databases of known individuals, including government watchlists. Such as, increased accuracy in deep learning algorithms can now identify a person from low-resolution images or non-frontal angles. It was first used to secure high-security areas like airports and border crossings but is now applied in public spaces, protests, and on the Internet as well.

The second area of AI in use is predictive analytics. By analyzing huge datasets extracted from social media, online financial transactions, cell networks, and travel patterns, AI models can potentially anticipate terrorist activity by detecting shifts in behavioral patterns, linguistic markers, or geospatial motifs. Often, these tools are used within counter-radicalization programs that allow for measuring the likelihood of violent extremism and mapping the distribution of interventions precisely. AI-powered autonomous drones transformed aerial surveillance and tactical attacks as well. They are not deployed just for surveillance for targeted killing in counter-terrorist operations for occasions where they might be engaged at a distance with little or even no human surveillance. Drones equipped with thermal imaging and motion detectors can cover tough terrain and hone in on suspects with a relatively short lag time.

2.2 Case Examples: Global Practices

Countries have developed their own models for applying AI to counterterrorism, some more powerful but also contentious than others. In the United States, the National Security Agency's PRISM program, revealed by Edward Snowden in 2013, was one of the first instances of AI and machine learning being used to surveil digital communications, including via email, chat, and video conferencing. PRISM gained access to metadata networks from some of the biggest tech companies, including Google, Apple, and Facebook, which helped analyze data and find trends that were synonymous with terrorist behavior. As well as it did at producing actionable intelligence, it drew worldwide condemnation because it operated in secrecy and because of the intrusiveness of bulk data collection [4].

Skynet in China is among the largest and most sophisticated uses of AI surveillance globally. Now formally legitimated as public security policy, Skynet "operates" with well over 600 million AI cameras with facial, gait, and emotional recognition. The system has been celebrated as a safe way to goose cities and has been successfully deployed against terror targets, but critics have noted its use for large-scale human rights abuses, especially surveillance and control of the Uyghur in Xinjiang, under the banner of anti-extremism.

In India, the Crime and Criminal Tracking Network and Systems (CCTNS) project, which was launched as part of the National e-Governance Plan for Police, will also interlink 15,000 police stations across the country. The analytics using AI will help facilitate the sharing of real-time crime data and profiles of suspects for preventive policing. The Indian government rolled out AI-based social media surveillance tools as part of its broader counterterrorism effort, raising fears of overreach in surveillance and controversies over digital profiling.

2.3 Efficiency vs Ethical Controversy

While the ingression of AI into counterterrorism frameworks without a doubt streamlines and speeds up operations, it equally heightens ethical quandaries and governance contention. Perhaps the most significant benefit of AI technology, however, is the accuracy of AI systems in quantifying the potential threat, which minimizes human error, augments situation awareness, and allows rapid response teams to be activated. Algorithms can sift through terabytes of data in seconds, and intelligence agencies can spot networks that operate in the shadows and shut down plots before they're carried out. But that efficiency comes at the cost of civil liberties. This inscrutability of AI decision-making particularly of black-box models carries other issues of transparency, accountability, and due process as well. If an AI system identifies someone as a suspect, that person may be interrogated or detained, with no knowledge of the grounds for the designation, contrary to foundational tenets of justice and nondiscrimination.

The imbalances in datasets can magnify the inequalities that are already present in society today. It was shown that facial recognition technology has greater error rates for individuals with darker skin, and targeting of religious or ethnic groups on the basis of monitoring or reassurance could happen under the guise of preventative targeting. Artificial intelligence systems used for predictive policing, which were based on historical arrest data, would only reproduce historical patterns of biased policing risks, especially in those communities that were already over-policed. Allowing machines to make life-and-death decisions without real human involvement also poses deep moral, legal, and human-moral respect questions in war and law enforcement [5].

3 Doctrinal and Regulatory Landscape

With AI technologies being increasingly used in counterterrorism strategies across the world, the moment has come to understand how the present international, regional, and national legal arrangements will address the new ethical and legal challenges posed by these technologies. The issues with surveillance, profiling, and algorithmic decision-making, amplified by many technologies that make use of AI, speak directly to the rights to privacy, freedom of expression, liberty, and nondiscrimination. This chapter traces the contours of the yogic doctrinal and regulatory landscape, conditioning the intersection of AI, security, and human rights, and identifies new principles of specific relevance to the responsible development and use of AI.

3.1 International Human Rights Frameworks

The 1966 ICCPR, which has been ratified by over 170 states, continues to be the cornerstone of international law on the human rights of individuals and the obligations of governments both in times of peace and of security crisis. Article 17 of the ICCPR explicitly protects against "arbitrary or unlawful interference" with individuals' correspondence, family, and privacy. If the surveillance technologies are rolled out without sufficient legal protections under due process or public transparency, they have the potential to violate this foundational provision. Likewise relevant under Article 9 (right to liberty and security) and Article 14 (right to a fair trial) are cases involving the detention or profiling of individuals based on ambiguous or false algorithmic outputs produced by AI-based systems.

While the UDHR is not legally binding, at its heart, it explains the dignity, equality, and freedom that must be the foundation of all contemporary human rights law. The UDHR includes, in Article 12, protection against arbitrary interference with privacy and reputation, and in Article 19, protection for the right to the freedom of expression, a right that can be curtailed if the AI software misclassifies online speech as extremist material. In Europe, the ECHR/ECtHR are legally binding. Article 8 of the ECHR provides protection for the right to respect private and family life, and Article 10 protects freedom of expression [6]. The ECtHR has established a three-part test that governs any surveillance mechanism that must be "in accordance with the law," necessary in a democratic society and proportionate to the threat. With AI being rolled out rapidly in state surveillance, these legal principles are now being stress-tested, as in many member states, there are no explicit regulations governing algorithmic systems.

3.2 Regional Legal Instruments: GDPR and Convention 108+

The GDPR, 2018, is by far the most aggressive data protection regime in history. Binding on all of the European Union and with extraterritorial reach even beyond Europe, the GDPR features provisions of decisive importance with immediate relevance to AI in counterterrorism. Article 22 gives a right not to be subject to decisions solely on the basis of automated processing, like profiling, which has legal or similarly affecting effects. This provision is particularly pertinent where AI is used to recognize suspects or recommend police action.

Furthermore, GDPR necessitates Data Protection Impact Assessments (DPIAs) of high-risk processing of personal data a standard that must become integral to AI implementations in security. Article 5 sets out principles of legitimate, fair, and transparent processing, and Article 6 specifies under what conditions the processing of personal data may occur. Some national security measures are occasionally exempt from certain GDPR rules, yet these exemptions should be limited and appropriately justified.

The Council of Europe Convention for the Protection of Individuals with Regard to Automatic Processing of Personal Data (Convention 108) and the updated Convention 108+ represent a complementary solution. Convention 108+ provides data protection rights to all human beings regardless of the nationality or residence of the person and adds special provisions concerning algorithmic decision-making as well as transborder data flows. Its global and binding nature distinguishes it as a uniquely global privacy instrument and a necessary standard for states using AI in counterterrorism.

3.3 National Legislations: India's DPDP Act 2023 and IT Rules 2021

At the international level, many nations are increasingly legislating on data protection and privacy issues concerning AI. India, being a rapidly digitizing democracy and major counterterrorism actor, provides an evolving regulatory environment.

India's first general data protection law is the Digital Personal Data Protection Act (DPDP), 2023. Although it excludes national security and law enforcement organizations from its requirements, it enjoins significant rights such as consent, purpose, and correction and erasure [7]. However, Section 17(2) enables the Central Government to exempt any state agency from implementation in the exercise of sovereignty or in relation to public order provisions that are set to dilute protection when used in surveillance or profiling against terror.

To complement the DPDP Act, the Information Technology (Intermediary Guidelines and Digital Media Ethics Code) Rules, 2021, place responsibilities upon digital platforms to identify the "first originator" of reported messages by law enforcement agencies. With these rules in conjunction with AI-based content filtering software, freedom of expression and anonymity of the Internet are gravely compromised. The uncertainty over algorithmic transparency, user redress, and judicial review in these programs mirrors the need for more advanced regulation that meets the promise and risk of AI.

4 AI-Specific Principles: OECD AI Principles and UNESCO's Ethical Framework

Aware of the inadequacy of existing human rights instruments to better address the complexities of AI, multiple intergovernmental venues have drafted principles specifically geared toward regulating AI. The Organization for Economic Co-operation and Development (OECD) AI principles (2019), endorsed by more than 40 countries, G20 among others, focus on inclusive growth, human-centered values, transparency, resilience, and accountability in AI systems [8]. They are notably demanding explainable AI decisions and the application of AI that aligns with democratic values. The guidelines are not legally binding. However, the guidelines are increasingly informing national AI policy and establishing a reference point for rights-based approaches to AI as they relate to counterterrorism.

The world's first normative document on AI ethics was adopted by the United Nations Educational, Scientific and Cultural Organization (UNESCO) in 2021: its Recommendation on the Ethics of Artificial Intelligence. It also contains extensive guidance on topics such as algorithmic bias, surveillance, and the use of AI in war and data protection. It calls on states to ensure that AI systems respect human rights and democratic institutions, and it promotes impact assessments and suitability of AI technologies—most notably when deployed in sensitive areas like national security. The human control aspect, justice, and the "do no harm" principle are equally emphasized in both OECD and UNESCO approaches to AI, and this is especially relevant in the context of the potential use of AI in state coercive activities for counterterrorism.

5 Privacy and Civil Liberties Under Threat

The ascendancy of AI as a national security tool is certainly improving the capacity of states to detect and respond to threats. But its widespread use in counterterrorism campaigns has also opened a parallel pathway, one that undermines core human rights, particularly the right to privacy and the protection of civil liberties. For AI technologies that have become more autonomous, more holistic, and more integrated into security systems, unchecked adoption poses the risk of entrenching the surveillance state, undermining guarantees of due process, and further marginalizing already vulnerable communities. This section examines new forms of privacy and civil liberties threats that emerge from AI-fueled counterterrorism initiatives against the privacy and civil liberties they object to.

5.1 Surveillance Overreach and Mass Data Collection

Traditional AI-based methods used in counterterrorism usually rely on the aggregation of vast amounts of data from both private and public datasets. Enormous stores of data—from mobile phone call logs and social media posts to biometric identifiers and GPS locations—are collected, processed, and analyzed in real time by machine learning algorithms. While supporters have argued that surveillances like this are needed as a terrorism preemptive measure, the indiscriminate nature of this data mining often violates required standards of necessity and proportionality by international human rights law.

As the Electronic Frontier Foundation has reported, most governments are using "dragnet" systems of surveillance, collecting data on millions and millions of people without any specific suspicion about their individual conduct and without judicial authorization. ALQ|AI threatens this by enabling the automation of bulk review of connected databases in ways that will never have the oversight and humanized judgment involved, neither now nor ever. Such systems often circumvent conventional judicial scrutiny to the extent that citizens may never know that their data is being viewed, let alone used, by these systems.

Such as the UK, the Investigatory Powers Act 2016 ("Snoopers Charter") enables intelligence agencies to intercept and bulk store Internet records and metadata. Although there was an attempt to sell the Act as a response to an intensification of terror threats, human rights campaigners have lambasted the Act for enabling indiscriminate and disproportionate data spying. Again, the use of such legislation for AI technologies leads to greater obscurity of state surveillance and profound concerns about democratic accountability.

5.2 Facial Recognition and Profiling Issues

Facial Recognition Technology (FRT) is the most visible public-facing aspect of AI in the context of security and has become a potent lightning rod for counterterrorism policies. These are commonly known as FRT systems used to process thousands of faces per minute and match them against criminal records or watchlists in public and semi-public areas [9]. These technologies provide operational efficiencies, but they are a far more controversial topic because they are invasive and prone to error especially when not employed under strict legal safeguards. Research by the US National Institute of Standards and Technology (NIST) in 2019 showed that most facial recognition algorithms had higher false positive rates for women, people of color, and seniors. These disparities are not just bugs in the code but errors in the real world, resulting in wrongful arrest, unwanted surveillance, and stigmatization of already marginalized groups.

In countries such as France, where scanning crowds with AI has been challenged on constitutional grounds, deploying facial recognition is another worrying step. More than two dozen cities in the United States including San Francisco, Boston, and Portland—have since barred facial recognition by law enforcement as showing racial bias and a violation of civil liberties. But despite the backlash, facial recognition is still rolling out across the world, mostly secretly, with little regulatory scrutiny or public debate. In counterterrorism, this danger is especially elevated where FRT is combined with predictive analytics that identifies individuals as potential targets because they have been linked with or near-linked individuals previously, effectively creating digital personas based on inadequate signs of behavior or intent. This undermines the presumption of innocence and may lead to anticipatory punitive measures based on incomplete or presumptive information.

5.3 Lack of Informed Consent and Due Process

At the center of human rights law is the fact that individuals must be informed when their rights are being curtailed and must have recourse to remedies where their rights are violated. AI surveillance and profiling are also performed in environments that are not transparent, and as such, it is nearly impossible for the individuals to know that they are under surveillance, even less so to be in a position to challenge the legality of the actions.

Unlike visually conspicuous and focused conventional surveillance, AI-powered systems operate covertly in the background baked into social media platforms, mobile applications, airport scanners, and public CCTV networks. Ambient surveillance strategy deprives individuals of actual agency over their own data and eliminates the potential for full disclosure consent. It is not a requirement of the law in most jurisdictions that individuals are advised that they are being monitored by an algorithm or that their data has been put into an intelligence database [10].

Judicial recourse is likely to be unavailable or ineffective. Once individuals are labeled as potential threats by opaque AI systems, they are likely to fall into a Kafkaesque web of suspicion without any clear path to appeal, understand, or reverse the judgment of the algorithm. Under national security contexts, governments are prone to rely on secrecy doctrines to keep the algorithms and datasets out of sight, thereby preventing judicial review or legal advice. The European Court of Human Rights has long affirmed that surveillance practices must include "adequate and effective guarantees against abuse." But in the era of autonomous surveillance, these protections are more aspirational than operational, leaving even the most basic due process protections felt uncomfortably eroded.

5.4 Impact on Vulnerable Groups: Minorities, Dissenters, and the Marginalized

AI policing against terror is not a social vacuum. It frequently intersects with embedded social biases and institutionalized discrimination, thus amplifying the dangers for some groups. AI-driven profiling and monitoring disproportionately affect minority religious and ethnic groups, political activists, human rights defenders, and migrants. A computer program piloted in Los Angeles and Chicago used and analyzed data up to October 2023 about past criminals and current crimes, and has led to racial profiling of communities. They rely on analyzing past crime in the hope of anticipating areas of future "hot spots" of illegality and, therefore, stationing more officers within an already socioeconomically imbalanced neighborhood. As much as these instruments are framed as objective things, they carry the bias of the data they are trained on and even magnify it.

In authoritarian states, this means labelling activists and dissidents a threat to national security. Their communications are then monitored, movements tracked, and social mobilization efforts censored with the help of AI technologies [11]. In Iran and Turkey, for example, reports have shown that governments are using AI-enabled surveillance to profile protesters, which can lead to the preemptive arrest of protest organizers based on their online behavior. The humanitarian implications are a concern, too. Despite their vulnerability, asylum seekers and refugees increasingly face biometric registration and algorithmic risk screening by which their applications for asylum or humanitarian protection are granted. In many instances, those are built on incomplete or discriminatory data and can lead to unjust refusals of protection, as well as perpetuate systemic exclusion.

6 Algorithmic Bias, Opacity, and Redress Challenges

These advancements have pushed the boundaries of what is possible with security processes, including the arrival of AI in counterterrorism. But that technological leap has unleashed a new set of increasingly sordid challenges of bias, transparency, and the unaccountability of automated decision-making. These issues are not purely technical; they implicate the very nature of democratic governance, human rights, and the rule of law. In high-stakes domains like the national security domain, when the stakes are high, this can lead to wrongful accusation, abuse of civil liberties, and institutional injustice if bias and opacity plague the outputs of your AI system. This section examines how these concerns the mutually constitutive kind of algorithmic bias, black-box decision-making, an absence of mechanisms of redress, and strains of delegating agency to machines combined are particularly relevant for counterterrorism.

6.1 Technical Explanation of Bias in Training Datasets

Algorithmic bias does not typically come from the technology itself but from the data it's trained on. AI systems, especially ones that use machine learning, learn how to predict or classify things by observing patterns in historical data. If this training data carries social, institutional, or historical biases, then the AI model will reproduce and also amplify them. For instance, if the databases used by police are filled to a majority with entries on some ethnic or socioeconomic groups as a result of past over-policing, an AI that has been trained on them will consider these individuals to have higher risk levels regardless of behavior [12]. The condition, which has been termed "historical bias," creates skewed outcomes that mirror and reinforce existing inequalities. A 2020 Center for Security and Emerging Technology (CSET) report highlighted how machine learning algorithms used in threat detection are likely to perform poorly when applied to linguistically or culturally heterogeneous populations not represented in training data. Exclusion of dialects, accents, or behavioral norms from non-Western contexts can result in false positives, misclassification, and over-surveillance of certain communities. In addition, the propensity of labelling bias categories to divide training data created in terms of subjective human opinion has the potential to produce definitions that are imperfect of what is "suspicious behavior" or "radical language." These built-in distortions are difficult to determine and edit, especially when datasets are proprietary or subject to national security classifications.

6.2 AI and the Lack of Explainability

The characteristic of a great deal of modern AI, and surely a great deal of deep learning algorithms, is that they cannot be explained. Explained most commonly as "black-box" models, they have the capability of generating results their designers might be hard-pressed to fully understand or reverse-engineer. That is particularly ominous in counterterrorism, where AI-based results can lead to detention, watch-listing, and surveillance. The opacity of such systems overturns transparency, a core tenet of due process and democratic accountability. Individuals who are subject to action as a result of AI determination rarely provide a clear reason or explanation for why something has been done to them [13]. "Lack of interpretability" also hinders regulatory and judicial review, making it essentially impossible to make high-stakes decisions and, subsequently, making algorithmic error essentially unchallengeable. Progress made on explainability even through techniques like XAI (Explainable AI) is largely theoretical or academic. Most police forces are running commercially produced AI systems with weak or nonexistent transparency components, justified by various performance metrics and operational confidentiality. It creates a risky chasm between ability and legal accountability. Explainability is not only a technical issue, it is a governance issue. National security exceptions to the interpretability mandate could cover a wide variety of AI systems, leaving a regime of unreviewable, unaccountable decision-making in place.

6.3 Absence of Redressal and Accountability in Automated Decisions

This raises the urgent question of accountability when biased or erroneous decision-making occurs in AI systems used in counterterrorism. Nobody sits on a governing body under so-called traditional decision-making schemes based on known human actors, while AI systems function in decentralized, multi-actor environments with muddy lines of accountability. Take the example of an AI system built by a private contractor, sold to a state agency, and then operated by local police.

This accountability vacuum is supported by the absence of official redress mechanisms. Victims of algorithmic misclassification generally have no procedural protections to contest their classification or obtain redress. National security regimes tend to override transparency duties, and the ability of those affected to know that they have been flagged may be nonexistent, let alone an opportunity for them to contest the reasons behind having been flagged. The Special Rapporteur's 2022 report on the Promotion and Protection of Human Rights while Countering Terrorism was also critical of the "lack of effective grievance and oversight mechanisms for algorithmic systems used in intelligence and counterterrorism operations." Lacking proper checks, AI systems are bound to create automated injustice in the name of operational efficiency [14].

6.4 Ethical Implications of AI Autonomy in Counterterrorism

The greatest challenge might be one of ethics: whether it is ethical to farm out high-stakes security judgments to independent machines. AI systems are not just being created to enhance human judgment but to make judgments independently to identify suspects, categorize threats, or even select targets in drone warfare. This raises fundamental questions about moral agency and responsibility. Can a machine really grasp the social, political, and emotional context of a counterterrorism ruling? Can it measure the threat of surveillance against the dignity of the person being surveilled? Can it take extremist speech out of lawful dissent in highly politicized settings?

Without human judgment, there's a risk of AI systems enforcing rules and categorizations in a blunt, context-free fashion. Ethical dilemmas say, balancing individual liberties with the need for collective security requires nuanced judgment, contextual understanding, and sensitivity to nuance, none of which AI has shown evidence of developing. More dangerously, if humans unduly rely on AI systems, thinking of them as error- and bias-free or "objective," a moral hazard exists. This over-reliance on machine logic can erode ethical responsibility, where an operator will blame the algorithm or justify the actions as "technologically determined." These processes risk depersonalizing security governance and technocratizing impunity.

7 National Security vs Human Rights

The discussion around AI and counterterrorism is often framed in terms of a tension between national security and individual liberty. This zero-sum, however, is both wrong and self-negating. Security and human rights are not conflicting objectives; in fact, they are deeply interlinked. The absence of the rule of law, transparency, and respect for civil liberties can turn counterterror into unchecked surveillance and dictatorship. This section tangles the so-called dichotomy together into a more thorough consideration of the rhetoric of security loopholes, exploitative uses of "terrorism" labels, as well as ambiguous darkness areas in surveillance laws, not to overlook the most stringent rigorousness of proportionality tests and the necessity of artificial intelligence-guided national security executions.

7.1 Security Exemptions and Overbroad Discretionary Powers

In most jurisdictions, national security operates as a jurisprudential exception to state practices of data privacy, transparency, and accountability. Such security exceptions, if sometimes necessary to address a pressing danger, are usually drawn so vaguely or so broadly as to permit a disproportionate exercise of power by the state. These exceptions usually include AI-based surveillance systems, protecting their design and use from public scrutiny [15].

In the UK, the Investigatory Powers Tribunal has alleged intelligence agencies engaged in mass data collection without adequate statutory authority. Likewise, India and the UAE's national security provisions in law give state agencies authority to intercept and monitor electronic communications with limited oversight. When AI devices can do mass, real-time data analysis, while we took none of the appropriate steps to define the parameters of such authority and limit it, those exceptions become even less like exceptions. Free of delineating parameters or independent scrutiny, security exemptions risk the normalization of exceptional practice and damage public confidence while impairing the checks offered by our democratic institutions.

7.2 *Strategic Misuse of "Terrorism" Labels*

The generic label "terrorism," while technically accurate, has been used by foghorn governments as a weapon for suppressing political dissent, vilifying adversaries, or rationalizing invasive information technology. This misuse can become even more pernicious when it is compared to AI systems that are being explicitly designed to detect "extremist content" and "radical behavior" particularly in contexts where even those definitions are themselves nebulous or politically constructed.

Accusing journalists, students, and peaceful protesters to be "terrorists," they have tried to justify AI-enabled surveillance and detention. "The implementation of algorithmic policing technologies poses an increasing threat of their co-optation for the purpose of false suspiciousness concerning political speech across vaguely defined national-security mandates," the US Department of Homeland Security wrote in a corporate report in 2020. Such environments allow even lawful expression or gathering to be algorithmically misidentified, leading to predictive state intervention on the grounds of false or manipulated information. This tramples not only freedom of expression but also the rule of law, requiring that rules of law be published, predictable, and clear. When "terrorism" is a catch-all, AI systems trained on such data inherit the bias and copy it at scale, typically without human oversight or accountability.

7.3 *Case Analysis: Pegasus Spyware and the Telegraph Act*

India offers a useful case study of the means by which the existing legal systems and AI surveillance neighboring technologies can converge to circumvent constitutional safeguards. The Pegasus spyware affair, revealed in 2021 by an international collaborative of reporters, illustrated that spyware produced by Israel's NSO Group had been used to target Indian journalists, activists, opposition politicians, and even sitting judges. While the Indian government would neither deny nor confirm its involvement, invoking "national security" to justify withholding judicial ratification, it stonewalled efforts to determine the legitimacy of the eavesdropping [16].

The Pegasus case exposed the frailty of India's Indian Telegraph Act of 1885 and the Information Technology Act of 2000, the two statutory frameworks that regulate state surveillance in India. Neither Act was passed with new surveillance technologies in mind; both lack explicit provisions against AI, spyware, and bulk data harvesting. They allow communication to be intercepted on vagrant excuses like "public safety" and provide for executive orders without court warrants or third-party audits. This legal vacuum has led to a shadow surveillance system subverting constitutional safeguards guaranteed under Article 21 (right to life and personal liberty) and Article 19(1)(a) (freedom of speech and expression). The existing legal state remains largely unchanged despite numerous calls from jurists and civil society for end-to-end surveillance reform and data protection.

7.4 The Need for Proportionality and Necessity Tests

The main tenets of global human rights law is that restrictions to rights are to be scrutinized under legality, necessity, and proportionality. Any invasion of privacy or liberty must be done in a manner set by statute in furtherance of a legitimate aim and be the least restrictive as possible.

The UN Human Rights Committee, in its General Comment No. 16 on Article 17 of the ICCPR, emphasized that surveillance must be made subject to adequate safeguards against misuse and must be proportionate to the threat at issue. These are especially important for AI, where decisions might be automated, mass, and irreversible.

Subordinating these tests to AI systems entails several key steps, like impact assessments, to take into account the potential harm to rights before deployment. Algorithmic transparency requirements to enable oversight agencies to understand how systems work. Regular audits and sunset clauses are used to check for ongoing necessity and appropriateness [17].

8 Comparative Perspectives and Global Trends

The global practice of AI in counterterrorism efforts is under control, but its regulation differs from one part of the world to the other. Although efforts are emerging worldwide to create sound legal and ethical frameworks governing the use of AI, others have not yet undertaken these steps, which include promoting transparency, accountability, and respect for human rights. This chapter compares the strategies of the European Union (EU), the United States (US), and India, summarizes emerging best practices, and identifies effective oversight models that provide useful lessons for AI use in national security.

8.1 Comparative Study: European Union vs. United States vs India

This comparative study reveals substantial variations in the responses of the EU, US, and India to the governance of AI in counterterrorism. The EU also leads from the front with a proactive, rights-oriented regulatory framework that balances security with judicial oversight and popular control. The United States, technologically advanced as it is, prioritizes defense capabilities over the protection of civilians and lacks integrative control. Like many existing critical issues in India are also deeply entrenched in outdated legislation or weak institutional brakes, the absence of a common framework of AI governance has brought about the pressing need for legal reform to safeguard against its misuse and to foster the principles of democracy given the imminent AI-enabled threats (Table 1).

Table 1 Comparative legal approaches to AI governance in counterterrorism

Aspect	European Union	United States	India
Regulatory approach	Centralized, rights-based, and comprehensive	Decentralized, sector-specific, innovation-driven	Fragmented, evolving, lacking dedicated AI legislation
Key frameworks	EU AI Act (2021, proposed), GDPR	Executive Orders, NSCAI Reports, FISA Section 702	DPDP Act (2023), Indian Telegraph Act (1885), IT Act (2000)
Focus in AI use	Risk-based classification, strict oversight for high-risk applications like surveillance and counterterrorism	National defense, security innovation, limited transparency	General data protection; lacks targeted regulation for AI in security
Transparency & oversight	Mandatory transparency reports, conformity assessments, public AI registries	Minimal centralized oversight; oversight largely left to specific agencies	Weak oversight mechanisms, broad security exemptions
Human rights protections	Strong emphasis on data privacy, fairness, and redress	Civil liberties concerns due to mass surveillance and limited judicial review	Limited guarantees; operational opacity in national security applications
Public accountability	High– Includes independent regulators, public consultation, and appeal mechanisms	LowLimited public disclosure and legal recourse in national security contexts	Low– Absence of effective redress systems and citizen engagement

8.2 Best Practices in AI Governance in the Security Domain

Internationally, some best practices have emerged, offering pathways to reconcile the deployment of AI with the protection of human rights. High-risk AI systems especially those used for public surveillance or in the justice system will be carefully tested before going live based on their potential for harm when deployed, a chance for data bias or ethical risk. Algorithmic Impact Assessments (AIAs) also promote transparency and minimize discriminatory impacts. AI systems should never be allowed to operate with full autonomy to make independent security decisions without human involvement. Decision-making should be subject to judicial review and traceable to the public authorities. Some governments have mandated public disclosure of how surveillance tools are applied [18]. These reports may include technical details, contracts with vendors, and limitations on their purposes. Public transparency reports can assist public trust-building and (democratic) control. Giving technologists, lawyers, ethicists, and civil society a seat at the table in the design and regulation of AI systems has the benefit of incorporating more perspectives in the decision-making process as part of interdisciplinary review boards.

8.3 Examples of Successful Oversight Mechanisms

Canada weaves a good precedent in the shape of its Algorithmic Impact Assessment (AIA) tool, meaning that all federal departments that deploy AI systems are required to use it. The tool mandates an assessment of the privacy, ethical, and social implications of AI systems before government agencies use them. It also compels public disclosure and documentation of risk mitigation measures, thus promoting transparency and civic responsibility.

The EU's proposed reforms to its own law regulating AI are another big step. Beyond the high-risk systems, the Act establishes conformity assessments, human oversight requirements, and registration of AI systems in an open European database, for all of the above guarantee that the AI technologies that are used in law enforcement and counterterrorism are not only technically sound but also ethically and legally justified [19]. Federal control has been limited; in the United States, local governments have taken the lead on oversight reforms. One is a so-called Community Control Over Police Surveillance (CCOPS) program that's been enacted in cities such as Oakland and Seattle, which mandates public hearings and legislative approval before law enforcement agencies can use surveillance technologies, including AI tools.

9 Recommendations and Proposed Framework

This demands a transition away from a disjointed, reactive policy toward an integrated and preventive governance model of counterterrorism, one where AI is wielded as a tool for protection instead of oppression. This model needs to respect and protect fundamental rights and allow for democratic control and ethical innovation [20]. The following section presents the specific, recommended practical steps, grouped into four pillars—rights-based governance, algorithmic accountability, institutional oversight, and ethical procurement.

9.1 Rights-Based AI Governance Model

A rights-based approach is one that reconciles the technical use with the demands of legality, necessity, proportionality, nondiscrimination and accountability should be at the core of any regulatory framework for AI in counterterrorism. National security, however, cannot serve as a carte blanche exception to legitimize widespread intrusions into private life or random decision-making. Such a human rights-based model should include legal safeguards that set out the appropriate way applicable by law enforcement and intelligence services that use AI. There is an open definition of key concepts (terrorism, extremism, radicalization) as legislative rules for judicial oversight as well as legislative guarantees for the victims of AI-informed decision-making. Countries like Germany and Finland have directly embedded human rights values in their AI strategy, setting a good example for ensuring technological progress respects democratic standards [21]. This type of model will need to involve cross-border harmonization of principles, particularly in view of the worldwide context of terrorism and flows of information. The rights-friendly regulation of AI internationally may be made available through the Council of Europe's Modernized Convention 108+.

9.2 Mandatory Algorithmic Audits and Transparency Mechanisms

To address rising demands for equity, transparency, and anti-discrimination, countries need to mandate mandatory algorithmic auditing programs as routine checks on AI technologies implemented in security work to check against legality, ethics, and societal ramifications.

Algorithmic audits would look into the dataset composition for representativeness and history of bias [22]. These audits must be conducted by independent third-party evaluators, not merely by vendors or government developers. Furthermore, results must be disclosed in transparency reports so that civil society, journalists, and affected communities can hold decision-makers accountable. Such a requirement has been included in the EU's proposed AI Act, which can serve as an effective example of transparency without undermining operational secrecy.

9.3 Creation of Independent Oversight and Grievance Redressal Bodies

The other critical step is the establishment of independent monitoring bodies that will monitor, investigate, and determine the use of AI in counterterrorism. Such bodies should be technically competent, legally empowered, and operationally autonomous from executive or policing organizations [23]. Such bodies would review the procurement and deployment of AI technology, conduct investigations into AI system abuse or harm, recommend sanctions or reforms, and provide binding remedies to those unfairly flagged or monitored. A good example is the UK's Investigatory Powers Commissioner's Office (IPCO), which conducts audits and approves surveillance warrants. The same AI-specific authority could assist in ensuring that national security activities remain within constitutional and international law limits. Furthermore, there should be effective grievance redress mechanisms to which individuals have access and can appeal against or challenge AI-based decisions, most importantly in cases of profiling, detention, or surveillance. The mechanisms in place should also ensure the right to explanation, access to data, and independent review or appeal mechanisms [24].

9.4 Ethics-by-Design Procurement Policies

The procurement cycle continues to be undervalued in regulatory language yet lies at the heart of what makes AI systems act as they do. Governments must adopt ethics-by-design procurement standards, which require vendors to embed human rights impact assessments, explainability features, and bias avoidance technologies from the production stage onwards. Such structures would have to make the pre-contract ethical screening of AI providers mandatory. On data protection contractual clauses, purpose limitation, and user training contractual clauses in 2022, the OECD released a report proposing that public procurement policies include AI ethics requirements as a financing and acquisition requirement [25]. The procurement policies should be harmonized with international standards, such as the UN Guiding Principles on Business and Human Rights (UNGPs), to make sure that governments and private vendors are accountable for adverse impacts linked with AI deployment.

10 Conclusion

The application of AI in counterterrorism has transformed the capabilities of modern security agencies enabling predictive threat detection, mass surveillance, and evidence-driven interventions on an unprecedented scale. However, as this research has shown, the rapid deployment of AI in this area has a tendency to outpace the establishment of corresponding legal, ethical, and institutional safeguards. The findings demonstrate systemic risks: algorithmic bias arising from flawed datasets, black-box decision-making, deficient redress mechanisms, and an indiscriminate focus on vulnerable groups under vague responses to "security" prerogatives.

Although AI can lend itself to operational efficiency, its use in high-risk, rights-sensitive environments like national security must be grounded in a solid legal foundation. Human rights standards, both global and regional, are important, but significant recalibrating is needed to respond to the specific threat of predictive and autonomous technology. Domestic legislations especially in the Global South also need to adapt to fill governance gaps and block abuse on the back of lax security loopholes. As the UN Office of the High Commissioner for Human Rights reports (2022) stress, the use of unchecked AI surveillance risks normalizing the violation of rights framed as innovation.

From this day forward, the same balance must be maintained, accountability weighed against innovation, security sought without faceless exchange of the dignity of those whom it professes to protect. Mandatory impact assessments, independent review commissions, and ethics-by-design procurement are not blockers to a legal solution; they are democratic safeguards. AI deployed against terrorism can't be wild; it cannot exist in a lawless shadowland. Instead, it should be governed by a model based on openness, fairness, and human rights. Only by embedding these values at every step, from development to deployment, are societies able to ensure that AI will remain a tool for the common good, not a weapon for untrammelled state power.

References

1. Montasari, R. (2024). Addressing ethical, legal, technical, and operational challenges in counterterrorism with machine learning: Recommendations and strategies. In *Cyberspace, cyberterrorism and the international security in the fourth industrial revolution: Threats, assessment and responses* (pp. 199–226). Springer.
2. Hoxhaj, O., Halilaj, B., & Harizi, A. (2023). Ethical implications and human rights violations in the age of artificial intelligence. *Balkan Social Science Review, 22*(22), 153–171.
3. Ganor, B. (2021). Artificial or human: A new era of counterterrorism intelligence? *Studies in Conflict & Terrorism, 44*(7), 605–624.
4. Esmailzadeh, Y., & Motaghi, E. (2024). International terrorism and social threats of artificial intelligence. *Journal of Globalization Studies, 15*(1), 168–179.
5. Martini, A. (2024). AI, counter-terrorism and global governance: State of the art. *Revista de Paz y Conflictos, 17*.

6. Amadi, P. S., & Eti, H. B. (2021). Artificial intelligence and terrorism prevention: Finding a balance between privacy right and National Security. *Indian J. Artificial Intel. & L, 2*, 56.
7. Yu, S., & Carroll, F. (2022). Implications of AI in national security: Understanding the security issues and ethical challenges. In *Artificial intelligence in cyber security: Impact and implications: Security challenges, technical and ethical issues, forensic investigative challenges* (pp. 157–175). Springer.
8. Lubin, A. (2024). Big data and the future of belligerency: Applying the rights to privacy and data protection to wartime artificial intelligence. In *Research handbook on warfare and artificial intelligence* (pp. 197–215). Edward Elgar Publishing.
9. Rahman, A. A. S., Kaur, A., & Saroj, P. (2024, September). Artificial intelligence and international crimes against humanity: Challenges and solutions. In *2024 International conference on advances in computing research on science engineering and technology (ACROSET)* (pp. 1–5). IEEE.
10. Singh, T. (2023). AI-driven surveillance technologies and human rights: Balancing security and privacy. In *International conference on smart systems: Innovations in computing* (pp. 703–717). Springer Nature.
11. Montasari, R. (2024). Introduction: Cyberspace, cyberterrorism and the international security in the fourth industrial revolution: Threats, assessment and responses. In *Cyberspace, cyberterrorism and the international security in the fourth industrial revolution: Threats, assessment and responses* (pp. 1–15). Springer.
12. Lemieux, F. (2024). Moral and ethical considerations. In *Intelligence and state surveillance in modern societies* (pp. 223–246). Emerald Publishing Limited.
13. Nagy, N. (2024). "Humanity's new frontier": Human rights implications of artificial intelligence and new technologies. *Hungarian Journal of Legal Studies, 64*(2), 236–267.
14. Wall, C. (2025). The ghost in the machine: Counterterrorism in the age of artificial intelligence. *Studies in Conflict & Terrorism*, 1–27.
15. Esmailzadeh, Y. (2023). Potential risks of ChatGPT: Implications for counterterrorism and international security. *International Journal of Multicultural and Multireligious Understanding (IJMMU), 10.*
16. Batabyal, G. S. (2024). Ethics, laws on war and artificial intelligence-driven warfare. In *Artificial intelligence, ethics and the future of warfare* (pp. 187–215). Routledge India.
17. Klingberg, S. (2022). Countering terrorism: Digital policing of open source intelligence and social media using artificial intelligence. In *Artificial intelligence and National Security* (pp. 101–111). Springer.
18. Veress, C. B. (2022). The limits of protection of human rights in warfare led by AI. *Acta Universitatis Sapientiae, Legal Studies, 11*(2), 81–97.
19. Baig, K., Abbas, A., Sajjad, M. H., & Zafar, M. H. (2024). The counter-terrorism and human rights: An analysis in the context of Pakistan. *The Critical Review of Social Sciences Studies, 2*(2), 1389–1410.
20. Sharma, M., Dixit, A., & Rawat, P. (2024). The use of AI in surveillance to identify the potential threat of terrorist attacks. In *2024 IEEE 1st Karachi section humanitarian technology conference (KHI-HTC)* (pp. 1–7). IEEE.
21. Mannan, M. A. (2025). Surveillance and privacy: Examining the complex interplay between National Security and Individual Freedoms. In *Analyzing privacy and security difficulties in social media: New challenges and solutions* (pp. 465–486). IGI Global Scientific Publishing.
22. Filipenko, N., Lukashevych, S., Andrieieva, O., & Ivanović, A. (2024). Application of artificial intelligence and information and communication technologies: Socio-ethical problems. *Theory and Practice of Forensic Science and Criminalistics, 34*(1), 12–41.
23. Singh, B., & Kaunert, C. (2025). Intelligent machine learning solutions for cybersecurity: Legal and ethical considerations in a global context. In *Advancements in intelligent process automation* (pp. 359–386). IGI Global.

24. Khazanchi, D., & Saxena, M. (2025). Navigating digital human rights in the age of AI: Challenges, theoretical perspectives, and research implications. *Journal of Information Technology Case and Application Research*, 1–14.
25. Oyekunle, D. O. T., Boohene, D., & Preston, D. (2024). Ethical considerations in AI-powered work environments: A literature review and theoretical framework for ensuring human dignity and fairness. *International Journal of Scientific Research and Management (IJSRM), 12*(03), 6166–6178.

Legal Implications of Using AI in Security Operations

Gaurav Kumar Sharma and Fatima Zahra Ouariach

Abstract Through improvement in efficiency and promotion of innovation, artificial intelligence (AI) is transforming different sectors, such as healthcare, finance, transportation, and education. However, the rapid pace of developing AI technologies brings forth very complicated legal issues that need addressing before going on with implementation. This chapter focuses on the changing legal landscape associated with AI and examines key areas such as privacy protection, liability, intellectual property, and employment. Data privacy is one of those big issues that accompany AI. A lot of personal data are collected, stored, and analyzed by AI-driven systems. Increasing reliance on algorithmic decision-making models means that there must be very strong legal restrictions keeping unauthorized uses and breaches away from an individual. In such efforts, legislations such as the EU's General Data Protection Regulation (GDPR) and the California Consumer Privacy Act (CCPA) regarding the United States help construct key safeguards through the establishment of transparency, user consent, and very strict data processing norms. However, with advancing lines of AI, managing the friction created during the compliance process with innovation and security remains quite a tough challenge. Liability and accountability are yet another crucial legal area regarding AI. AI-driven choices can have consequences that are powerful enough to germinate quarrels about who should be found culpable once an AI system harms or makes mistakes. This shall further be a "fundamental legal question" on whether accountability rests on developers, end-users, or the AI systems themselves.

G. K. Sharma (✉)
ICFAI Law School, The ICFAI University, Jaipur, Rajasthan, India

F. Z. Ouariach
Abdelmalek Essaadi University, Tétouan, Morocco
e-mail: fatimazahra.ouariach@etu.uae.ac.ma

C. Kaunert et al. (eds.), *Artificial Intelligence for Global Counter-Terrorism*, Contributions to Security and Defence Studies,
https://doi.org/10.1007/978-3-031-99235-3_7

1 Introduction

AI is about the enhancement of computer-based capabilities so that tasks are done that typically require human intelligence. This would cover tasks carried out by AI through programming based on rules combined with deep learning and machine learning algorithms. Rooted in the processes of learning, AI gains enhanced abilities to gain knowledge and skills, thereby developing effectiveness in various fields. The ever-increasing importance of AI in modern times is fast becoming a widespread realization, especially in sectors like banking, insurance, telecommunications, etc., and legal services. In fact, traditional coverage of liabilities may not comprehensively cover the complexities of autonomous decision-making, and therefore, new legal doctrines and regulatory mechanisms for fair and effective accountability warrant development for the new age.

The unique introduction of artificial intelligence opens the law of intellectual property (IP) also to tests. Questions like ownership over AI-generated content, patentability of inventions driven by AI, and legal protection for AI innovations also ignite controversy among legal scholars and policymakers. Such laws conventionally recognized for the premises in IP do not provide for autonomous creation and/or inventing processes and remain contentious with respect to rights enjoyment by the AI developer, company, and even the AI. Such interrogatories require a reconsideration of the patent, copyright, and trademark lexicon to lie in line with the current generation of AI-formed works.

Understanding and discussing AI applications in the workplace raises fresh dimensions with respect to employment and labor rights. Automation and AI-centric technologies are transcending boundaries when it comes to the job market, thereby creating panic over future job losses and the immediate need to upskill the workforce. Labor laws need to be proactively established by governments and policymakers to shield workers' rights in the economic adaptation promoted through such measures. For example, the formation of policies that will enable upskilling initiatives, bring about fair labor practices by policy interventions, and address ethical issues surrounding automation in workplaces are some of such efforts. AI can unleash phenomenal opportunities for development in all sectors, and its application can raise great legal and ethical issues at the same time. There are essential protective measures that have to accompany the establishment and adoption of AI technologies for the rights of individuals, standards of privacy, and equitable legal accountability to be in place. To create a legal environment conducive to enabling and fostering innovation while safeguarding fundamental societal values, it is important that policymakers, legal professionals, and industry stakeholders work collaboratively. So, as expected, proactive and adaptive regulations are going to be important to keep AI technologies serving humanity in a very responsible and ethical manner in the time to come.

The Indian legal profession, however, has been slow so far in adopting AI-driven means of operation, maintaining the pace of technology. A number of legal practices remain old-fashioned, relying on methods that were developed decades earlier. But

AI could improve the entire legal domain by equipping lawyers with fast access to vast reservoirs of legal knowledge and expertise. The legal arena is inherently complicated and dynamic, so AI shall also serve as added assistance in the accurate navigation through this complexity [1].

AI has traditionally been designed to be a closed and integrated framework comprising software and hardware facets. On the software side, the major element that weighs on AI development is its algorithms. One such major area of development is the artificial neural network (ANN) that resembles the structure and workings of the human brain. This essentially interlinks a network of neurons where neurons share information among themselves through weighted connections, thereby identifying complex, nonlinear patterns within humongous datasets. AI systems keep learning algorithms by continuing to train with the information that has referenced different inputs with errors they have encountered, thereby enhancing their prediction and decision-making capacities.

Integrating AI into industries and various domains has raised concerns regarding the attendant risks, such as incidental errors and data breaches. The risks of an AI-induced error can be life and death to patients in places where AI is considered in high-risk sectors such as health care. Abiding under specific conditions, it also raises huge legal and ethical imputations on privacy, surveillance, bias, discrimination, and the role of human judgement in the decision-making process. The swelling adrenaline of new AI-driven digital technologies has, in fact, also amplified fears of data security, as AI systems might become new sources of vulnerabilities.

While the Indian legal sector is faced with many such challenges, AI presents the most exceptional opportunities for it [2]. There are already areas where the value propositions of AI tools have found adoption:

- Contract review: AI tools can create an effective and efficient contract review.
- Legal analytics: AI can analyze very large legal datasets to render insights, predict outcomes, and provide better decision-making.
- Outcome prediction: AI models are capable of studying the history of judicial rulings, allowing them to predict how certain cases may turn out.
- Legal research: High efficiency in legal research with AI, hammering down the retrieval of case laws and other relevant precedents.
- Documentation automation: AI facilitates the automation of document-draughting processes, reducing the tediousness of paperwork for lawyers.
- Intellectual property management: AI can assist in the protection, monitoring, and enforcement of intellectual property rights.

With advancing technologies, AI will keep up with the changing needs of lawyers and clients. The promise of AI to transform the legal field is huge when we talk about a great reduction in costs and an increase in efficiency. AI has the ability to save a considerable amount of time with legal research and document draughting, which in turn allows lawyers to devote their energies to the more challenging and strategic dimensions of their work. While AI presents many powerful tools, it cannot replace one of the most precious sentiments enshrined in legal practice—human beings. Clients will always seek seasoned legal advisors who will know how best to apply modern technology in a human-related, personable approach toward legal services [3].

The legal profession is not the only sector transformed—others are looking in finance, transportation, education, and all the other AI-generated diameters. These AI technologies have advanced to a level that creates indelible legal implications and challenges that require scrutiny. By automating decision-making and predictive analytics, integration into everyday life creates corruption; however, critical legal issues arise on the way to accountability, transparency, privacy, liability, intellectual property, and ethics.

The privacy rights issue is among the foremost legal concerns surrounding artificial intelligence (AI). AI is a data-intensive system reliant on vast amounts of information and hence raises questions regarding data protection, user consent, and surveillance. Further complicating these issues is the opacity of AI decision-making in terms of both its transparency and accountability—the most critical applications, such as criminal justice and health care, create greater confusion. Another legal problem is deciding about liability with respect to AI-based decisions that lead to injury, as the traditional concept of responsibility blurs in the face of the integrity of autonomous activity by artificial intelligence, raising fundamental questions as to whether responsibility should be conveyed to the developer, end-user, or even perhaps the machine itself [4].

Then, of course, the old laws won't be able to keep pace with the new creatures they are giving birth to; these very artificial intellectual properties introduce entirely new conflicts in ownership, patentability, and infringement, and that too not only at the national but also at the global levels. To top it all, ethics becomes an important factor in terms of AI governance with issues related to fairness and non-discrimination and respect for human dignity. This becomes a requisite for holding all such systems to ethical standards in preventing bias, discrimination, and detriment to society.

The legal hurdles in AI demand concerted multi-disciplinary efforts from policymakers, legal practitioners, technologists, ethicists, and even other stakeholders. This will develop proactive legal frameworks and regulatory infrastructures to harness this transformational power while minimizing its risks and safeguarding fundamental rights and values within societies. AI regulation will therefore promote innovation while ensuring accountability and fairness and maintaining public trust in systems driven by AI [5].

2 Legal Implications of Artificial Intelligence in India

Artificial intelligence (AI) has taken the world by storm, making its way into various fields, creating a whole new hype in everyone's lives—how we are to perform our roles and how we will deal with technology in the near future. The former human intelligence comparison usually applies where computers simulate cognitive functions like problem-solving, decision-making, and language comprehension. Simply put, it enables computers to do things that require human intelligence, such as problem-solving, decision-making, and communication in different languages. The development of AI has affected most parts of an ordinary person's life, influencing everything from recommendations on some digital platforms to developing analytical reports. AI has many applications: search engines that can even break into the most advanced recommendations from sites like YouTube, Amazon, and Netflix; virtual assistants such as Siri or Alexa; and autonomous vehicles like Tesla's self-driving cars [6].

2.1 Regulatory Framework for AI in India

As of now, India does not have any specific legislation framing AI in its judicial or administrative systems, but there are some laws that already exist or others that are waiting for enactment which take an expected view on some aspects of AI-both directly and indirectly; chiefly in subjects related to data privacy and cyber security. These are:

1. The Information Technology (IT) Act, 2000: This Act mainly focuses on data protection and cybersecurity and also regulates electronic transactions, so it is related to point AI applications considering sensitive digital information.
2. The Proposed Digital Personal Data Protection Bill, 2022: This bill mainly envisages regulating data privacy, consent-based data processing, and principles of personal data handling. AI technologies would have been heavily data-centric; thus, an expected effect of this bill would be on governing AI-centered technologies.

Recognizing the transformational power of AI, the Indian government has taken positive and proactive steps to integrate AI into the legal, economic, and technological framework of the country. Under this effort, the Ministry of Commerce and Industry constituted an Artificial Intelligence Task Force in 2017 to examine the integration of AI into all fields, particularly including governance and legal affairs. In addition, the Ministry of Electronics and Information Technology has set up four expert committees to prepare a strategic framework for the AI policy establishment.

In that line, to address AI's implications in the legal field, the government launched the Centre of Excellence for Artificial Intelligence in the Legal Field (CEAILF). This initiative aims to research what AI can deliver in legal research, case management, and increased judicial efficiency. In another broad context, NITI Aayog, the apex policy think tank in India, released the national strategy for artificial intelligence—a foundational document for AI governance and regulation in India. NSAI lays out possible applications for AI, associated risks, and regulatory considerations before continuing to bring forward any significant step toward developing AI-specific legislation [7].

2.2 AI and Cybersecurity: Strengthening Digital Defenses

With the continuing evolution of AI and machine learning technologies, an increasing role is being played by them in cybersecurity. High amounts of data can be analyzed by AI-enabled systems in mere seconds to find intrusions, phishing, or any user behavior events that are deemed suspicious. With these capabilities, one can rather term AI indispensable within the digital security frameworks.

The pace at which cyber threats are evolving is incredible, which essentially means that security professionals need to move with time and enhance their arsenal with cutting-edge technologies to cope with and protect networks, infrastructure, and the most critical asset, sensitive organizational data. AI cybersecurity developments further improve detection capabilities, automate response mechanisms, and improve overall security infrastructure. Hence, AI becomes increasingly integral for modern cybersecurity strategies, especially concerning online businesses and banks that deal with a large number of digital transactions.

2.3 Impact of AI on the Legal Profession

The legacy of traditionalist practices, developed over the decades, was now facing a technological transformation affected by AI in India's legal sector. Just like their counterparts in the rest of the world, Indian lawyers are slowly opening up to using these new AI tools to bolster efficiency in legal work. AI technology is changing the legal sector by augmenting legal research, contract draughting, case analysis, and due diligence with much higher accuracy, speed, and productivity.

AI-powered legal tools help lawyers by flagging inconsistencies in case law, contract review automation, and tight legal research gained through AI and analysis of vast amounts of legal documentation. These tools allow a lawyer to devote time to higher-order legal reasoning and client advocacy rather than repetitive administrative tasks. AI could change the existing legal system; however, it does not necessarily mean that it will replace lawyers completely. Rather, it will be an adjunct to fulfil the purpose of legal service better: to provide access to justice and efficiency in court proceedings [8].

If the Indian legal system aligns itself with global tech advancements, this will strengthen its footing in the international AI arena. International collaboration for AI research and regulatory frameworks could serve India in juggling AI's ethical and legal conundrums while also promoting innovation and responsible AI development. In due time, AI, if developed with sufficient foresight, could help forge a more amiable and productive ecosystem of legal service delivery for the benefit of everyone downstream, from the legal practitioner to society as a whole.

3 Artificial Intelligence and Current Scenario in India

India is the fastest-growing market in the world. It may transform different sectors such as p., finance, agriculture, and governance. As the most populous country, AI creates opportunities as well as challenges, with respect to regulation and data security. A typical legal gap in India is unaided by the absence of a dedicated law governing artificial intelligence and a data protection act.

Currently, there is some semblance of law on protection of data in India under Sections 43A and 72A of the Information Technology Act, which lays the foundation for protection against the unlawful disclosure of personal information. These provisions may be the result of considerable achievement, but juxtaposed against the EU's framework of the GDPR, they lack that depth. In light of all this increased immergence in AI technology, it is crucial for a country to start allocating enough time toward the development of clear draft policies that regulation would prescribe in regard to the AI system's transparency, accountability, and security in its implementation [9].

In fact, the various committees set up by the Indian government address the holistic view, including the legal and ethical aspects, along with the technical aspects, of AI development and implementation. The regulatory framework that is being structured here in the EU can be expected to set the standard for India and other nations, much as the GDPR did for developing laws on data protection across the globe. Also, in 2017, the Supreme Court of India, in its celebrated judgment on the right to privacy, recognized the right to privacy as a constitutional fundamental right, strengthening the need for robust regulations for AI to help protect an individual's rights in an increasingly digital world.

3.1 Government Initiatives and Industry Adoption

Now, here is an important and serious fact—it is advancing its AI by such leaps and bounds that its industries and businesses are adopting AI-enabled solutions much more quickly than the regulations can come in for effect. Companies are training their employees on AI technologies to provide higher productivity and to spark new opportunities and innovation. In particular, in 2018, NITI Aayog, which is the country's top-level policy think tank, brought out several AI initiatives, and among them were the two big, which are "Responsible AI" (February 2021) and "Principles for Responsible AI" (August 2021), both of which put forth ethical guidelines and strategies for the use of AI for development in India. Besides, the Indian government has taken up the National AI Portal to centralize information and disseminate research and policy developments in AI. In addition to that, a National AI Strategy is being drafted to steer AI innovation and deployment across more than one sector [10].

3.2 Expansion of AI in Indian Industries

Industries around India are quickly adopting AI to help them improve the efficiency of their work, optimize processes, and enhance the customer experience. AI integration is particularly emphasized in:

1. Information technology and services: Be it as regards the IT operations, customer support, and cybersecurity, AI-based automation and machine learning techniques will revolutionize them all.
2. Healthcare: The application of AI in early detection of diseases, precision medicine, and predictive analytics will make healthcare much accessible and outcomes even better.
3. Finance and banking: The financial sector is transforming with AI-based fraud detection, risk assessment automations, and personalized financial services.
4. Agriculture: Using AI applications of precision farming, crop monitoring, and predictive analytics benefits farmers in maximizing yield and reducing wastage of resource.

3.3 AI Startup Ecosystem and Academic Research

India has a vibrant and rapidly growing startup ecosystem, with many startups using AI technologies that are coming up in different sectors. These startups are developing cutting-edge solutions in areas such as:

- Healthcare diagnostics (AI medical imaging and early disease detection)
- E-commerce and personalization (AI recommendation engines and chatbots)
- Smart manufacturing (AI automation and predictive maintenance)
- Fintech (fraud detection, credit score, and robo-advisors)

AI research and education are being actively sponsored by many Indian academic institutes. Top-tier universities and research institutions conduct specialized AI courses, degrees, and dedicated research programs to train the next generation of AI professionals and spur innovations [11].

3.4 Challenges and Future Prospects

Following the rapid advancement of AI, there are many challenges that still persist:

- Data privacy and security: The absence of substantial data protection regimes gives rise to violations of data privacy and misuse.
- Ethics: Unbiasedness, transparency, and fairness are major concerns regarding AI systems.

- Skill development: The demand for AI-skilled professionals is on the rise, and thus, investment in AI education and training must be increased.

All these challenges require cooperative action from the government, the private sector, universities, and civil society to evolve responsible AI policies and frameworks. With India's commitment to advancing AI research, supporting innovation, and framing comprehensive regulations, the country is poised to emerge as a leading force in AI [12].

AI is expected to become the backbone of every sphere of life in the foreseeable future, with reverberations into governance, economic growth, and technological forwardness. The essence of sustainable advancement of AI lies in the development of ethical, inclusive, and futuristic road maps that will help harness AI's benefits and, at the same time, protect fundamental rights and societal interests.

4 Worldwide Development of Artificial Intelligence

A domain in which artificial intelligence (AI) developed into the discipline of study was 1956, and since then, technology has changed in a revolutionary manner. Over the decades, AI has been penetrating various sectors from legal institutions and law firms to governments across the globe. Understanding the need for a pan-European legal frame, the European Union (EU) has now launched the AI Act, which aims at creating a unified legal and governance structure for artificial intelligence across its jurisdictions.

So much weight is given in the AI Act toward the promotion of internal transparency and accountability for the development of AI in the ethical dimension, and thereby to eliminate risks. This regulatory learning perspective particularly favors India as it infers a lot in terms of shaping its own AI governance framework while reducing the adverse consequences [13]. While seemingly somewhat slow when taking into account the rapid advance of AI in the twenty-first century, it is still undeniably a lot more advanced, thanks primarily to highly technical statistical machine-learning algorithms that are very efficient in solving complex problems, both in academia and in the industry. AI saw in recent years unparalleled global investment and innovation through countries' initiatives such as the United States, China, and top European economies propelling research and development efforts into the field. AI research institutes, technology startups, and human resources have also done much in strengthening this capacity.

Several countries have started to draw national AI strategies to accelerate their development in research, investment, education, and regulatory oversight of AI technologies. Such countries should define how to use AI in an economic and societal environment. AI applies to a variety of industries-from healthcare to finance, manufacturing to agriculture, transportation to entertainment. AI-enabled solutions from predictive analytics to natural language processing drive businesses toward better efficiency and innovation, as well as reshape business processes.

But the proliferation of AI brings about many ethical and regulatory dilemmas concerning data privacy, algorithm biases, accountability, transparency, and workforce displacement. Governments, examiners, and institutions are now striving to institute ethical principles, regulatory standards, and legal frameworks so that AI monopolizes the process of development and application. There is an international picture of AI that hangs competition and collaboration, among cross-border research partnerships, global AI conferences, and multinational initiatives creating opportunities for sharing and progress in technology.

As a result of the rapid growth in the adoption of AI, there is an increasing trend in demand for skilled professionals in AI-related departments. Institutions of education, as well as online learning resources and training from industries, are increasingly being stretched to cater to this rising demand for AI skills. It will take workforce development and pacing strategies to comprehend the current and future artificial intelligence environment in order to create a steadily expanding cohort of future professionals equipped to transform society as it moves toward AI [14].

Another critical aspect of AI governance entails security concerns: cybersecurity risks, data protection, intellectual property rights, and ethical implications of fully autonomous AI systems. Governments, private stakeholders, and international organizations engage in policy-making and collaborative efforts toward the realization of such objectives. Global AI governance institutions must be established to ensure the alignment of technological development with morality and societal well-being.

Such a dynamic and constantly evolving trajectory of artificial intelligence is metamorphosed due to rapid innovation and technology diffusion, as well as intricate challenges. As the future unfolds with AI, responsible governance and international cooperation will ensure that the full potential of this technology is harvested and that its risks are mitigated. The integration of technological progress with ethical consideration will be the balanced approach needed to provide equitable and sustainable AI-driven solutions for all.

5 Intellectual Property and Artificial Intelligence

The intersection of artificial intelligence (AI) and legal innovation has introduced a host of fresh challenges, particularly in the field of intellectual property (IP). The questions of ownership, authorship, and patentability of works generated by AI, as systems increasingly take part in the creation of content and advancements in technology, have started to emerge. Traditional IP laws, which for ages have recognized human creators as the sole proprietors of intellectual property, are now being challenged due to the emergence of machine-generated works and innovations [15].

One complex issue arises with the determination of the true owner and creator of works generated by AI. Historically, intellectual property laws have accorded rights solely to human authors. The increasing utilizations of AI in creative processes throw that framework into disarray. The ruling of the US Copyright Office in Zarya of the Dawn is an example. A 2023 comic book with art made using Midjourney, an

AI tool, was ruled such that while the particular individual who compiled and arranged the comic book work would be entitled to copyright over that work as a whole, copyright could not be claimed over the specific images made by AI. This was so because Midjourney did not afford enough control over the creative process, making any attribution in the traditional sense contestable.

These highlight the changing nature of intellectual property laws in response to the increasing advances in artificial intelligence. Legal systems worldwide need to adapt to such changes as artificial intelligence is becoming more involved with creativity and technology to create tensions pertaining to the promotion of innovation while still adhering to the basic tenets of authorship and ownership in intellectual property law.

6 Advantages of Artificial Intelligence in Enhancing Cyber Security

Artificial intelligence plays the prime role in strengthening cybersecurity by studying the behavioral patterns of business organizations and strikingly detecting any changes that signal security threats. It also strengthens the organization by further enhancing network security and risk mitigation through its advanced capabilities. Mere human efforts would not have been enough to figure out every such possible security threat that an organization might be facing. The AI-powered systems, on the other hand, would detect as well as analyze and even potentially stop a cyber threat before it brings huge ruin. It means a real-time and continuous threat detection in the form of constant monitoring that should provide a proactive approach in protecting the digital infrastructure. The enormous volume of data that flows daily between business and user makes the protection of such information from cyber threats, malware, or unauthorized access much more serious than ever. AI security ensures confidentiality and integrity while preventing compromise of sensitive business data by malicious parties [16].

AI will contribute the most to the research of vulnerability management because it will scan for successful threats and find ways to patch any weaknesses in an organization's security groundwork. Security protocols are monitored continuously; hence, AI supports optimizing defense mechanisms and mitigating the chances of cyberattacks. In other words, those cybercriminals have been active in developing their new tactics to penetrate the walls of business networks. Therefore, with the increasing hacking strategies, organizations are required to build more and more stronger systems to defy those strategies. These adaptive intelligent systems are AI-driven adaptive and intelligent cybersecurity solutions that look at the simple future of defense mechanisms against the probably most penetrating threats.

7 Challenges for Artificial Intelligence

AI advancing so quickly outside and into almost every field is thus creating levels of efficiency and innovation. The legal field, which in many respects has been a latecomer to technology, is witnessing the growing application of AI-driven tools that serve to enhance the productivity of the various aspects of legal practice. Such tools are increasingly deployed by legal professionals to facilitate legal research, document analysis, and contract review, thereby maximizing productivity and accuracy.

That said, conversely, such transformation comes with a variety of complex problems requiring due diligence. One of the central issues is how far legal practitioners should go in relying on AI outputs and the ramifications of such dependence. The quality and reliability of AI-generated results are always greatly determined by the data sets on which training has been given; thus, this raises questions of data bias, transparency, and ethics. As AI continually affects the legal landscape, it is the right time for the legal practitioner to assess the tools responsibly, ensuring their integration into the system ensures fairness, accuracy, and justice [17].

8 Impact of AI on Legal Practices

1. Advanced legal functions: The use of advanced data analytics enables swift and thorough treatments by very large legal datasets, significantly improving the efficiency and accuracy of legal research. With technology-based assistance, legal practitioners will quickly identify relevant case laws, precedents, statutory provisions to enable a smooth and attempt-efficient research process.
2. Automated review and analysis of documents: The automation of legal document review actually accelerates complex tasks such as contract analysis, due diligence, and even e-discovery. Legal professionals would have enough time to review and assess massive volumes of documents through application of advanced algorithms and artificial intelligence without any compromise in accuracy and without the time that rigorous manual scrutiny consumes.
3. Legal drafting and documentation: Leading-edge technology can facilitate the drafting of legal documents, including contracts, legal briefs, and high-quality contracts. Legal drafting will be automated and yield better results with regard to compliance with laws and consistency of document formation but also greatly reduce risks of human error and omission in the legal drafting exercise.
4. Improved client interaction and legal services delivery: AI-enabled legal systems bring about all-day access for hassle-free responses to clients' most asked legal questions and better communication with clients. Such technologies would probably allow appointment scheduling, provide legal consultation, and ensure proper correspondence between attorneys and clients toward better optimization of client engagement and services provided.

9 Understanding the Legal Issues Surrounding AI

There is a rapid transformation taking place in the AI legal landscape, and this has become a wonderful labyrinth of regulations, challenges, and risks. Basically, AI systems work on a backbone of heavy data processing and analysis, thereby identifying patterns through a machine-learning mechanism and generating an output based on user input. Nevertheless, unrestrained reliance on data-driven learning brings forth a number of legal issues. Biases or incompleteness in datasets, poorly defined AI frameworks, and opacity in the decision-making processes tend to engender ethical and legal dilemmas [18].

A serious question of concern in the legal field is the liability of lawyers—especially in front of their respective regulatory bodies—using AI in their practice and having an understanding of the limitations and potential risks that AI embraces. Inappropriate use of AI in the legal setting will lead to wrong results, ethical breaches, and violations of confidentiality to their clients. Another equally giant concern that has arisen is where AI with matters of public interest has become the focus of scrutiny in major ongoing lawsuits. For instance, some of the world's largest corporate technology giants, such as Microsoft and OpenAI, are mired in lawsuits concerning AI-generated content and copyright infringement. These cases underscore the bigger disturbances caused to intellectual property rights by the tension that exists concerning the authorship, ownership, and fair use of works made from AI.

The very lawyers and law firms are not exempt from the loss caused by misuse of AI-driven tools. The rapid growth of AI-assisted legal research, contract analysis, and predictive analytics could bring opportunities as well as challenges. AI, if dutifully applied, could better aid the work of lawyers in terms of efficiency and accuracy, but wrongful application—by relying excessively on the outputs of automation or not verifying the information it provides—can induce professional misconduct and raise liability issues. As AI technology evolves, the need for comprehensive regulations, ethical guidelines, and properly informed legal oversight becomes an ever-urgent necessity to alleviate any risks and ensure responsible integration of AI into the legal profession [19].

10 Legal Risk Associated with Gen AI Models

Nowadays, almost all generative artificial intelligence (AI) tools give disclaimers that assure the users they have no guarantee that what will be produced would be accurate or reliable. Rather, the users are told to be careful, as they remain accountable in assessing any fact. An AI output may probably contain inaccuracies and biases from its training data or even utter something misleading. Besides that, there are also major concerns regarding data privacy, as many of these AI tools possess the authority to utilize inputs or data fed by the users as training data. This poses a danger once sensitive or private information is inputted. On top of that, the emergence of new regulatory frameworks with regards to the technology raises further legal and ethical challenges. For example, issues of transparency, accountability, and compliance with emerging regulations complicate AI usage in professional realms [20].

Take, for instance, the new laws that the European Union has just passed, which regulate the generative AI tools and are proof of growing scrutiny across the globe on how these technologies impact society. While they regulate their operations strictly, industries like healthcare will soon come up with their own ethical frameworks on how to use such technologies in their activities in tandem with the specific standards. Ethical issues also abound in the legal field, where professionals will have to develop risk-mitigation strategies while maximizing AI's use in legal research, case analysis, or documentation. Since very serious ethical and legal stakes are at play, responsible AI usage in legal work would need an alignment with evolving laws, transparency measures, and ethical considerations.

10.1 Accuracy

The core concept underpinning artificial intelligence is that of accuracy, which forms the basis for making appropriate predictions and decisions with the given data. The level of accuracy directly determines the reliability and utility of AI systems in different fields, such as medical diagnosis, financial risk assessment, and autonomous driving. Thus, AI models must be tested against a very high standard for precision that would compromise neither quality nor speed of decision-making. This would call for rigorous training on clearly defined and high-quality datasets and pertinent algorithms, followed by careful validation and testing. But then again, due to the inherent complexities and unpredictability intrinsic to real-world data, accuracy might never be fully granted. Developers must somehow straddle the line between enhancing accuracy and dealing with the inherent limitations of AI technologies. Therefore, the continual development and maintenance of these highly adaptive systems—with adaptive learning capabilities and consistent monitoring of algorithm performance—will have to be put in place in order to enhance their performance with time. Nevertheless, as long as AI continues to develop, it will remain important to achieve the claim of accuracy against its ethical and technical compromises, thereby harmonizing AI technologies to user utilities and societal needs [21].

10.2 AI Bias and Fairness

The ethical implications of artificial intelligence (AI) are a matter of much concern these days, especially with regard to bias and fairness. AI technologies, not properly designed and implemented, may end up reinforcing existing social inequalities and injustices in very insidious ways. Different sources of bias in AI include skewed or unrepresentative training data, algorithmic flaws, or even highly prejudiced decision-making mechanisms. This would result in unfair and discriminatory outcomes for people or groups in terms of race, gender, or economic background.

Fairness in AI calls for a multi-pronged process that goes from identifying and curating training datasets. The data used to derive AI-built models in assessment of diverse and inclusive attention to blocking societal prejudices should be highly prioritized. Equally important is iterating through algorithms to remove unintended bias in decision-making. Openness and accountability also play a vital role in attaining AI fairness because they enable stakeholders to view critically how decisions, through AI, take place and whether they adhere to standards of truth and fairness [22].

The AI bias issue is a much bigger one that requires technical inputs. It touches on moral and societal responsibility. A collaborative comprehensive action involving AI developers, policymakers, legal persons, ethicists, and community representatives must strive toward a robust framework that provides for equity, inclusivity, and the ethics of deploying AI. It also involves establishing stricter measures, auditing at regular intervals, and promoting discussions across disciplines.

10.3 Data Labeling Challenges

Data labeling is somehow central to the design of AI models by serving as the basis for training algorithms to recognize patterns and make independent decisions and outputs. Nevertheless, several significant challenges are associated with this process and tend to affect the accuracy, reliability, and acceptability of AI systems. One of the concerns here is bias being injected during the labeling process whereby human annotators could unintentionally import their subjective opinions into the dataset. Such concern would become even bigger in cases where AI is being used to make a vital decision—an example being when an absolute precision in labeling uncertainties of road safety would have to be employed by autonomous vehicles, or when a subject would have to categorize data into positive or negative in sentiment analysis systems, based on human emotions that are often extremely nuanced [23].

The accuracy and consistency of labeled data are among the main issues to tackle, given the possibility that human labelers label data inconsistently due to different judgments or different interpretations. This is more likely to be the case in situations involving complex datasets, be it unstructured text or images, where the possibility of discrepancies based upon essentially subjective differences, that is, differences in interpretations, arises. In addition, certain niche domains or specialized fields would also call for domain-specific expertise, which in turn makes it almost impossible to find qualified annotators who would be able to appear on the data-labeling records. The conundrum is further worsened in high-stakes situations, such as AI being used for medical diagnosis, legal analysis, or financial forecasting, where even minor deviations concerning data labeling can give rise to grossly wrong predictions from the AI with serious ramifications [24].

Another major challenge in data labeling is its scalability. AI models keep on growing in complexity and require larger and diverse datasets, yet traditional manual labelling processes are hardly efficient and practical anymore in these terms. The time and cost of manually labelling huge masses of data present a gigantic hurdle for many an organization to overcome in terms of AI development, especially for those not having deep pockets. To meet such challenges, innovative data-labeling techniques under exploration now include active learning, in which AI models select the most informative data points to humans for labeling; semi-supervised learning, in which both labeled and unlabeled data are utilized to make a model more accurate; and crowdsourcing, which are dividing the labeling tasks across a broad network of contributors.

AI-driven validation tools can help in reducing inconsistencies and improving data integrity. Thus, by adopting these new-age labeling strategies and quality control measures, AI developers can also improve the accuracy, fairness, and robustness of AI systems, which, in the end, would lead to even more reliable and less biased outcomes in many applications.

11 Conclusion

Through integration with the Indian legal system, AI has the potential to ramp up both efficiency and accuracy. Fundamental issues of accountability and transparency must nevertheless be resolved to have AI acting in ethicality and impartiality. One major challenge at a global level is the lack of a well-defined regulatory structure for how AI should be used. Keeping pace with rapid advancements across a variety of technological areas, AI technology is developing faster than ever, presenting serious ethical and legal concerns. Therefore, setting up safeguards becomes crucial to securing the safe, responsible, and fair use of the AI system.

The main risks posed by AI include bias and discrimination, infringement on privacy, and threats to human life and safety. Such issues accentuate the need for proper regulations that can be put in place to mitigate potential damages while enabling innovation. Positive steps taken in this respect include the formation of some bodies and committees, such as the Centre for Ethics and Artificial Intelligence in Law and Finance (CEAILF), and the publication of NITI Aayog's National Strategy for Artificial Intelligence (NSAI) discussion paper. AI could be a game-changer for human affairs and could probably become the most impactful invention in history. How AI systems are engineered, implemented, and regulated affects society as a whole with long-lasting consequences.

Key aspects of AI governance are outlining policy dilemmas, settling ethical disputes, clarifying legal ambiguities, and keeping AI and data analytics solutions simply transparent. The decisions about the development of AI software, thereafter, will affect AI-driven decisions and their integration into institutional settings.

Understanding these mechanisms, therefore, assumes greater importance as they will affect public life significantly in the time to come. AI tools can play a vital role in the vast and evolving Indian legal framework in offering other perspectives and providing insight in a matter of seconds. Traditionally, legal research was a time-consuming and resource-intensive process and frequently affected operational efficiency in law firms. But an AI-enabled legal research system can democratize access to legal knowledge by allowing small and medium firms to be able to carry out their work in a complete and thorough manner without compromising on quality.

AI is quickly becoming the centerpiece of many industries in India, such as healthcare, banking, and transportation. Yet that means very rapidly entering a concern with AI bias. Bias is said to be present in an AI system when an algorithm consistently produces results skewed in favor of one group or in disfavor of another. This tends to raise a serious concern about fairness and discrimination in matters of extreme importance, such as employment, lending, and criminal justice. For the marginalized sections, acceptance of the consequences of bias would come as a heavy burden, necessitating potent anticounter violence to avoid or mitigate such an injustice from entering society in the first place.

AI bias arises from deep-rooted human prejudices that are present in the datasets used to train the AI system, as well as in the algorithms extended for this training. Sample bias, non-representative data preferences, several algorithmic distortions, and so on are quite a few manifestations of such bias. Understandably, it is paramount that we identify these forms of bias and rectify them to ensure that temperate AI systems exist and operate fairly, inclusively, and justly. With a serious set of ethical principles for AI, protective legal structures, and an open system of governance, India is set to lead the charge in the responsible application of AI systems across sectors to shield people from the impact of algorithmic discrimination.

References

1. Rehan, H. (2024). AI-Driven cloud security: The future of safeguarding sensitive data in the digital age. *Journal of Artificial Intelligence General science (JAIGS) ISSN 3006-4023, 1*(1), 132–151.
2. Marsico, F., & Amigo, M. (2025). Ethical and security challenges in AI for forensic genetics: From bias to adversarial attacks. *Forensic Science International: Genetics, 76*, 103225. https://doi.org/10.1016/j.fsigen.2025.103225
3. Abdullayeva, F. (2023). Cyber resilience and cyber security issues of intelligent cloud computing systems. *Results in Control and Optimization, 12*, 100268. https://doi.org/10.1016/j.rico.2023.100268
4. Goyal, S. (2021, May 21). Anti Terrorism Day 2021: List of 8 major terror attacks that shook India. Jagranjosh.com. https://www.jagranjosh.com/general-knowledge/list-of-major-terror-attacks-that-shook-india-1590080570-1
5. Stepanov, L. V., Koltsov, A. S., & Parinov, A. V. (2021). Evaluating the cybersecurity of an enterprise based on a genetic algorithm. *Lecture Notes in Electrical Engineering*, 580–590. https://doi.org/10.1007/978-3-030-71119-1_57

6. Aota, M., Kanehara, H., Kubo, M., Murata, N., Sun, B., & Takahashi, T. (2020, July). Automation of vulnerability classification from its description using machine learning. In *2020 IEEE Symposium on Computers and Communications (ISCC)* (pp. 1–7). IEEE.
7. Hafeez, A., Topolovec, K., & Awad, S. (2019). ECU fingerprinting through parametric signal modeling and artificial neural networks for in-vehicle security against spoofing attacks. In *2019 15th International Computer Engineering Conference (ICENCO)*, 29–38. https://doi.org/10.1109/icenco48310.2019.9027298
8. Santos, C. H., & de Lima, S. M. (2022). Artificial-Intelligence-Based Antivirus Specialized in Citadel Malware Pattern Recognition. https://doi.org/10.21203/rs.3.rs-2052263/v2
9. Kumar, K. S., Nair, S. A. H., Roy, D. G., Rajalingam, B., & Kumar, R. S. (2021). Security and privacy-aware artificial intrusion detection system using federated machine learning. *Computers & Electrical Engineering, 96*, 107440.
10. Iwendi, C., Rehman, S. U., Javed, A. R., Khan, S., & Srivastava, G. (2021). Sustainable security for the internet of things using artificial intelligence architectures. *ACM Transactions on Internet Technology (TOIT), 21*(3), 1–22.
11. Pawlicki, M., Kozik, R., & Choraś, M. (2019). Artificial neural network hyperparameter optimisation for network intrusion detection. *Lecture Notes in Computer Science*, 749–760. https://doi.org/10.1007/978-3-030-26763-6_72
12. Bhardwaj, A. (2024). Secure framework against cyberattacks on Cyber-Physical Robotic Systems. Smart Home and Industrial IoT Devices: Critical Perspectives on Cyberthreats, Frameworks and Protocols, 98–127. https://doi.org/10.2174/97898152567101240100006
13. Chithaluru, P., Al-Turjman, F., Kumar, M., & Stephan, T. (2023). Computational-Intelligence-Inspired adaptive opportunistic clustering approach for industrial IoT networks. *IEEE Internet of Things Journal, 10*(9), 7884–7892. https://doi.org/10.1109/jiot.2022.3231605
14. Wiafe, I., Koranteng, F. N., Obeng, E. N., Assyne, N., Wiafe, A., & Gulliver, S. R. (2020). Artificial intelligence for cybersecurity: A systematic mapping of literature. *IEEE Access, 8*, 146598–146612.
15. Zhang, Z., Ning, H., Shi, F., Farha, F., Xu, Y., Xu, J., Zhang, F., & Choo, K.-K. R. (2021). Artificial Intelligence in cyber security: Research advances, challenges, and opportunities. *Artificial Intelligence Review, 55*(2), 1029–1053. https://doi.org/10.1007/s10462-021-09976-0
16. Promyslov, V. G., Semenkov, K. V., & Shumov, A. S. (2019). A clustering method of asset cybersecurity classification. *IFAC-PapersOnLine, 52*(13), 928–933. https://doi.org/10.1016/j.ifacol.2019.11.313
17. Millar, K., Cheng, A., Chew, H. G., & Lim, C. C. (2020, December). Operating system classification: A minimalist approach. In *2020 International Conference on Machine Learning and Cybernetics (ICMLC)* (pp. 143–150). IEEE.
18. Kure, H. I., Islam, S., Ghazanfar, M., Raza, A., & Pasha, M. (2021b). Asset criticality and risk prediction for an effective cybersecurity risk management of cyber-physical System. *Neural Computing and Applications, 34*(1), 493–514. https://doi.org/10.1007/s00521-021-06400-0
19. Hashmi, E., Yamin, M. M., & Yayilgan, S. Y. (2024). Securing tomorrow: a comprehensive survey on the synergy of Artificial Intelligence and information security. *AI and Ethics*, 1–19.
20. Bellaby, R. (2024). The ethical problems of 'intelligence–ai'. *International Affairs, 100*(6), 2525–2542. https://doi.org/10.1093/ia/iiae227
21. Singh, B., & Kaunert, C. (2024). Intelligent machine learning solutions for cybersecurity. *Advances in Computational Intelligence and Robotics*, 359–386. https://doi.org/10.4018/979-8-3693-5380-6.ch014
22. Habbal, A., Ali, M. K., & Abuzaraida, M. A. (2024). Artificial Intelligence Trust, risk and security management (AI trism): Frameworks, applications, challenges and future research directions. *Expert Systems with Applications, 240*, 122442. https://doi.org/10.1016/j.eswa.2023.122442
23. Han, N., Li, H., & Yang, G. (2018). Study on Counter-Terrorism Strategy based on the Characteristic of the Terrorism Communication. In *Proceedings of the 2018 International*

Conference on Management, Economics, Education and Social Sciences (MEESS 2018). https://doi.org/10.2991/meess-18.2018.57
24. Rivera, D., Monje, F., Villagrá, V. A., Vega-Barbas, M., Larriva-Novo, X., & Berrocal, J. (2019). Automatic translation and enforcement of cybersecurity policies using a high-level definition language. *Entropy, 21*(12), 1180. https://doi.org/10.3390/e21121180

Leveraging AI and Cybersecurity for Proactive Counterterrorism: Strategies, Risks, and Future Trends

Vijeta and Shashank Solanki

Abstract The integration of artificial intelligence deep learning alongside cybersecurity technologies enables present-day counterterrorism operations to identify threats in advance while offering reduction solutions and obtaining highly precise real-time intelligence data. This research explores the effects of predictive analytics with artificial intelligence and machine learning algorithms and facial recognition systems, together with natural language processing (NLP), for identifying extremist content on today's counterterrorism operations. Security agencies gain improved surveillance capabilities by analyzing big data through a combination of artificial intelligence assessment models and deep learning behavioral patterns detection to protect cybersecurity from terrorist threats. This chapter investigates AI applications in worldwide counterterrorism operations through real-time studies that analyze autonomous systems and drone technology as well as real-time AI software capabilities for detection. The analysis focuses on the consequences of AI deployment in counterterrorism operations, particularly in relation to privacy, human rights, ethical considerations, and the associated legal implications. The investigation examines two emerging trends: blockchain cybersecurity systems and quantum encryption security through quantum computing technology as well as AI-based forensics capabilities to enhance counterterrorism defenses. This research project develops an extensive framework that unites strategic recommendations about counterterrorism AI utilization and deep learning techniques to protect ethical limits alongside security requirements with new technology advancements.

Vijeta
School of Law, CHRIST University, Bengaluru, India

Christ University, Ghaziabad, India

S. Solanki (✉)
School of Law, CHRIST University, Bengaluru, India
e-mail: shashank.solanki@law.christuniversity.in

C. Kaunert et al. (eds.), *Artificial Intelligence for Global Counter-Terrorism*, Contributions to Security and Defence Studies,
https://doi.org/10.1007/978-3-031-99235-3_8

1 Introduction

Independent networked groups have appeared in the twenty-first century because of terrorism's evolution, while adopting modern technology for carrying out specific terrorist operations. Through digital communication systems, along with encrypted messaging and dark web access, terrorist organizations obtain extensive operational capabilities that simplify their activities. The combination of neighboring technologies enhances terrorist capabilities for recruitment and enables dissemination of propaganda while protecting their structures. Security forces must create extensive countermeasures based on technology to stop complex attacks between countries. Large databases become easy to analyze through AI processing methods, which detects terror activity symptoms precisely in real time. Security agencies employ machine learning algorithms to study big data assets, thus enabling them to detect unusual suspect behaviors while anticipating future threats so that they can take preventive measures [1].

Critical infrastructure security and declassified information require reliable cybersecurity systems to protect against terrorist cyberattacks aimed at disrupting systems and extracting data for propaganda purposes. Applications of artificial intelligence (AI) serve counterterrorism operations during multiple operational settings. Through its military operations, the Israel Defense Forces developed the artificial intelligence programs "The Gospel," "Lavender," and "Where's Daddy." Through AI programming, the Israel Defense Forces allows their security departments to perform extensive air-based attacks on discovered militant operations. Implementing AI battle applications raises significant safety problems since they cause damage to civilians, alongside challenging moral dilemmas about AI utilization in military combat. Current counterterrorism approaches develop continuously through joint action between law enforcement and the military because of both proliferation of terrorism and developing security procedures [2]. The implementation of AI-based cybersecurity measures enables protected counterterrorism efforts and guards' national critical infrastructure through dual security and safety protection.

1.1 Objectives of the Chapter

The focus of this research is the use of artificial intelligence technology in counterterrorism instruments for cybersecurity, with the end goal of achieving the fundamental objectives outlined here:

- Integration of machine learning, natural language processing and facial recognition enhances the capacity of security forces to identify terrorists in counter terrorism operations. The study measures the performance metrics and operational risks associated with such systems if selected to be part of existing security formats.

- Predictive analytics equips security forces with strong tools to employ advanced predictive counterterrorism methods to identify future terrorist attacks in advance. The ability of threat prediction models to identify true security issues is evaluated, along with their overall performance.
- The analysis of counterterrorism AI and cybersecurity will thoroughly scrutinize the embrace of blockchain for bringing encrypted data shielding, and in particular the use of quantum encryption, to strengthen cyber systems. The discussion is dedicated to the use of state-of-the-art solutions for addressing the ongoing operational challenges, as well as improving the outcomes of further counterterrorism operations [3].
- The evaluation has to cover ethical considerations in addition to the existing laws related to AI and cybersecurity in counterterrorism. This region is defined by anticipation of legal liability and respect for international human rights norms (special attention is paid to privacy protection and removal of systematic bias).

2 Theoretical Foundations and Technological Framework

2.1 Fundamentals of Cybersecurity in Counterterrorism

In addition to purely defensive uses, cybersecurity in counterterrorist roles itself becomes a critical enabler in digital operations. By enacting disciplined technologies and process-driven safeguards the protection against digital threats to systems and networks and to applications and data is brought into effect [4]. Several critical aspects show the way operations manifest the utilization of cybersecurity as an instrument in counterterrorism policy:

- Safeguards are put in place to guard against illegal access to important intelligence, surveillance, threat reporting, and internal departmental communication. The safeguards are based on advanced encryption standard (AES) encryption and also encompass public key infrastructure (PKI) protections.
- Uncertainty or defects in intelligence may compromise the success of operations. With the help of blockchains and hashing technologies, such counterterrorism operations can build reasonable and unchangeable proof-of-concept databases and secure logs for communication.
- Consistent availability of intelligence applications for decision-making is necessary for operating systems to function efficiently. Accomplishing the desired results is less probable when systems needed for coordination go offline. Redundancy plans succeed because of counterterrorism cybersecurity features, which include DDoS protection and automatic failover capabilities [5].
- The reason for these principles is to keep possible threats from harming the reliability and stability of AI systems. The persistence of AML threats is a consequence of continued updates by adversaries to the information used for training

and to the resulting model outcomes. Artificial intelligence design that resists exploitation is facilitated for cybersecurity professionals by the IBM Adversarial Robustness Toolbox. Professional cybersecurity workers pay particular attention to tracing online misconduct associated with the dark web, crypto currency, and encrypted voice over internet protocol (VoIP) communications [6]. Integrating deep packet inspection (DPI) analysis with artificial intelligence and threat intelligence systems serves to detect and manage unusual events and their automatic defenses.

2.2 *Synergizing AI and Cybersecurity: A Conceptual Framework*

Due to AI-augmented cybersecurity solutions, advanced security teams can identify threats at early stages and neutralize them accordingly [7]. We present here a step-wise framework depicting the convergence of AI technologies into cybersecurity tools against terrorism.

Layer 1: Secured Data Acquisition and Preprocessing

The mechanism behind the system's operation utilizes rigorous security actions to enhance the security of its data transfer procedures. Secure multi-party computation (SMPC), in collaboration with PII anonymization and encryption, guarantees conformity to main data protection frameworks such as general data protection regulation (GDPR), international covenant on civil and political rights (ICCPR), additional requirements.

Layer 2: AI-Driven Analysis and Threat Modeling

The AI system utilizes structured and unstructured data to produce risk assessments by embedding predictive behavioral analysis and suspicious behavior assessment methods. Data is sorted and alerts for anomalies are generated by the system using a variety of supervised and unsupervised techniques, and the responses of the system are fine-tuned accordingly from a reinforcement learning point of view. The system automatically alerts end-users to the presence of unforeseen variation in patterns of communication and financial dealings linked to indicators of threat available to the service agents.

Layer 3: Strategic Decision-Making and Response Optimization

The system produces real-time alerts, as well as aid tool and visual summary, based on its analysis findings while performing. Post intervention, based on analysis, the system provides recommendations on surveillance distribution to the operation and strategic units [7]. The system will utilize AI and past successful results to predict threat patterns and suggest strong defensive actions, utilizing.

Looking at Fig. 1, one sees secure data is analyzed through cybersecurity stages and introduced to AI threat detection and ends with the production of strategic decision-making abilities. It is clear from the diagram that AI serves to heighten

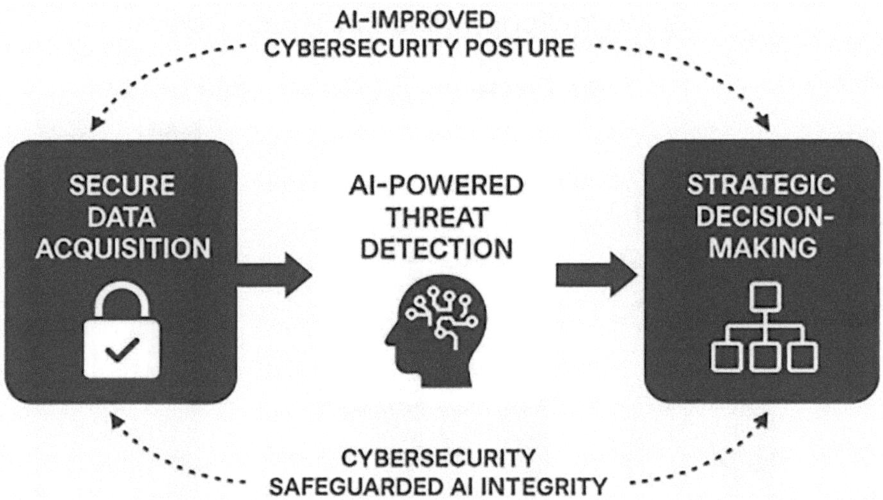

Fig. 1 Conceptual integration of AI and cybersecurity in counterterrorism

cybersecurity, and that cybersecurity defenses likewise safeguard AI against vulnerabilities.

3 Predictive Analytics and Threat Detection

3.1 Machine Learning Algorithms in Early Threat Detection

Upon launch, threat detection systems leverage machine learning algorithms to handle copious amounts of data in order to identify subtle signs of future terrorist activities within a complex information system. The presented analysis examines the efficacy of Random Forest classifiers and Artificial Neural Networks (ANNs) in the field of counterterrorism based on their practical use and overall usability. Random Forest's attention to ensemble techniques—in which training yields a collection of decision trees—and the method used to combine their predictions results in higher accuracy and robustness, necessary for discerning benign from malicious actions, given how alike the actions may be [8]. Random Forest algorithms, created with past terrorist data, effectively and accurately identify potential early extremists. Artificial Neural Networks employs its skill at processing nonlinear information to generate detailed models relating attributes like modified communication, special financial behaviors, and unusual travel routines with occurrences of organized terrorism. Upon introducing new information and applying continuing backpropagation and appropriate weight modifications, the models' forecasting effectiveness is improved accordingly. The rapid reaction of adaptive systems plays

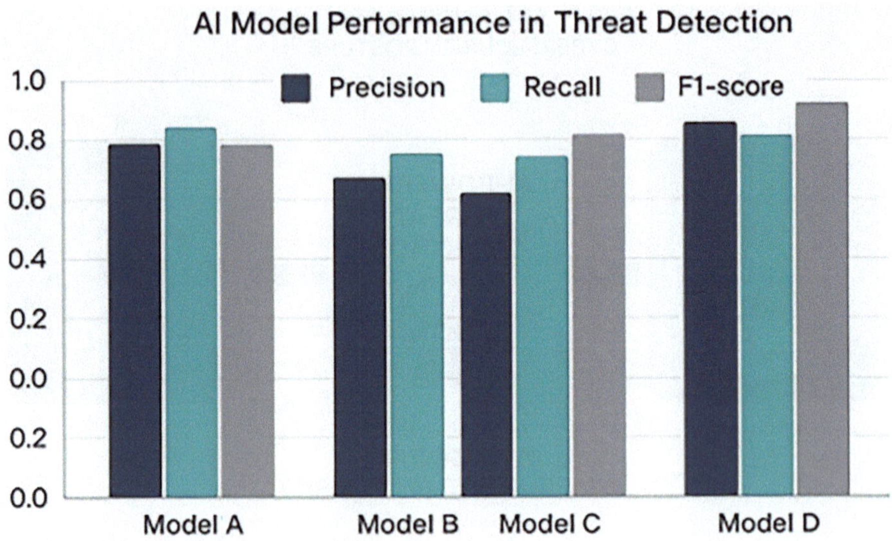

Fig. 2 AI model performance in threat detection

an important role in managing terrorism, as swift threat detection heavily improves protective actions [9].

Figure 2 shows a comparison of precision, recall, and F1-score via a bar graph for the AI models used in threat detection. This visual aid assists in identifying the efficiency of each model in different operational situations. The analysis of the performance characteristics and limits of each model helps practitioners and policymakers to make recommendations as to the type of AI solutions to pursue for counterterrorism activities applications. The graphical representation not only fits the numerical findings discussed above but also provides an applicable structure for further development and implementation of AI in the detection of threats.

4 Advanced Surveillance and Intelligence Systems

The cybersecurity-based artificial intelligence is leveraged by developments in surveillance and intelligence systems to complement counterterrorism. Current surveillance setups require professional interception and inherent evaluation processes to track and deal with terrorist movements [10]. Real-time collection and processing of key data sources have become an essential need to meet the present global security needs. These days, security infrastructures tie different sensors and IoT devices to sophisticated algorithms, which enable security operators get timeous and reliable data to stop terrorism.[11].

4.1 Natural Language Processing (NLP) for Extremist Content Detection

Still, the key instrument of identifying extremist content in digital platforms is the application of NLP technologies, combined with modern approaches of artificial intelligence. New digital tools are used by terrorist networks for developing new mechanisms for spreading the message, recruiting members, and organizing their activities. Security agencies take advantage of NLP technologies to perform an effective analysis and monitoring of extremist content. Through NLP, the machine systems use computational approach to analyze and produce written work on the basis of human expression. NLP-based systems are increasingly integral to counterterrorism efforts that perform identification of possible extremist feelings and intentions over large text datasets throughout social media and web forms [12]. Sentiment analysis as a technique measures text by revealing emotions through words and topical modeling to reveal the themes that dominate large text collections.

4.2 The Implementation of NLP for Extremist Content Detection Typically Follows a Multistep Process

- Data collection: During the operational stage, numerous online sources are used to gather massive data.
- Preprocessing: In the process of text manipulation, researchers are sure that data is cleared from irrelevant information and standardized and extremist language structures are protected.
- Feature extraction: During this stage, extraction of linguistic markers for extremist content, in the form of unique phrases and keywords, takes place, along with the analysis of their semantic structures.
- Model training and classification: Using the assistance of trained learning abilities, staff-operated machine learning models interpret the extracted features and detectors to identify content as extremist or nonextremist.
- Alert generation and response: The authorities should be notified by these alerts immediately after extremist content is identified by the system.

NLP helps fight terrorism by reviewing extremist content distributed in several languages by extremism supporters. The use of NLP systems in detecting extremist material is constrained by recurring technological problems [13]. Because they cannot detect sarcasm, metaphors, or slang, NLP systems frequently make errors in understanding language. To accomplish this, it is necessary to use general assessment, suitable laws, and awareness of why complete software solutions are not enough. Successful application of NLP systems tailored to specific needs and democratic requirements depends on persistent joint efforts among specialists in technology, linguistics, law, and ethics [14].

5 Autonomous Technologies and Real-Time Applications

Such agencies employ autonomous systems, together with real-time artificial intelligence tools, to boost their processes for detecting and eliminating terrorist threats. Because terrorist threats today emerge from advanced and unpredictable systems spread over disconnected networks, traditional security methods are largely insufficient for protecting national and international security. Currently, arm-tackling counterterrorism largely depends on AI drones, supported by real-time software, as its principal operational component [15]. These innovations improve operations by delivering urgent and tailored services and by safeguarding personnel working in the field. We analyze technical features comprehensively, revealing the positive and negative aspects of ongoing counterterrorism units through real-life situations.

5.1 AI-Powered Drones and Autonomous Systems in Field Operations

Beyond traditional counterterrorism efforts within buildings, AI-powered drones—also known as unmanned aerial vehicles—offer significant advantages in the field. Even in situations with limited GPS access, AI-supported systems enable drones to decide accordingly through object recognition and computer vision, either fully or partially on their own. Highly accurate location tracking distinguishes drones of this kind. By combining sensor and information technology, the drone plays an important role in carrying out targeted attacks and preserving the integrity of civilian buildings, as described in [16]. Persistent tracking of a target becomes possible when several AI drones are combined, thanks to the drones' greater operational radius. Command centers are updated instantaneously on odd events that drone sensors with motion, infrared, and facial recognition, employing machine learning, recognize. Drone technology is valuable for its high operational efficiency, which is considered on par with other benefits. Unmanned intelligent drones, thanks to their autonomous capabilities, have the freedom to perform and make superior decisions in flight and mission activities as compared to manned aircraft and reconnaissance planes. Since autonomous operations allow drones to participate in conflicts instantly without requiring human input, emergency responses are considerably faster. Current drone use is unable to fully address the difficulties caused by their use [17].

In present-day AI algorithms, it is common not to notice newly arising problems when wandering into unknown and constantly changing terrains, which can provoke the chain of false alarm or prevent seeing the threats. When offensive operations happen to kill civilians, militaries purchasing unmanned systems impose massive ethical questions about accountability. Whether or not the Geneva Convention can be reliably applied to determine the proportionality and distinction in deploying lethal autonomous systems is a subject of intense legal scrutiny because of the obscurity of international humanitarian law for lethal autonomous systems. Because of their open susceptibility, such systems are susceptible to many security risks, which result from constant electronic threats. The computers that control drones and AI-run operations are still vulnerable to cyberattacks that could potentially turn off command networks or change data, fooling the AI into thinking that its autonomous choices are right. The security of deployed hardware needs to be protected from security risks by constant encryption and robust cybersecurity protocols. The responsibility of field operations can only be transferred to AI drones if they are used in an ethical manner, and within the humane strictures of the current laws and technical security [18].

5.2 Case Studies: AI Deployment in Active Counterterrorism Scenarios

The case studies feature practical counterterrorism operations demonstrating that artificial intelligence delivers operational success and enhances its roles in securing active operations in defense. Israeli Defense Forces receive AI drones from Navi Sight and Sky Hopper, which search independently for targets in areas with poor GPS coverage. Drones are engineered to carry out automated monitoring of border areas and interrupt militant efforts while securing on-site workers. The Replicator program that forms part of the Defense Department's Project Maven demonstrates the dependency of the US military on artificial intelligence as a keystone of drone warfare and increased potential to analyze threats. The two autonomous vehicle initiatives aim at generating a high number of unmanned systems that can perform missions in harsh operational environments. Ukraine offers another compelling example. Ukrainian military forces use AI-powered drones in conflicts, while their older systems deliver only 75% higher strike accuracy from object detection; this combined insight into operational effectiveness is elevated [19].

The implementation of autonomous systems makes operational processes easier, enlarging their potential, since operators do not require extensive training to control autonomous systems effectively. In South-East Asia, real-time AI surveillance undertakings allow the authorities to detect members of the prohibited ISIS and Al-Qaeda terrorist networks in towns and the countryside. The analytical platform is a vital tracking solution whereby online recruitment tactics and real-time combat-training exercises are tracked through movement data and communication insights. Tests during practices demonstrate that AI systems are beneficial in contemporary counterterrorism efforts, highlighting the need to create sufficient regulatory systems [20]. Regulatory standards globally and mutual ethical standards should concern proper identification, technological flaws rectifications, and proper utilization of autonomous systems. The inclusion of autonomous technology systems is employed to carry out predictive precision operations, which represents a hallmark of future national terrorism responses in a new counterterrorism paradigm.

6 Ethical, Legal, and Human Rights Implications

There is a need for assessment of AI and cybersecurity applications in counterterrorism in order to maintain ethics and protect constitutional rights. The use of facial recognition data and high levels of algorithms, in addition to AI in security measure, poses a threat to guaranteeing individual rights under the government authority. Remedies from these tools can significantly enhance timeliness to address terrorism by security agencies, while presumptuous or immoral use may inadvertently weaken the democratic norms and legal assurances that the tools are supposed to support. These significant aspects are explicated in this section, beginning with the interpretation of privacy–security dichotomy, followed by evaluation of legal dimensions across international borders, and, finally, the resolution of globally accepted ethical conventions [21]. The effective application of artificial intelligence toward counterterrorism is not possible without comprehensive measures that stand on the constitutional limits and do not contradict the international standards of human rights to be able to keep the trust of the public. It is vital that ethical bounds are set by governing bodies controlling AI counterterrorism operations, because these not only safeguard national security besides legal rights but also personal freedom [22].

6.1 Balancing Privacy with Security

Those who create AI-based counterterrorism surveillance systems should first plan a timeline that boosts national security while protecting privacy before scaling up. Digital systems are responsible for operating facial recognition and predictive analytics in law enforcement detection tasks. There are novel problems for the protection of people's rights that develop with the widespread use of surveillance technologies here. Biometric and artificial intelligence drones used at the 2024 Paris Olympics contributed to more straightforward threat recognition and better crowd feedback [23].

People increasingly worry about more effective security solutions, thanks to the risk they pose to essential rights and the greater risk of misuse. Administrative bodies are tasked with creating thorough surveillance rules and making certain they are consistently assessed. Enhancing privacy with these technologies is achievable if both committee oversight and open dialogue with the community are included. Using privacy technologies alongside anonymization reduces data hazards and guarantees that freedom rights are upheld within security systems [24].

6.2 Legal Considerations in National Contexts

Governments keep an eye on AI surveillance in antiterrorism efforts in order to protect privacy alongside safeguarding the public. In 2024, US bodies turned to artificial intelligence to bolster security measures and pursued the most suitable ways to diminish unnecessary surveillance and threats to civil liberties. At present, laws governing artificial intelligence systems are designed to protect citizens' freedoms and do not permit any breach of constitutional rights. Indian authorities have not carried out any serious public oversight of AI monitoring activities in India. India's confidential rights face risk because there is no special law governing AI surveillance at this time [25]. If there is a national emergency according to the Digital Personal Data Protection Act (DPDPA)—an Indian legislation enacted in 2023 that governs the processing of digital personal data to protect individuals' privacy rights— the government may ignore privacy rules and perform tasks without needing individuals' permission. Clear proof now shows that enforceable standards are needed to manage AI surveillance and discourage criminal behavior. Human rights standards must form the foundation for lawmaking processes in every country. When AI is used, each instance must obey legal requirements by putting in place needed security measures and organizational guidelines to ensure the protection of basic human rights and to outline their applicable boundaries [26]. It should be ensured that regulatory systems have in place a strong monitoring structure, complaint management processes, and regular inspections to sustain individual rights during protective security actions.

6.3 Ethical Frameworks for Responsible AI in Counterterrorism

The adoption of security frameworks that occur in the course of counterterrorism work makes sure that modern AI systems incorporate the consideration of ethics to maintain both rights and democratic replacements. The UNESCO Recommendation on the Ethics of Artificial Intelligence is a guide to countries in imposing AI system rules and regulations that protect human dignity, equality, and diversity [27].

The Council of Europe developed the Framework Convention on Artificial Intelligence and Human Rights and Democracy and Rule of Law to validate vital principles that control AI practices and respect human rights and democratic concepts. The incorporation of public engagement and transparency in the framework guarantees that ethical values are seen essentially throughout the AI system development stages, in line with the convention [28]. Multidisciplinary control organizations need to work together and carry out international impact studies to come up with these ethical systems. Social trust can only be assured if the agencies responsible for security incorporate ethical guidelines into the development of AI and obey them when protecting the rights in the counterterrorism endeavors. Artificial intelligence is central in helping societies to maximize on security, protect privacy,

Table 1 Comparative Overview of National Legal Frameworks on AI Surveillance Jurisdiction Key Legislation AI Surveillance Provisions Limitations/Challenges

United States	USA PATRIOT Act; various state laws	Smoothens data transmission with regard to safety to allow such surveillance system to be established to fight against terrorism. Each country has its legal system, while some jurisdictions try to regulate.	Balancing national security interests with the protection of individual privacy rights; variability in state-level regulations leading to inconsistencies.
India	Information Technology Act; Proposed Personal Data Protection Bill	It provides selective oversight with government endorsement and protects data collected with strong legal safeguards.	Absence of robust data protection legislation; concerns over government surveillance infringing on privacy rights.

European Union General Data Protection Regulation (GDPR); Proposed AI Act Places privacy at the top of the list; it requires organizations to secured a bright consent when dealing with personal information. Underpinned by risk assessment as the basis for its functioning, proposed AI legislation mandates strict supervision of high-risk systems and curtails real time biometric monitoring to major crime events. Ensuring uniform compliance across member states; addressing concerns over the use of biometric data in public spaces
United Kingdom
Investigatory Powers Act
AI surveillance for individual freedoms to be maintained
Carries out strategies whose mechanism includes interception to fetch large scale data
Besides controlling communication networks, it uses colossal data per AI surveillance legislation
Legal challenges concerning the proportionality and oversight of surveillance measures, particularly regarding their impact on privacy rights. China Cybersecurity Law; Various Regulations Implements extensive Uses advanced AI techniques such as those of facial recognition and predictive analysis to improve national security and social governance
Significant human rights concerns; criticisms over mass surveillance practices and potential misuse of personal data

maintain binding legal systems, and maintain ethical standards for the protection of human dignity and democratic values [29] (Table 1).

7 International Legal Frameworks Governing AI and Cybersecurity in Counterterrorism

The fast-paced implementation of AI and cybersecurity systems for counterterrorism purposes exceeded the time needed to establish proper legal guidelines, thus producing complex regulatory structures broken down into multiple sections. At present, it is imperative to create extensive international legal frameworks that will merge national security legislation and establish joint international security operations and basic human rights protection [30]. Multiple international treaties and initiatives, along with their execution processes and worldwide security operation effects, form part of the research about governing AI and cybersecurity applications in counterterrorism [31].

7.1 The Framework Convention on Artificial Intelligence

Artificial intelligence faced rapid advancement across all industries, so the Council of Europe established the Framework Convention on Artificial Intelligence through its September 5, 2024 proclamation. Foremost, as the first international agreement of its kind, the treaty establishes protocols that ensure AI operations full respect for human rights and democratic principles and legal principles and support technological progress simultaneously [32]. The Convention utilizes fundamental principles from its core, which defends human dignity while maintaining individual autonomy, yet upholds equality standards and nondiscrimination rights in combination with privacy protocols, personal data protection, transparency systems, oversight mechanisms, accountability measures, responsibility tests, reliability standards, and safe innovation guidelines [33]. Under the Convention, both government organizations and private sector entities need to execute detailed evaluations of AI system effects on human rights as well as democratic processes. The Convention provides affected people with ways to access defensive measure procedures supported by effective redress mechanisms. The Framework Convention establishes standards to protect AI technology from misuse and prevents misuses, which often occur in the distribution of fake news and biased counterterrorism operations [34].

8 Emerging Trends in AI and Cybersecurity for Counterterrorism

The modern-day terrorist activities demand innovations in security measures because their operations persistently transform in present times. This part evaluates how blockchain, alongside quantum computing and AI practice, enhances counterterrorism capabilities through protected information management, secured communications networks, and advanced investigative methods [35]. Also, the quantum computing and AI practice enhances counterterrorism capabilities through protected information management, secured communications networks, advanced investigative methods [35].

8.1 Blockchain Technologies for Secure Data Management

The permanent digital records on blockchain create decentralized data protection methods whose main purpose is to support counterterrorism operations. Blockchain distributes data across various interconnected nodes, which protects information from cyberattacks that result from system breakdowns. Blockchain utilizes cryptographic encryption principles for bulletproof security functions, which protect data from unauthorized modifications. The implementation of blockchain in counterterrorism functions through protected intelligence databases and a system that enables agency verification of sources and tamper-proof connection building between information providers [36]. When implementing blockchain technology for this specific domain, multiple challenges appear during the delivery phase. System scalability encounters major obstacles due to increasing data volumes, because this data expansion generates efficiency slowdowns and necessitates extensive processing capabilities. The current systems experience difficulties when working with new protocols, because standardized integration protocols are missing for smooth system-to-system connections. Blockchain enables reliable data maintenance through transparent features; however, appropriate management is necessary to protect sensitive national information. Joint action between technology professionals and security experts, alongside policymakers, must create operational frameworks to balance blockchain benefits against security needs and operational requirements for proper resolution of these challenges [37].

8.2 AI-Based Digital Forensics and Intelligence Operations

Digital forensics technology received major transformation alongside intelligence operations through the implementation of artificial intelligence technology that delivered investigation tools, which accelerate both speed and increase accuracy in counterterrorism measures. The large processing capability of AI algorithms detects warning indicators that serve to identify terrorist activities [37]. AI tools allow digital forensics teams to create predictive threat assessments during financial record analysis and digital communication evaluation, as well as entity online collaboration examination. Machine learning AI trains network surveillance to detect particular security cues, thus permitting analysts to deal with complex tasks, while programmed processes continue to run automatically. The enhanced functionality of AI-based surveillance tools occurs through their live streaming data analysis for threat detection, which results in instantaneous investigator intervention [38].

The AI systems need organizations to address multiple operational and ethical issues during their deployment for digital forensic and intelligence tasks. The effectiveness of AI algorithm operations depends on organizations establishing valid analytical decisions that undergo proper validation processes to stop inaccurate information delivery. Public surveillance systems controlled by AI produce privacy concerns that police officials must safeguard along with the fundamental privacy rights of citizens. Standard accountability systems are essential in reports because law enforcement wants to verify data that their AI systems obtain [39]. The combination of previous ethical guidelines that create oversight mechanisms with AI counterterrorism technology enables organizations to utilize its ethical and beneficial applications. Public security problems actively benefit from counterterrorism solutions delivered through blockchain networks, which use AI systems to build foundations with quantum encryption capabilities [40]. Proper leadership approaches need implementation to address joint obstacles and challenges of novel security tools, which enhance capabilities, communication systems, and investigation processes. Countless research efforts, along with social collaboration, combined with flexible policy solutions, create the conditions needed to attain maximum benefits from new technologies in counterterrorism operations (Table 2).

Table 2 Emerging technologies and their counterterrorism applications technology application area key advantages potential limitations

AI forensics	Digital evidence analysis	Automated, real-time data processing; scalability	Standardization challenges; risk of algorithmic bias

Blockchain Data integrity and audit trails Immutable records; decentralized architecture Scalability issues; lack of global regulatory norms Quantum Encryption Secure communications Superior cryptographic security; future-proof High implementation cost; immature infrastructure

9 Strategic Recommendations and Policy Framework

A critical demand exists to appropriately deal with AI technological developments and counterterrorism cybersecurity because of their swift evolution. A comprehensive plan already exists for AI counterterrorism operations that implements both legal requirements and technical specifications, along with moral standards. This part establishes three sequential levels of directives that guide governments, as well as policymakers and security agencies, together with researchers to practice AI-powered counterterrorism responsibly[41].

9.1 Roadmap for Future Research and Technological Evolution

The sustained relevance of AI-based counterterrorism strategies requires permanent dedication to research, together with innovation and critical thinking. The upcoming roadmap includes essential priorities for research development through studies about new technologies alongside multidisciplinary work and law-focused prediction.

The initial research priority centers on developing emerging technologies that include quantum computing platform with blockchain infrastructure and neuromorphic artificial intelligence architecture. The encryption method based on quantum technology offers tomorrow's standard security, which makes existing hacking techniques irrelevant. The combination of immutable blockchain data storage methods with neuromorphic artificial intelligence systems enables created tamper-proof records that enhance threat detection models through brain-inspired contextual processing [42]. The domain calls for scientists to unite across computer science, law, and ethics fields with political science and behavior understanding disciplines. The responsible usage of AI requires knowing how AI shapes radicalization tendencies, how machine systems affect society, and how laws must adjust to new technological developments. Research organizations, including the Center for Security and Emerging Technology (CSET) and MIT's Lincoln Laboratory, have started modeling collaborative approaches for counterterrorism efforts. In addition to this institution-based research activity, there should be development of simulation platforms and scenario-based forecasting models to predict AI responses across different terrorist operations, such as critical infrastructure cyberattacks, coordinated drone attacks, and deepfake data manipulation [43]. The created models enable organizations to spot upcoming challenges and generate updated response plans accordingly. Globally recognized research efforts are required to develop AI governance models. Research needs to evaluate different AI management structures for counterterrorist use by studying how boards responsible for ethics governance, along with algorithm assessment protocols and stakeholder assessment meetings, could become a permanent part of the system. Such institutionalization requires continuous work. The fast speed of AI innovation creates the likelihood that current laws will lose their validity in short order. Due to technological speed up, it is essential to adopt agile governance practices that use iterative policy development, stakeholder feedback systems, and testing phases to maintain legal conformity with technology. The proposed framework establishes an ethical security architecture through proper legal frameworks and scientific methods that is prepared for future developments [44].

10 Conclusion

Security organizations use artificial intelligence systems for counterterrorism operations through cybersecurity methods, which generates both fast and precise outcomes. The database investigation process becomes faster by combining deep learning technology with machine learning algorithms for terrorist behavior detection, and natural language processing and facial recognition systems enable exact extremist searches in surveillance missions. The implementation of drone systems controlled by artificial intelligence allows tactical deployment due to their functional ability to transfer information while observing in real time. The identification of privacy intrusions and decision biases in modern technological solutions needs thorough examination before deployment, because these problems result from current technological advancements. AI technology requires permanent evaluation, which follows the operational and justice requirements outlined by the Budapest Convention [45]. Future counterterrorism protection standards built on AI and cybersecurity require transparent algorithm structures that ensure human rights compliance in every nation across the world. Research development progresses through policy implementation for blockchain security with quantum encryption communication systems that handle data security. AI shows itself as a worldwide security transformer, because it needs continuous collaboration between those who make laws and technology experts, as well as artificial intelligence specialists, for protecting privacy and human rights internationally [46].

References

1. Adeyinka, K. I., & Adeyinka, T. I. (2024). *Cybersecurity measures for protecting data. In Advances in information security, privacy, and ethics book series* (pp. 365–414). https://doi.org/10.4018/979-8-3693-9491-5.ch016
2. Lee, N. (2024). *Counterterrorism and cybersecurity*. Springer eBooks. https://doi.org/10.1007/978-3-031-63126-9
3. AI-Driven Counter-Terrorism: Enhancing global security through advanced predictive Analytics. (2023a). IEEE Journals & Magazine I IEEE Xplore. https://ieeexplore.ieee.org/abstract/document/10328769
4. Baumgartner, H., & Őszi, A. (2024). Artificial intelligence in crime prevention and counterterrorism. https://oda.uni-obuda.hu/handle/20.500.14044/25874
5. Ahmed, S. (2024, September 30). *The Evolution of Terrorism: New trends and counterterrorism strategies*. https://journals.fari.org.pk/index.php/FJGASS/article/view/11
6. Bazarkina, D. (2023). *Current and future threats of the malicious use of artificial intelligence by terrorists: Psychological aspects* (pp. 251–272). Springer eBooks. https://doi.org/10.1007/978-3-031-22552-9_10
7. Benouachane, H. (2024). *Cyber security challenges in the era of artificial intelligence and autonomous weapons* (pp. 24–42). CRC Press eBooks. https://doi.org/10.1201/9781003441700-3
8. Masyhar, A., & Emovwodo, S. O. (2023). Techno-prevention in counterterrorism: Between countering crime and human rights protection. *Journal of Human Rights Culture and Legal System, 3*(3), 625–655. https://doi.org/10.53955/jhcls.v3i3.176
9. Buttar, A. M., Shahid, M. A., Arshad, M. N., & Akbar, M. A. (2024). Decentralized identity management using Blockchain technology: Challenges and solutions. In *Signals and communication technology* (pp. 131–166). https://doi.org/10.1007/978-3-031-49593-9_8
10. Chitadze, N. (2024). Artificial intelligence, terrorism, and cyber security. In Advances in computational intelligence and robotics book series (pp. 87–106). https://doi.org/10.4018/979-8-3693-7540-2.ch005
11. Baig, M. a. A. (2024, June 28). Artificial intelligence, Emerging Technologies and national security of Pakistan. https://www.journal.ciss.org.pk/index.php/cissinsight/article/view/363
12. Çıtak, E. (2024). *Current technological trends and developments in the field of security* (pp. 11–23). CRC Press eBooks. https://doi.org/10.1201/9781003441700-2
13. Dodiya, K. R., Varayogula, S. N., & Gohil, B. V. (2024). *Rising threats, silent battles* (pp. 123–150). IGI Global eBooks. https://doi.org/10.4018/978-1-6684-9800-2.ch006
14. Esmailzadeh, Y., & Motaghi, E. (2024). International terrorism and social threats of artificial intelligence. *Journal of Globalization Studies, 15*(1), 168–179. https://doi.org/10.30884/jogs/2024.01.09
15. Gritzalis, S., Γκρίτζαλης, Σ., Συστημάτων, Σ. Τ. Π. Κ. Ε. Τ. Ψ., & Συστημάτων, Α. Ψ. (2024). Advancements in Open Source Intelligence (OSINT) Techniques and the role of artificial intelligence in Cyber Threat Intelligence (CTI). https://dione.lib.unipi.gr/xmlui/handle/unipi/16306
16. Gumenyuk, V., Nikitin, A., Bondar, O., Zhydovtsev, I., & Yermakova, H. (2025). The role and significance of state-building as ensuring national security in the context of artificial intelligence development. *AI Magazine, 46*(1). https://doi.org/10.1002/aaai.12207
17. Ige, T., Kolade, A., & Kolade, O. (2023). Enhancing border security and countering terrorism through computer vision: a field of artificial intelligence. In Lecture notes in networks and systems (pp. 656–666). https://doi.org/10.1007/978-3-031-21438-7_54
18. El-Bably, A. Y. (2023). Societal risks of using cyber metaverse technology. In Advances in digital crime, forensics, and cyber terrorism book series (pp. 114–125). https://doi.org/10.4018/979-8-3693-0220-0.ch006
19. Karamifar, F., Tabibian, S., & Rezaei, S. A. (2023, April 1). *The role of international treaties in combating cyber terrorism: A legal analysis*. https://www.jlsda.com/index.php/lsda/article/view/16

20. Kaur, R., Gabrijelčič, D., & Klobučar, T. (2023). Artificial intelligence for cybersecurity: Literature review and future research directions. *Information Fusion, 97*, 101804. https://doi.org/10.1016/j.inffus.2023.101804
21. Khan, A. (2024, September 30). Artificial intelligence in national Security: opportunities and risks. https://journals.fari.org.pk/index.php/FJGASS/article/view/8
22. Lemieux, F. (2024). *Cyber intelligence*. Emerald Publishing Limited eBooks, pp. 171–184. https://doi.org/10.1108/978-1-83549-097-620242011
23. Marsili, M. (2023). Morals and ethics in counterterrorism. *Conatus, 8*(2), 373–398. https://doi.org/10.12681/cjp.34495
24. Martini, A. (2025). AI, counter-terrorism and global governance: state of the art. *Revista De Paz Y Conflictos, 17*, 205–221. https://doi.org/10.30827/revpaz.17.31319
25. McNeil-Willson, R., & Romaniuk, S. N. (2024). *Cyber counter-terrorism*. CRC Press eBooks, pp. 240–245. https://doi.org/10.4324/9780429426063-30
26. Meena, G., Raha, S., Selvakumar, P., Mohit, N., Satyanarayana, P., & Vats, C. (2025). The role of AI in combatting extremism and radicalization on social media. In Advances in social networking and online communities book series (pp. 63–90). https://doi.org/10.4018/979-8-3693-9904-0.ch004
27. Montasari, R. (2023). Cyber threats and the security risks they pose to national security: An assessment of cybersecurity policy in the United Kingdom. In Advances in information security (pp. 7–25). https://doi.org/10.1007/978-3-031-21920-7_2
28. Montasari, R. (2024a). Addressing Ethical, Legal, Technical, and Operational Challenges in Counterterrorism with Machine Learning: Recommendations and Strategies. In Advanced sciences and technologies for security applications (pp. 199–226). https://doi.org/10.1007/978-3-031-50454-9_10
29. Montasari, R. (2024b). Analysing ethical, legal, technical and operational challenges of the application of machine learning in countering cyber terrorism. In Advanced sciences and technologies for security applications (pp. 159–197). https://doi.org/10.1007/978-3-031-50454-9_9
30. Montasari, R. (2024c). Assessing the effectiveness of UK Counter-Terrorism Strategies and alternative Approaches. In Advanced sciences and technologies for security applications (pp. 27–50). https://doi.org/10.1007/978-3-031-50454-9_3
31. Montasari, R. (2024d). Introduction. In Advanced sciences and technologies for security applications (pp. 1–15). https://doi.org/10.1007/978-3-031-50454-9_1
32. Montasari, R. (2024d). Machine learning and deep learning techniques in countering cyberterrorism. In Advanced sciences and technologies for security applications (pp. 135– 158). https://doi.org/10.1007/978-3-031-50454-9_8
33. Pillar, P. R. (2023). *Counterterrorism* (pp. 452–467). Routledge eBooks. https://doi.org/10.4324/9781003247821-32
34. Maity, S. (2024). Evolution and the dynamism of fintech and its regulation. In Advances in finance, accounting, and economics book series (pp. 239–268). https://doi.org/10.4018/979-8-3693-3803-2.ch010
35. Radanliev, P. (2024). Cyber diplomacy: defining the opportunities for cybersecurity and risks from Artificial Intelligence, IoT, Blockchains, and Quantum Computing. *Journal of Cyber Security Technology, 1–51*. https://doi.org/10.1080/23742917.2024.2312671
36. Rani, N., Jindal, K., Chikkara, R., & Malik, N. (2024). *Empowering defense*. Wiley, 289–310. https://doi.org/10.1002/9781394234028.ch16
37. Saleh, A. M. S. (2024). Blockchain for secure and decentralized artificial intelligence in cybersecurity: A comprehensive review. *Blockchain Research and Applications, 5*(3), 100193. https://doi.org/10.1016/j.bcra.2024.100193
38. Sanclemente, G. L. (2023, October 16). Digital tools: Safeguarding national security, cybersecurity, and AI bias. https://cebri-revista.emnuvens.com.br/revista/article/view/154
39. Sarjito, A. (2024). Enhancing National Security: Strategic policy development in defense management. *Journal Pelita Nusantara, 2*(1), 56–68. https://doi.org/10.59996/jurnalpelitanusantara.v2i1.524

40. Shafik, W., Tufail, A., Apong, R.a. a. H. M., & Balasubramaniam, S. (2024). Future directions in cybersecurity, digital forensics and biometric systems (pp. 238–263). CRC Press eBooks. https://doi.org/10.1201/9781032702377-13
41. Sholeh, M. B., & Iswanti, A. (2024). Countering cyberterrorism: the confluence of artificial intelligence, cyber forensics and digital policing in US and UK national cybersecurity Countering cyberterrorism: the confluence of artificial intelligence, cyber forensics and digital policing in US and UK national cybersecurity, by Reza Montasari, United Kingdom, Springer, 2023, xv+164 pp., £139.99 (hardback), ISBN 9783031219191. Intelligence & National Security, 39(6), 1103–1107. https://doi.org/10.1080/02684527.2024.2312629
42. Vance, T. R. (2023). Geopolitical Implications of Artificial intelligence in Cybersecurity: A Comprehensive analysis. Zenodo (CERN European Organization for Nuclear Research). https://doi.org/10.5281/zenodo.8214594
43. Role of AI in combating cyber terrorism. (2023, September 20). IEEE Conference Publication | IEEE Xplore. https://ieeexplore.ieee.org/abstract/document/10275910
44. Yamin, M. M., Ullah, M., Ullah, H., & Katt, B. (2021). Weaponized AI for cyber attacks. *Journal of Information Security and Applications, 57*, 102722. https://doi.org/10.1016/j.jisa.2020.102722
45. Yue, Y., & Shyu, J. Z. (2024). A paradigm shift in crisis management: The nexus of AGI-driven intelligence fusion networks and Blockchain trustworthiness. *Journal of Contingencies and Crisis Management, 32*(1). https://doi.org/10.1111/1468-5973.12541
46. Nair, A. J., & B, S. R. A. (2025). Confluence of AI and global security paradigms. In Advances in finance, accounting, and economics book series (pp. 161–182). https://doi.org/10.4018/979-8-3693-7036-0.ch008

The Algorithmic Panopticon: Artificial Intelligence, Mass Surveillance, and the Death of Privacy

Shailja N. Vyas and Mithilesh Narayan Bhatt

Abstract As the UN High Commissioner for Human Rights has stated, "Artificial Intelligence has the potential to either amplify human dignity or erode fundamental freedoms—it is up to us to decide its course." Artificial intelligence (AI), with its pros and cons, has brought extraordinary changes in the field of governance, industries, and even in our day-to-day life. Extensive use of AI in sectors such as healthcare, finance, communication, and law enforcement calls for combating the urgent issues relating to human rights. The sudden rise in mass surveillance, undisclosed algorithmic workings, and data exploitation has made problems with privacy, transparency, and accountability much worse. Artificial intelligence has largely promoted discrimination in service delivery and police activity, heightening the dangers to both civil liberty and due process, mainly because of its reinforcement of systemic biases in datasets. Because AI is largely opaque and regulations are lacking, resolving harm is much harder. Although the General Data Protection Regulation and similar regulations may be helpful, it remains evident that they are unable to fully address the speed with which AI evolves. Even so, for the ethical deployment of AI to happen, strong global rules concentrated on guaranteeing privacy, transparency, and accountability are indispensable.

1 Introduction

Since the start of the present century, advances in artificial intelligence (AI) have been remarkably fast and have transformed major areas of human life. In several sectors, including trade, regulation, and communication, and interpersonal relationships, there has been considerable change. Because of the impressive innovation and performance of AI technology, the field is now confronted with key ethical

S. N. Vyas · M. N. Bhatt (✉)
Department of Law, Sardar Patel University of Police, Security and Criminal Justice, Jodhpur, Rajasthan, India

C. Kaunert et al. (eds.), *Artificial Intelligence for Global Counter-Terrorism*, Contributions to Security and Defence Studies,
https://doi.org/10.1007/978-3-031-99235-3_9

problems, along with legal issues and the protection of human rights. Privacy rights in contemporary digital spaces primarily deal with human rights dilemmas as their main concern. Because AI and computers are now part of healthcare, law enforcement, finance, and social media, it is imperative to evaluate the ways data is gathered, how individuals are watched, whether algorithms are biased, and how human rights consent is gained.

"Privacy" is a pertinent International Human Right, identified by Article 12 of the Universal Declaration of Human Rights (UDHR) [1] and Article 17 of the International Covenant on Civil and Political Rights (ICCPR) [2]. Privacy now goes through dramatic changes. Data is being perceived as a valuable asset, and thus, blurred lines are generated between places that were once private or public. Extensive dataset analysis is required for the operation of AI technologies, but these systems are operated in such a manner that people can't sense how data collection and distribution processes are taking place [3]. Wider concerns have arisen about decreased civil liberties and widespread surveillance due to the deployment of AI in surveillance systems, using facial recognition technology, predictive policing capabilities, and decision-making algorithms.

However, in democratic states, privacy serves to protect us from government intrusion, but unrestricted AI tool development threatens our freedom, as well as our human dignity [4]. Human rights of the population groups under the watchful eye of authoritarian regimes, who employ AI-based surveillance systems, are substantially threatened [5].

At this stage, India is at a decisive one, because it has moved from a very fast transforming digital economy space to that of a leading center for AI technology development. As the use of AI technologies by state and private institutions in India increases, Indian democracy thus faces an urgent need for privacy rights analysis and needs serious data protection legislation. The significant ruling in Justice K.S. Puttaswamy (Retd.) v. Union of India (2017) [6] has also declared "privacy" as a constitutional fundamental and laid down legislative standards for judging the effect of AI technological specifications. The enforcement of this right faces major obstacles because of the combination of opaque algorithms with technological dominance.

This chapter seeks to interrogate the ambivalent limits of AI by shedding light on its potential benefits while also identifying the callous threats it poses to the pivotal liberties. The chapter further advocates for finding a balanced approach that will promote AI investment while making sure that there exist viable mechanisms for strong protection from human rights abuses.

2 Understanding AI: Meaning and Types

Although AI used to be envisioned solely in science fiction, it is now fundamentally important in guiding industry operations, regulatory development, and common everyday actions. Because of the rapid growth of AI, efforts must be made now to create accurate definitions for AI concepts and their particular subfields. When AI foundations are firmly established, it becomes possible to both understand its present applications and to forecast the consequences for law and society.

2.1 Definition

AI makes use of computer systems for the purpose of allowing machines to emulate important human cognitive skills. All of the components—learning, understanding sets of rules, making decisions, and automatic correction—are considered part of AI [7]. Machines, by utilizing AI, are now capable of completing tasks that demand the same fundamental capabilities that humans possess, for instance, perceiving images, understanding speech, making decisions, and translating different languages. According to John McCarthy, AI was inaugurated as "the science and engineering of making intelligent machines" when he first introduced the term [8]. The growth of AI has caused the definitions to grow, and they now cover both computer systems that replicate human thinking and machines that can act independently after considering captured data.

2.2 Types of AI

Artificial intelligence (AI) can be categorized into three primary heads on the basis of its abilities and functions:

1. **Artificial narrow intelligence (ANI):** Weak AI, as it is known, is artificial intelligence created to perform a particular set of tasks, including facial recognition, internet searching, and giving voice assistance. ANI systems operate according to clear limitations and are not endowed with either consciousness or general intelligence. Common instances of this technology include Siri, Alexa, and Google Translate [9].
2. **Artificial general intelligence (AGI):** Often termed Strong AI, AGI signifies an artificial entity capable of grasping, acquiring, and utilizing knowledge in a manner that mirrors human cognitive functions. It can carry out any intellectual activity that a human can perform. Currently, AGI exists only as a theoretical concept and continues to be a topic of active investigation and discussion [10].
3. **Artificial superintelligence (ASI):** Artificial superintelligence (ASI) is a term used for a hypothetical threshold in artificial intelligence where machines outperform humans in every domain, including creativity, problem-solving, and emotional intelligence. At this stage, computers are believed to think like humans and achieve outcomes beyond those of humans. Both academic and technical communities regularly engage in wide-ranging discussions about the ethical and existential risks associated with ASI [11].

Thus, this categorization aids in comprehending the development as well as possible future directions of artificial intelligence. Currently, the majority of AI applications are categorized as narrow AI; however, swift progress is extending the limits toward broader, more generalized abilities.

3 AI in Everyday Settings: A Human Rights and Legal Lens

Artificial intelligence technology continues its steady advancement into standard human practices, which reshapes communication methods and work approaches as well as the delivery of services and legal procedures. The innovations enabled by these technologies enhance operational performance yet generate fundamental legal questions along with ethical dilemmas about human rights protections. The current legal system requires modification to navigate the modern technological landscape through an equilibrium between innovation and human rights protections.

3.1 AI in Healthcare: Right to Health and Data Privacy

The field of healthcare is being transformed with the help of artificial intelligence (AI) that allows early detection of diseases, predicting treatment outcomes, and offering tailored medical care to patients. Medical imaging is being evaluated by AI, illnesses are anticipated to progress by AI, and electronic health records are overseen by AI. For instance, IBM Watson assists healthcare professionals by suggesting treatment options based on data derived from tremendous datasets. But these advancements provoke fears over both the right to health and the right to privacy, in relation to the organization of sensitive health information. The opacity in the decision-making process of AI amplifies the chances of misuse of data and implementation of discriminatory practices [12]. The regulation of health data used by AI technologies in India is expected to be greatly affected by the legal framework set under the Information Technology Act of 2000, and also the Digital Personal Data Protection Act, which is to be enacted soon.

3.2 AI in Criminal Justice: Fair Trial and Due Process

Applications of artificial intelligence (AI) in the criminal justice system are growing, including uses of predictive policing, facial recognition, and determining risk for bail. One good example is the use of the correctional offender management profiling for the alternative sanctions system in the United States, known as COMPAS, to assess the risk of recidivism on the defendant. While these technologies are meant to minimize the error and bias introduced by humans, a study showed that they continue promoting typical discrimination against minority groups [13]. This reliance on nontransparent algorithms can infringe upon basic rights, including the right to a fair trial, the presumption of innocence, and the right to seek remedies. Similarly, the deployment of AI in law enforcement in India, as exemplified through the Automated Facial Recognition System (AFRS), raises important questions about the legal protections and mechanisms of judicial oversight, as there is lack of clarity.

3.3 AI in Employment: Right to Equality and Nondiscrimination

The use of artificial intelligence (AI) in human resource management is expanding into the recruitment field and is now impacting resume screening, virtual interview questions, and performance reviews on potential and existing employees. However, these uses are designed to make algorithms more effective and reduce human biases, but may create algorithmic discrimination—an algorithmic way of denying any candidate because he or she belongs to a particular gender, caste, or socio-economic category. The very situation is also of concern regarding the right to equality and nondiscrimination sanctioned under international human rights law, as also under the constitution of India under Articles 14 and 16. For that reason, accountability of biased algorithms is vitally important, and policymakers need to identify, today, how to address the lack of clarity around this accountability.

3.4 AI in Education: Right to Education and Data Protection

The educational landscape has been redefined by AI-powered platforms with personalized learning experience, automated grading, and virtual classrooms. Nevertheless, they rely on the collection and processing of huge amounts of student data, regarding which there are concerns relating to data protection, user consent, and equitable access to digital resources. While AI implementation can equally serve for the betterment of the countries in which it is implemented, without proper framing of regulations, without appropriate regulation, they might just be exacerbating the disparities that currently exist pertaining to access to quality education, especially in countries like India, where access to and usage of digital technologies among citizens is still a huge gap to fill. As laid down in Article 21A of the Indian Constitution and in Article 26 of the Universal Declaration of Human Rights, the right to education entails protection against surveillance and discrimination in digital learning settings [15].

3.5 AI in Governance: Participatory Rights and Transparency

Artificial intelligence (AI) is increasingly being used by governments across the globe to assist them in the improvement of the efficiency of public service delivery through chatbots, automated systems at complaint boxes, and tracking of welfare payments. It can certainly work on making access more accessible to citizens, but there can be a danger in that being used to restrict public engagement and transparency, especially when decisions are made by algorithms with no accountability. Significant problems with democratic rights, freedom of expression, and access to legal recourse become obvious in this situation [16]. Faced with the challenge of bringing about digital governance in India through initiatives such as Digital India and the adoption of AI in administrative tasks (such as tax compliance and social security payments), there are many issues to be taken into account as for the possible violations to citizens' fundamental rights, primarily among rural and excluded communities.

The wide use of artificial intelligence (AI) in day-to-day life could lead to big legal and human rights system implications. Advantages of AI are many in fields such as healthcare, education, justice, and governance, but dangerous if not regulated appropriately; on this, it can crush existing rights. To ensure that AI is used responsibly, legal protections must adapt to ensure that, first of all, rights of privacy, equality, and same treatment accorded under similar circumstances and due process, as well as the rights to health, human dignity, access to justice, and exemption from punishment and cruel, inhumane, and degrading treatment, are preserved and fulfilled. To achieve this, it requires a joint work of lawmakers, technology specialists, human rights advocates, and representatives of civil society to create policies with a human values focus in the development of AI.

4 Challenges Posed by AI in Human Rights and Privacy Concerns: A Global and Indian Perspective

The escalating adoption of artificial intelligence in various sectors is raising serious concerns regarding human rights and privacy. Because artificial intelligence is advancing at a rapid pace, it becomes ever more pressing to understand and address the wide range of challenges it raises for human rights and privacy. The challenges at hand have practical implications, which become especially clear when we think about distinct Indian circumstances. These problems are exacerbated by more factors such as extensive surveillance, challenges related to data collection and use of AI that raise ethical issues, and the potential for artificial intelligence algorithms to support biased outcomes without intention. In view of the above, a complete and reflective study of these conditions is needed to reveal the dynamic relationship between technological growth and principles, such as dignity and autonomy. This research will provide meaningful support to policymakers and practitioners and also stimulate critical discourse on the increasingly important role of individual rights in a digital era.

4.1 Absence of Specific AI Legislation

At present, the landscape shows a clear deficit in lawsuit regulations created particularly for artificial intelligence. The absence of legislation in this field causes major difficulties in governing AI technologies and safeguarding basic human rights. As AI technologies continue to advance quickly, it is increasingly apparent that existing legislative frameworks—including those relating to data protection and intellectual property—may not address the particular and difficult safety issues posed by AI. Lack of regulation in this area lets AI applications expand unregulated, raising the likelihood of serious infringements of individual rights, especially with regard to privacy and discrimination. Because of this, a comprehensive examination of socio-technical components and regulatory interpretations that perpetuate these issues is needed in order to motivate the development of new regulatory approaches suited for managing AI in society.

Global The aim of introducing the AI Act in the European Union is to introduce clear regulation for AI systems based precisely on how much risk they present [17]. Even so, a number of important countries, most notably the United States, have yet to develop specific AI laws or governance frameworks, which causes a mix of differing regulations globally [18]. Such a regulatory void has important effects since it introduces a lot of unpredictability for stakeholders, urgently calling for harmonization between legal systems. Such an effort, properly carried out, has the potential to establish a unified regulatory system that would ensure user protection and promote innovation in the rapidly growing area of artificial intelligence.

India Currently, depending on obsolete legal structures, largely the Information Technology Act of 2000, clearly points to the insufficiency of these laws for managing the new legal problems resulting from AI. Because AI is being used more often in sectors such as surveillance and finance in India, there is now a pressing demand for regulatory frameworks that can effectively manage the special challenges arising from AI technologies [19]. As a result, it becomes clear that lawmakers must update existing legislation and that all stakeholders should participate in building a system that is both resilient and ready to adjust to rapid developments in digital technology. In addition, these regulatory frameworks will explain the different impacts of AI, assisting in more thoughtful dialogue among policymakers, developers of technology, and the general community about safeguarding rights and decreasing potential risks.

4.2 Data Privacy and Protection

The fast growth and frequent extensive usage of personal data of the user, for complex artificial intelligence systems, are causing deep concerns about maintaining transparency and privacy. There is a significant increase in use of unauthorized data and surveillance, which poses risk to their ethical usage. This serious challenge is driven by the fact that AI systems must use extensive datasets, many of which include confidential and personal information about individuals. In fact, many people have little knowledge about the ways in which their personal information is being utilized and managed. For the most part, people do not give informed consent, or understand the consequences of their consent, and this can result in significant and harmful breaches of their privacy. The discussion that follows will closely examine these intricate problems in order to raise awareness among multiple stakeholders, including researchers, policymakers, and the public, about the pressing need for improved safeguards. These safeguards can preserve both technological development and individual privacy rights, thereby protecting personal freedom and dignity from threats posed by AI.

Global The General Data Protection Regulation (GDPR) was created in the European Union (EU) to preserve and maintain data security and observe privacy protections worldwide. However, as more organizations and states have started implementing AI-based systems, the prevalence of facial recognition in public surroundings increases concerns related to both mass surveillance and unauthorized privacy invasions [3]. AI systems are becoming ever more essential in data-driven economic systems. But these tools could seriously harm the right to privacy everywhere. A major issue is that AI relies heavily on datasets that are typically gathered with lack of consent or lack of transparency. As a consequence, there is a risk that it will encourage widespread monitoring, targeting of populations, and attempts to influence human actions [3]. Governments, together with private businesses, now use AI surveillance technologies such as facial recognition and biometric scanning. In most cases, such systems allow individual monitoring in real time, usually without the subject's knowledge or authorization. China employs facial recognition to oversee public spaces extensively, and the United States has law enforcement that relies on personal citizen information within predictive policing methods [20]. AI systems, even in the EU, governed by the GDPR, often fail to respect the current legal protections designed to safeguard privacy, making people's data more vulnerable to unethical uses. Because AI algorithms work in ways people cannot easily see, users struggle to understand the uses of their data, and automated sorting of individuals undermines their control over personal information [21]. The growth of these advancements brings difficulties for both Article 12 of the Universal Declaration of Human Rights and Article 17 of the International Covenant on Civil and Political Rights, which support privacy.

India In India, the Supreme Court's decision in Justice K.S. Puttaswamy v. Union of India (2017) [6] made "privacy" a fundamental right. However, the absence of a deep data protection law holds back privacy protection efforts, with concerns regarding increasing use of artificial intelligence (AI) in such applications as surveillance and biometric recognition [22]. The precise constitutionality of the right to privacy in India is, relatively, laid down by the landmark decision in Justice K.S. Puttaswamy (Retd.) v. Union of India [6] affirming privacy in Article 21 Indian constitution is a significant step toward protecting privacy of its citizens. Regardless, the preexisting legal constructions in India are yet not sufficient to control AI systems that might violate this right [23]. AI technologies such as biometric identification systems, including Aadhaar or facial recognition, at the public level and governance through predictive analytics, among others, pose enormous privacy problems. Such technologies serve frequently in nontransparent ways with no sufficient oversight, consent processes, or practices to reduce data collection [24]. India does not have a broad-based data protection law in its regulatory regime. Although the Digital Personal Data Protection Act, 2023 is a step forward, it does not specifically cover the regulatory aspect of AI or describe governance mechanisms for AI algorithms specifically, in terms of transparency, purpose limitation, and user agreement [25, 26]. This, in turn, creates a vacuum in regulation, which weakens effective protection of the right to privacy as far as AI technologies are concerned.

4.3 Algorithmic Transparency and the Black Box Problem

Challenge: The lack of transparency in various AI algorithms, the so-called black box issue, makes clarification of what is taking place in the AI systems' decision-making processes troublesome, a major worrying factor in the context of human rights. Reason: AI algorithms, and most especially those where deep learning techniques are applied, operate in ways that are not readily understandable even to those who construct them. This opacity complicates the assessment of whether AI-generated decisions will meet legal rules and human rights to a fair hearing and challenge decisions that affect one's life.

Global The deployment of AI systems in the decision-making processes, for instance, in the judicial process of sentencing or recruitment, reveals an important aspect of the lack of the means of transparency on a global scale. The individuals whose decisions are made in this manner typically do not have the tools at their disposal with which to understand, challenge, or appeal the results generated by these systems [27]. The absence of transparency presents an existential danger to the foundation of principles of fairness and due process.

In the field of artificial intelligence (AI), a major challenge is the issue of algorithmic transparency, paradigmatically demonstrated by the "black box problem." In a similar way, and as AI grows in sophistication, especially in deep learning–based systems, the methods that these systems use to give results become opaque, even to the engineers that build them. Such an immanent obscurity generates a wide range of legal and ethical quandaries, especially where critical rights are concerned, such as the context of criminal justice, healthcare, employment, and finance [28].

Eventually, the lack of explanation found in AI systems, in the long run, undermines fundamental democratic values such as openness, accountability, and the right to effective recourse. For instance, in the performance of AI technologies that analyze creditworthiness, designate parole eligibility, or guide hiring practices, involved people often fail to identify reasoning or challenge algorithmic decisions because of the lack of transparent reasoning [29]. This phenomenon is incompatible with procedural fairness and due process rights as enshrined in international human rights agreements, such as Article 8 of the European Convention of Human Rights and Article 14 of the International Covenant on Civil and Political Rights.

Moreover, the lack of transparency in AI systems intensifies the likelihood of continuing the biases inherent to the system with little control. This was made even worse when creating AI models in one jurisdiction and their use in another one, without taking into consideration the local legal or cultural context [27].

India In India, the use of artificial intelligence (AI) in public services (AI-based surveillance or automated decision-making process across areas such as law enforcement and recruitment) is rising. Nevertheless, the current absence of transparency and noncreation of mechanisms of providing explanations for AI decisions prevent citizens from their ability to find redress or vent their challenges to rather unfair results [14]. AI's shadowy character throws tremendous legal and moral dilemmas, especially in relation to decision-making in the public sphere. As the way government work shifts more to artificial intelligence (AI) for functions such as policing, surveillance, and governing, which include: predictive policing tools, facial recognition technology, and AI-guided welfare distribution, the lack of algorithmic accountability endangers citizenship, due process, and account. For instance, there are AI applications implemented by the Crime and Criminal Tracking Network & Systems (CCTNS) and Automated Facial Recognition Systems (AFRS) that routinely function without clearly defined guidelines for how they decide or correct any errors, or rules to where a citizen can challenge incorrect? This ambiguity is especially alarming in a country that exists in a society with large socio economic and caste differences in which mechanized systems could unintentionally exacerbate present inequities. Notwithstanding the recognition of privacy, a fundamental right, in the case of Justice K.S. Puttaswamy (Retd.). v. Union of India (2017) [6], Indian regulatory structures do not provide any adequate standards to be followed with regard to explaining or auditing an AI system currently. Also, the recently established Digital Personal Data Protection Act, 2023, as much as it deals with aspects of data governance, does not take firm hold of issues of transparency and accountability of algorithms in decision-making processes [25, 26]. Without a law similar to the European Union's AI Act, India currently does not have enforceable legal obligations that require public or private sectors to ensure AI systems are transparent, auditable, and, however, also contestable, therefore putting citizens' rights at risk in AI-influenced living spaces.

4.4 Bias and Discrimination in AI Systems

AI systems can increase rather than preserve biases exhibited in training data to bring biased outputs in vital areas such as recruitment, policing, and credit assessment. The cause of that is the fact that AI algorithms are essentially determined by the data used for their training. When the training set contains the existing societal bias, like the ones related to gender, race, or social class, the AI systems might unwittingly perpetuate and exaggerate these biases, bearing unjust or discriminatory consequences.

Global Prompted by the increasing racial bias concerns, in the United States, the usage of artificial intelligence (AI) in law enforcement, and specifically in the use of facial recognition and predictive policing, has raised numerous concerns. It has been found that while in many cases these AI systems wrongly identify people of color at a much higher rate, it can lead to unwarranted surveillance and policing [30]. In addition, the recruitment AI systems have shown a penchant for male would-be employees over their female counterparts because of the bias in the training data. Instead of being impartial or neutral, AI systems tend to be biased replicas of the societal biases that exist in the data they are trained with. This may give rise to the algorithmic discrimination in which AI makes decisions primarily affecting people according to their race, gender, socioeconomic class, or other protected groups [30].

This problem has real worldwide implications. One such example is the work of ProPublica on the COMPAS algorithm used in the US criminal justice system, and also found to be more prone to falsely classifying Black defendants as high risk than their counterparts—white defendants [13]. Also, gender bias has been noted from hiring algorithms as they have degraded resumes with words that are commonly associated with female job seekers [14, 31]. Such cases reveal that there are possibilities for AI to sustain discrimination in essential areas such as law enforcement, employment, and credit rating. Such a bias compromises fundamental human rights values, particularly "equality" and "nondiscrimination," as highlighted in Article 7 of the Universal Declaration of Human Rights (UDHR) and Article 26 of the International Covenant on Civil and Political Rights (ICCPR). Despite a growing understanding of such challenges, there is still a lack of dedicated legal architectures present in many regions to review or control biased outputs produced by AI. While the AI act proposed by the European Union groups together risk-based governance, which would take the form of tighter regulations for AI systems that exist within contexts where fundamental rights are under threat [17].

India Caste discrimination is a continuing problem for India, and AI systems adopted for use in recruitment and policing can worsen the situation. Lack of scrutiny during the design of these AI systems further deteriorates the scenario, triggering increasing calls for an ethical structure that encourages fairness and usability [14, 31]. The severity of problematic algorithms and discrimination becomes especially vital in India, where the social environment is multifaceted and can be described by the use of caste, religion, gender, and economic disparities. AI use cases in areas such as enforcement, banking, and recruitment use datasets that not only reflect but reinforce systemic inequality, thus high chances that their results will perpetuate discrimination or make it worse [13]. For instance, the adoption of facial recognition technology in policing rekindled fears of discrimination against certain religious sections, such as Muslims and Dalits. Studies prove that these systems tend to be less accurate in the case of people with darker skin, setting up more false positives and wrongful surveillance [24]. In the spheres of employment and credit evaluation, AI models may be discriminatory against regional accents, educational credentials, or names connected with castes [32]. Despite the acknowledgment of equality by the Indian Constitution through Articles 14 and 15, the declaration of privacy and dignity as fundamental rights by the Supreme Court, and the absence of any considerable number of cases related to algorithmic discrimination, India does not have specialized legal norms for evaluation or treatment of algorithm. While the Digital Personal Data Protection Act, 2023, in combination with the IT Act, 2000, does not include the mentioned requirements for AI explainability, fairness assessments, or means of mitigating biased outcomes. This lack of regulation allows biased AI systems to operate with no responsibility.

4.5 Accountability and Liability in AI Decision-Making

Determining liability and accountability in cases where AI systems cause harm is a significant legal issue, as conventional responsibility models struggle to address the complexities of autonomous systems. AI systems, especially those that function independently, can make decisions that result in harm, which raises questions about who should be held accountable—the developer, the user, the owner, or the AI itself. This ambiguity in accountability highlights a critical deficiency in the existing legal frameworks at both global and national levels.

Global In the context of autonomous vehicles, establishing liability when an AI-operated car is involved in an accident presents significant challenges. Questions arise regarding whether the responsibility lies with the manufacturer or the vehicle's owner. The ambiguity surrounding AI liability regulations complicates the process for victims seeking justice [33, 34]. One of the key legal and ethical issues in global AI governance is the identification of accountability when AI systems inflict harm. Traditional legal systems are tailored for human actors and entities like businesses or government bodies. In contrast, AI systems, particularly those that are autonomous or capable of self-learning, can behave in ways that do not directly relate to any single human action, thus making it difficult to pinpoint legal responsibility [33, 34]. In high-stakes environments such as autonomous vehicles, algorithmic trading, and medical diagnostics, failures in AI decision-making can lead to serious consequences. The critical question is: Who should be responsible—the developer, user, manufacturer, or the AI system itself? Many legal jurisdictions currently lack specific frameworks to address AI accountability, leading to challenges for courts and regulators in applying existing tort, contract, and criminal laws to AI-related cases [35]. The European Union has sought to tackle this issue with proposed regulations, such as the AI Act, which introduces a risk-based liability model that mandates enhanced oversight and documentation for high-risk AI applications. Furthermore, the European Union's Product Liability Directive is being revised to encompass damages caused by AI systems, streamlining the process for consumers to seek compensation even when the workings of the AI are not transparent [17]. However, on a global outset, there remains a dearth of agreement on whether AI systems should be classified as a legal subject, agent, or object; and whether frameworks like "electronic personhood" may be necessary. Until a clearer understanding is made out, establishing accountability for AI-caused harm remains inconsistent, opaque, and often inadequate.

India India is experiencing critical problems with the implementation and control of artificial intelligence (AI), more so as this technology is spreading to core fields such as autonomous driving and medicine. Lack of definition of legislation concerning AI liability has led to a situation where persons affected cannot tell who is responsible for any losses that may emanate from AI systems [36]. The problem of establishing responsibility for AI-powered choices is becoming more relevant as India embraces AI in control, finance, health care, and policing. There is however no specific legal framework yet that addresses the specific harms associated with AI or makes a clear demarcation of the liability if autonomous systems cause harm or violate rights [19].

For example, an AI-based credit scoring system can wrongly reject a person's application for a loan because of poor data processing or a system of bias. Whereas under the current Indian laws, the person harmed by such a decision would find it difficult to determine whom do they hold responsible, the financial institution or the algorithm's author, the software company. The Information Technology Act of 2000 and the Digital Personal Data Protection Act of 2023 do not provide sufficient regulation of accountability with regard to automated decision-making processes. In addition, AI technologies are becoming more widely used for law enforcement operations, such as facial recognition and predictive policing, but while appropriate in the private sector, there is no enforceable legal requirement for transparency, documentation, or audits of AI-based decision-making in the public sector governance. Such a lack of accountability may actually violate such fundamental rights as equality, privacy, and due process (as provided under Articles 14 and 21 of the Indian Constitution) (Justice K.S. Puttaswamy (Retd.) v. Union of India, 2017) [6].

As a result, the Indian legal specialists and policymakers are calling for an extensive regulatory system for AI, which would define the responsibility, deploy fairness audits, and provide human control. Unless such legal reforms are made, the responsibility for gaining from harms done by AI will remain unclear, posing major concerns both for consumer protection and constitutional justice maintenance.

4.6 Jurisdiction and Cross-Border Enforcement of AI Laws

Challenge The interconnected nature and global pervasiveness of AI systems have made it more challenging to identify and establish the relevant legal jurisdiction, especially when matters pertaining to any conflicts or breaches occur. Reason: AI systems often function in a crossover manner across different countries situated in different nations, its servers being placed in different countries. This transnational nature makes it cumbersome to determine which regulations shall apply in instances of legal conflicts or transgressions of rights, thus adding to the levels of complication regarding the enforcement and responsibility.

Global Potentially, the people from one nation that has been affected by the AI system existing in another country may face major difficulties trying to pursue legal action. For example, if AI systems worked in the United States but were used by a European firm, judgments made might contradict European laws, creating something of a legal quagmire to navigate [18]. The very nature that artificial intelligence (AI) technologies have no borders presents major challenges to legal systems that are founded historically on national sovereignty. AI systems, in particular those controlled through cloud services, can be developed in one country, deployed in another, and affect consumers in a third one. This complex connection of jurisdictions and players creates confusion as to the jurisdiction and confounds the application of laws and human rights safeguarding [37]. One of the main problems is determination of the applicable legal frame when the damage is caused as a result of AI usage. For example, a case where an AI system is used for content moderation by a social media platform in the United States, censors political expressions in the European Union, or labels content wrongly in Africa may be difficult to determine which country's data protection or human rights laws apply. US free speech laws and EU privacy regulations might conflict, as evidenced by current conflicts over data transfer over the Atlantic and the practices related to algorithmic moderation [38]. More importantly, the absence of binding international agreements that control the conduct, accountability, and remedial measures of AI weaken enforcement efforts. As valuable as initiatives such as OECD AI Principles and the UNESCO Recommendation on the Ethics of Artificial Intelligence can be, they lack legal enforceable ability. The AI Act and the General Data Protection Regulation (GDPR) by the European Union try to use AI governance and privacy standards globally, but other countries frequently oppose compliance and national sovereignty [17].

India India's legal framework is currently facing significant challenges, particularly due to the rising integration of artificial intelligence (AI) across various sectors, such as e-commerce, banking, and healthcare, all of which involve cross-border data interactions. The paucity of a unified global regulatory framework for AI systems complicates enforcement, especially when systems formed by foreign entities have implications for Indian citizens [22]. As India rapidly enhances its presence in the global digital economy, it encounters formidable obstacles in asserting jurisdiction over international AI technologies and in safeguarding legal protections for its citizens against foreign AI providers. The nation's reliance on global platforms and AI solutions primarily based in regions like the United States, Europe, and China exacerbates difficulties in seeking legal recourse and enforcing data protection, particularly when breaches occur outside Indian territory [39].

The Indian judiciary has emphasized the importance of digital privacy, notably in the landmark case Justice K.S. Puttaswamy (Retd.) v. Union of India (2017) [6], which recognized privacy as a fundamental human right. However, the practical enforcement of this right against foreign AI entities remains limited. For instance, when overseas social media platforms or algorithmic systems breach privacy or disseminate misinformation within India, the lack of effective cross-border enforcement mechanisms becomes evident due to jurisdictional uncertainties and the absence of bilateral treaties aimed at addressing AI-related harms [40].

Even though legislative enactments such as the Information Technology Act of 2000 and the Digital Personal Data Protection Act of 2023 have been put in place to guide digital platforms, they cannot have extraterritorial applicability. Although Section 75 of the IT Act allows certain extraterritoriality regarding offenses affecting Indian networks, enforcement of such laws in the real world—validation and prosecution—is not sufficient without mutual legal assistance treaties (MLATs) or special AI governance international agreements [41]. In order to tackle these problems, India will need to play an active role in the global regulatory cooperation, perhaps through G20, BRICS, or the Global Partnership on AI (GPAI), to introduce enforceable standards for accountability in cross-border use of AI.

5 Ethical and Legal Oversight of AI: A Human-Centered Perspective

The rapid growth of artificial intelligence (AI) has caused a need for well-developed ethical and legal guidelines that declare that technological development is in consonance with democratic ideals and human rights. Critical aspects of this conversation encompass ethical guidelines, policies regarding data protection, and the role played by AI in enhancing access to justice.

5.1 Ethical Frameworks and Global Governance Models

Essential principles on which ethical governance of artificial intelligence (AI) has a foundation include fairness, accountability, transparency, and explainability. Such values are essential for the accountable introduction and use of AI systems to avoid discrimination in the automated decision-making and make the process meaningful and understandable for users, as well as traceable back to human control.

Transparency is particularly relevant for dealing with problems of "black box" algorithms; fairness intends to overcome bias in datasets that can cause discrimination in society [42]. In different parts of the world, many organizations have versions of a framework that would support these principles. The coming AI act of the European Union has proposed a law that will apply risk assessment as its regulatory means to require effective measures for high-risk AI systems [17]. The OECD Principles on AI encourage inclusive growth, further emphasize on human-centered values, and recommend strong accountability measures [43]. UNESCO's Recommendation on the Ethics of AI (2021) provides for a broader perspective as regards to the field, addressing cultural and environmental concerns alongside gender issues in studying AI ethics.

In India, "Responsible AI for All," a vision for responsible AI use being inclusive, safe, and transparent, has been proposed by NITI Aayog. This document describes the main ethical principles and requires rules adapted to certain industries that concentrate on explainability and fairness of AI implementation [44]. It also puts emphasis on the need to utilize a decentralized governance model where many stakeholders are involved. Furthermore, public-private partnerships (PPPs), the role of which increases in AI governance, are becoming more important. These partnerships utilize industry insights combined with public accountability in the development of standards for compliance and innovation. For instance, corporate responsibility can bring itself in accord with the public good as programs such as Microsoft's AI for Good and Google's AI Principles are coming to show.

5.2 AI and Data Protection Laws

The dependence of artificial intelligence (AI) upon enormous datasets should promulgate matters of privacy, consent, surveillance, and profiling. AI systems tend to process sensitive personal information that is received without informed consent from people, victimizing them to privacy violations and misuse opportunities. Inclinations such as biometric surveillance, facial recognition, and automated decision-making regularly pretest the boundaries of privacy protections. The EU's General Data Protection Regulation (GDPR) is known to be a pioneering model for privacy protection in the AI age. It calls for informed consent, pushes data minimization, and gives people rights to explanation and review of automated decisions [45].

Besides, India has also stepped up its game by passing the Digital Personal Data Protection Act in 2023, which provides duties to data fiduciaries, provides penalties in case of infringements, and establishes a Data Protection Board. Nevertheless, the Act has limitations regarding AI-specific regulations and lacks clear guidelines on algorithmic accountability and AI auditing [46]. There is a growing demand for data protection standards tailored to AI, especially to regulate automated profiling and the international transfer of data.

5.3 AI and Access to Justice

The incorporation of artificial intelligence (AI), particularly in legal systems suffering from resource insufficiency, poses tremendous opportunities for making justice more attainable. Now, systems are utilizing legal help chatbots, predictive analytics, and AI-powered document review tools to augment efficiency and access to legal services. AI has the capability, by streamlining case control workflows and enhancing legal research, to mitigate the stagnation in court progression.

India is actively working on court system automation through initiatives aimed at increasing transparency, like the e-Courts Initiative. The development of SUPACE (Supreme Court Portal for Assistance in Court Efficiency) has been undertaken by the Supreme Court, which assists the judges in retrieving relevant facts and legal information, thus accelerating the judicial proceedings. Notwithstanding these advantages, the absence of AI algorithm-related bias transparency and the risk of assigning decision-making power to a machine remain core concerns. Training AI systems on archival legal decisions may embed biases, which run counter to the fundamental aims of achieving justice [47].

6 Recommendations for Formulating AI Policy Centered on Human Rights

With the growing impact of AI technologies on society, it is crucial to incorporate human rights into the foundation of AI policy to promote fairness, accountability, and social justice. The subsequent unified recommendations outline fundamental principles for a human rights-focused AI framework, providing specific insights relevant to both global and Indian contexts.

6.1 Develop Comprehensive Legal and Ethical Frameworks for AI

- ***Global context:*** It is vital for the global nations to work together and develop certain international agreements, legislation, or equivalent frameworks that would reinforce ethical principles pertaining to artificial intelligence, as proposed by international organizations such as UNESCO and the OECD. These frameworks should be made compulsory, and these must incorporate the most quintessential principles, such as fairness, openness, and accountability within algorithms [15, 43, 48].
- ***Indian context:*** India should take what it is doing on the ground level, such as NITI Aayog's Responsible AI for All, a step further and have an all-encompassing AI Act. This legislature should contain enforceable codes of ethics, human rights

guarantees, and punishments for violations of the codes of ethics. There is an urgent need for former strategies that have merely been suggestions for a policy to become enforceable in the letter of the law [44].

6.2 Ensure Data Protection and Privacy in AI Systems

- ***Global context***: The existing global data protection law needs to be improved on a similar scale as the European Union's General Data Protection Regulation (GDPR), but with stipulations specific to the AI-based processing of data. Nothing should be more pressing than affirming informed assent, the right to clear clarifications, and care to protect people from profiling and surveillance mechanisms used by artificial intelligence systems [45].
- ***Indian context***: The Digital Personal Data Protection Act came in force in 2023 in India. However, it does not include narrowed provisions dealing with artificial intelligence. Amendments to this legislation are absolutely vital to include clauses that speak to issues surrounding algorithmic transparency; the need to obtain consent in processes involving use of automated decision-making; and the provision of individual redress mechanisms, as identified by PRS Legislative Research in 2023 [46].

6.3 Create Independent AI Oversight Mechanisms

- ***Global context***: Establishment of regulatory bodies, at the international and local levels, should be done to make them responsible for the auditing and surveillance of AI systems. Such entities would act independently and would be composed of multidisciplinary teams capable of evaluating compliance with standards of ethics and examination of suspected human rights violations involving AI technologies [42].
- ***Indian context:*** India needs to take the decisive step of creating an AI Ethics Council, which can provide oversight of artificial intelligence in several industry sectors. Composed of experts in law, technology, and ethics, as well as representatives of the civil society, this council should be diverse. Embracing this inclusive process will help us to ensure the AI systems that we operate in our country do so with transparency and within regulatory boundaries of meeting all citizens' rights.

6.4 Promote Digital Literacy and Public Engagement

- ***Global context:*** It is vital for the governments of the world to use their finances to generate efforts toward AI awareness and digital literacy programs. Such investments are critical if citizens are to have an understanding of their digital rights. That knowledge is essential because it increases democratic participation in discussions about AI regulation and develops a popular need for ethical and responsible AI usage in society [48].
- ***Indian context*:** India, thus, needs to focus on introducing digital literacy programs, particularly in rural and semi-urban setups, to enhance public understanding of the rights associated with AI technologies. It becomes critical to enable citizens with knowledge on data privacy, consent procedures, and channels to find redress if they are harmed. They are essential in a country that is characterized by levels of technological awareness and accessibility.

6.5 Foster Inclusive and Nondiscriminatory AI Development

- ***Global context*:** It is quintessential that AI systems must be built on heterogeneous and representative datasets, in order to avoid the occurrence of algorithmic bias, if any. There is a need to press for worldwide AI policies that require fairness evaluation and diversity audits during and upon completion of the development and deployment processes [42]. This approach should be embraced to come up with equitable and just AI technologies.
- ***Indian context*:** In India, there must be no onus that allows AI to reflect or perpetuate cast, gender or socio-economic status-based prejudices. We should champion the government-sponsored programs that undergo strict bias testing and build inclusive datasets. This is all the more important for public sector usage, such as the distribution of welfare, surveillance, and policing, where fairness and equity are of supreme importance.

6.6 Leverage AI to Strengthen Access to Justice and Public Welfare

- ***Global context:*** It is highly important to accept the embrace of integration of AI in order to enhance legal aid, ease procedures in courts, and enhance ways of delivering public services. But we should place human oversight and transparency over this journey first. We have to keep our guards up because it is necessary to eliminate swap of life-lying human judgment by confusing AI systems [47].
- ***Indian context:*** India has an excellent opportunity to develop its model successes, like SUPACE and the e-Courts Project. In doing this, it will be able to

implement crucial safeguards against which AI will not end up promoting bias or ignoring marginalized people. It is so very important that legal-tech tools are designed with explainability, fairness, and inclusivity as underlying features. These steps, when undertaken, will not only improve the justice system but make sure that every community is treated equally.

7 Conclusion

There has to be an attentive review of the technologies of AI in relation to its implication on human rights. The attention to the basic concerns should be projected in the form of lines, as the boundaries to the AI technologies are being established. Countries present a variety of ways on how they address AI's challenges, some being proactive seekers of policies and others scrambling to keep up with these developments.

AI-aided decision-making and surveillance elicit concerns of an individual's right to privacy, equality, and discrimination. Not only do identities get obscured in the walls of nontransparentAI systems that contain algorithm biases, but the presence of surveillance is salt on the wounds and threatens individual freedoms and marginalized oppressed sections of society. These concerns can be seen in India, whereas no comprehensive frameworks in discussion of surveillance and AI exist. They lack strong data protection legislation, restrict regulators, and authorize unfettered surveillance in a public sphere.

Application of AI in policing, social welfare spread, and governmental actions demonstrates the loud call for solving biases of algorithms, increasing transparency, and encouraging the fair distribution of benefits from technologies. Despite the imminent Personal Data Protection Bill and the discussion about the ethicality of AI being a positive move in the right direction, directing AI technology to the frameworks of human rights necessitates far greater work.

There is an immediate need to have global and national policymakers to create the verticals of equity and responsibility fully complemented by the broad policies that address access, governance, and accountability. Careful coordination across borders, proactive law-making, and ongoing discussion of the ethics of AI are necessary not only to rein in its risks but also to realize its benefits to society. The case of India is that the legal and institutional arrangements designed to ensure respect for fundamental human rights in the use of AI technology need urgent development if the technology is to be served by, and not serve to undermine, the rights of all citizens, especially vulnerable groups.

Ultimately, the challenge lies in finding the right balance between technological innovation and protection of human dignity, privacy, and freedom concerns. Thus, it is firmly asserted that AI must be developed and deployed with a human-centric perspective, wherein the rights and freedoms take more precedence over every innovation and algorithmic decision-making process. Legal frameworks, both nationally and internationally, must be taken up to meet the unique challenges that are posed by AI, ensuring that it becomes a tool for empowerment rather than oppression. Adherence to these principles can help shape a future where technology uplifts humanity, rather than diminishing it.

References

1. United Nations. (1948). Universal declaration of human rights. https://www.un.org/en/about-us/universal-declaration-of-human-rights.
2. United Nations. (1966). International covenant on civil and political rights. https://www.ohchr.org/en/instruments-mechanisms/instruments/international-covenant-civil-and-political-rights.
3. Zuboff, S. (2019). *The age of surveillance capitalism: The fight for a human future at the new frontier of power*. PublicAffairs.
4. Tufekci, Z. (2015). Algorithmic harms beyond Facebook and Google: Emergent challenges of computational agency. *Colorado Technology Law Journal, 13*(1), 203–218.
5. Mozur, P. (2019, April 14). One month, 500,000 face scans: How China is using AI to profile a minority. *The New York Times*. https://www.nytimes.com/2019/04/14/technology/china-surveillance-artificial-intelligence-racial-profiling.html.
6. Justice K. S. Puttaswamy (Retd.) v. Union of India. (2017). 10 SCC 1.
7. Russell, S., & Norvig, P. (2021). *Artificial Intelligence: A modern approach* (4th ed.). Pearson.
8. McCarthy, J. (2007). What is artificial intelligence? Stanford University. http://jmc.stanford.edu/articles/whatisai/whatisai.pdf.
9. Kaplan, A., & Haenlein, M. (2019). Siri, Siri, in my hand: Who's the fairest in the land? On the interpretations, illustrations, and implications of artificial intelligence. *Business Horizons, 62*(1), 15–25. https://doi.org/10.1016/j.bushor.2018.08.004
10. Goertzel, B., & Pennachin, C. (2007). *Artificial General Intelligence*. Springer.
11. Bostrom, N. (2014). *Superintelligence: Paths, dangers, strategies*. Oxford University Press.
12. World Health Organization (WHO). (2021). Ethics and governance of artificial intelligence for health: WHO guidance. https://www.who.int/publications/i/item/9789240029200.
13. Angwin, J., Larson, J., Mattu, S., & Kirchner, L. (2016). Machine bias: There's software used across the country to predict future criminals. And it's biased against blacks. ProPublica. https://www.propublica.org/article/machine-bias-risk-assessments-in-criminal-sentencing.
14. Raghavan, M., Sandvig, C., & Karahalios, K. (2020). Bias in AI: An examination of its impact on discrimination and fairness. *IEEE Transactions on Technology and Society, 7*(2), 57–72.
15. UNESCO. (2021). AI and education: Guidance for policy-makers. https://unesdoc.unesco.org/ark:/48223/pf0000376709.
16. Latonero, M. (2018). Governing artificial intelligence: Upholding human rights & dignity. Data & Society Research Institute. https://datasociety.net/library/governing-artificial-intelligence/.
17. European Commission. (2021). Proposal for a regulation laying down harmonised rules on artificial intelligence (Artificial Intelligence Act). https://eur-lex.europa.eu/legal-content/EN/TXT/?uri=CELEX%3A52021PC0206.
18. Binns, R. (2020). AI regulation and the global governance of artificial intelligence. *Harvard Law Review, 133*(6), 1012–1025.
19. Aggarwal, A. (2020). Artificial intelligence and the Indian legal system: Challenges and prospects. *Indian Journal of Law and Technology, 16*(1), 1–25. https://ijlt.in
20. Feldstein, S. (2019). The global expansion of AI surveillance. Carnegie Endowment for International Peace. https://carnegieendowment.org/2019/09/17/global-expansion-of-ai-surveillance-pub-79847.
21. Wachter, S., Mittelstadt, B., & Floridi, L. (2017). Transparent, explainable, and accountable AI for robotics. *Science Robotics, 2*(6), eaan6080. https://doi.org/10.1126/scirobotics.aan6080

22. Krishnan, M., & Muralidhar, S. (2020). Privacy and data protection in India: A legal perspective. *Journal of Indian Law and Society, 25*(4), 202–214.
23. Bhandari, V. (2020). AI and the law: The case for a rights-based approach in India. Carnegie India. https://carnegieindia.org/2020/01/29/ai-and-law-case-for-rights-based-approach-in-india-pub-80923.
24. Kumar, N., & Choudhury, R. (2021). Facial recognition in India: A threat to privacy. Centre for Internet and Society. https://cis-india.org/internet-governance/blog/facial-recognition-in-india-a-threat-to-privacy.
25. Internet Freedom Foundation. (2023). Analysis of the Digital Personal Data Protection Act, 2023. https://internetfreedom.in.
26. Internet Freedom Foundation. (2023). Concerns with the Digital Personal Data Protection Act, 2023. https://internetfreedom.in.
27. Pasquale, F. (2015). *The black box society: The secret algorithms that control money and information*. Harvard University Press.
28. Burrell, J. (2016). How the machine 'thinks': Understanding opacity in machine learning algorithms. *Big Data & Society, 3*(1), 1–12. https://doi.org/10.1177/2053951715622512
29. Wachter, S., Mittelstadt, B., & Floridi, L. (2017). Why a right to explanation of automated decision-making does not exist in the general data protection regulation. *International Data Privacy Law, 7*(2), 76–99. https://doi.org/10.1093/idpl/ipx005
30. Eubanks, V. (2018). *Automating inequality: How high-tech tools profile, police, and punish the poor*. St. Martin's Press.
31. Raghavan, M., Barocas, S., Kleinberg, J., & Levy, K. (2020). Mitigating bias in algorithmic hiring: Evaluating claims and practices. Proceedings of the 2020 Conference on fairness, Accountability, and Transparency, 469–481. https://doi.org/10.1145/3351095.3372828
32. Chaudhuri, S. (2021). Algorithms and inequality in India. *The India Forum*. https://www.theindiaforum.in/article/algorithms-and-inequality-india.
33. Scherer, M. (2016). The legal and ethical implications of AI in autonomous vehicles and robotics. *Journal of Robotics and AI Law, 4*(1), 1–15.
34. Scherer, M. U. (2016). Regulating artificial intelligence systems: Risks, challenges, competencies, and strategies. *Harvard Journal of Law & Technology, 29*(2), 353–400.
35. Pagallo, U. (2013). *The laws of robots: Crimes, contracts, and torts*. Springer.
36. Das, A. (2020). Regulation of artificial intelligence in India: An assessment of legal and ethical issues. *Journal of Indian Law and Society, 31*(4), 101–116.
37. Kuner, C., Svantesson, D. J., Cate, F. H., Lynskey, O., & Millard, C. (2017). The governance of cross-border data flows: Four principles for the future of data regulation. *Vanderbilt Journal of Transnational Law, 51*(4), 977–1000.
38. Bradford, A. (2020). *The Brussels effect: How the European Union rules the world*. Oxford University Press.
39. Mehta, A. (2022). Artificial intelligence and India's regulatory challenges: Towards a new digital governance paradigm. ORF Occasional Paper No. 337. https://www.orfonline.org/research/ai-india-digital-governance.
40. Bhandari, V., & Kulkarni, P. (2021). Regulating AI in India: A constitutional and legal framework. Vidhi Centre for Legal Policy. https://vidhilegalpolicy.in.
41. Chaudhuri, S. (2023). Cross-border AI regulation and India's digital sovereignty. *The India Forum*. https://www.theindiaforum.in
42. Floridi, L., Cowls, J., Beltrametti, M., Chatila, R., Chazerand, P., Dignum, V., et al. (2018). AI4People—an ethical framework for a good AI society: Opportunities, risks, principles, and recommendations. *Minds and Machines, 28*(4), 689–707. https://doi.org/10.1007/s11023-018-9482-5
43. OECD. (2019). OECD principles on artificial intelligence. https://www.oecd.org/going-digital/ai/principles/.
44. NITI Aayog. (2021). Responsible AI for all: Part 1—principles for responsible AI. https://www.niti.gov.in/sites/default/files/2021-02/Responsible-AI-22022021.pdf.

45. Voigt, P., & Von dem Bussche, A. (2017). The EU general data protection regulation (GDPR): A practical guide. *Springer*. https://doi.org/10.1007/978-3-319-57959-7
46. PRS Legislative Research. (2023). The Digital Personal Data Protection Act, 2023. https://prsindia.org/billtrack/the-digital-personal-data-protection-bill-2023.
47. Surden, H. (2019). Artificial intelligence and law: An overview. *Georgia State University Law Review, 35*(4):1305–1339. https://readingroom.law.gsu.edu/gsulr/vol35/iss4/8.
48. UNESCO. (2021). Recommendation on the ethics of artificial intelligence. https://unesdoc.unesco.org/ark:/48223/pf0000381137.

The Role of AI in Enhancing Predictive Policing to Prevent Terrorism

Shailja Thakur and Chetan Trivedi

Abstract The introduction of artificial intelligence (AI) in predictive policing has been a game-changer for law enforcement, ushering in data-driven methods for crime prevention and resource allocation. Machine learning algorithms, advanced data analytics, and predictive models used in AI-powered systems identify crime patterns, assess high-risk areas, and estimate risk for any precautionary measure. Such systems push a large amount of previous crime data, enabling the police force to better predict terrorist activities, effectively manage patrols, and decrease response time. Such technological advancement also paved the way for a shift from reactive policing to proactive terrorist prevention methods. Facial recognition, anomaly detection, natural language processing, and automated surveillance systems have all contributed to investigative capabilities evolving, thanks to AI-driven technologies. These advanced tools help in tracking criminal syndicates, detecting any suspicious activities, and analyzing social behavior trends effectively, empowering authorities to act upon any emergent threats instantly. This chapter identifies the utility of AI in predictive policing and how it benefits, challenges, and impacts law enforcement as a whole. Additionally, it delves into the ethical implications, the need for a regulatory framework, and the technological advancements required to make AI an instrument of justice, not a vehicle for injustice. Although an AI ecosystem in policing can contribute to preventing crime more effectively, a well-regulated AI ecosystem in policing can also ensure that law enforcement practices are just, ethical, and transparent.

S. Thakur (✉) · C. Trivedi
University Institute of Legal Studies, Chandigarh University, Punjab, India

C. Kaunert et al. (eds.), *Artificial Intelligence for Global Counter-Terrorism*, Contributions to Security and Defence Studies,
https://doi.org/10.1007/978-3-031-99235-3_10

1 Introduction

With ongoing changes in rapid technology and shifting criminal behavior, police departments are seeking digital AI solutions for predictive policing. Examining the operational logic of predictive policing, this chapter explores the role that AI plays in preventing acts of terror. This section explores the complex interplay between AI systems and security operations—addressing simultaneously the benefits that AI provides for anticipating criminal activity and the complications and challenges it poses. By analyzing data in real time, law enforcement agencies are better able to allocate resources where necessary and implement targeted preventative measures in high-risk areas, leading to improved safety for the public as a whole. However, the use of artificial intelligence in predictive policing raises important ethical, legal, and societal concerns. One major change in how public safety authorities approach crime prevention is the use of AI in predictive policing, made possible by new technology combined with changing law enforcement and community beliefs. Traditional approaches to policing operate using historical data combined with human judgment at a time when these approaches suffer from both human biases and limited funding availability. AI systems currently process massive amounts of data to identify both broad patterns and unknown outliers that individual human analysts would miss. The identification system then pinpoints higher-risk areas along with individuals, so security personnel are able to halt the act before it occurs [1].

Machine learning algorithms analyze social media, financial data, and any communication patterns to detect indications of radicalization or attacks being planned. By employing natural language processing, AI technology examines communications for important terms that point toward extremist behavior, thus creating useful intelligence assets for law enforcement officers. The predictive systems powered by AI help identify when certain law enforcement areas need additional surveillance efforts because they can predict the probability of specific criminal activities within defined locations. Counterterrorism operations have experienced multiple impacts because of artificial intelligence implementation. The intelligence and law enforcement sectors currently employ artificial intelligence through predictive counterterrorism operations to uncover possible threats, along with elements of terrorism specified as concerning.

The progression of AI technology, together with expanding digitalization across all life aspects, creates enhanced opportunities for implementing AI in predictive counterterrorism deployments. Imagining a future in which artificial intelligence (AI) will be instrumental in the prevention of domestic terrorism is not an unreasonable one, boasting both facial recognition in widespread public infrastructures such as government buildings, major sporting events, transportation hubs, and open marketplaces. They are capable of discovering potential threats in real time, which allows law enforcement to respond quickly, and in some cases intervene, so an attack can be avoided completely. But despite the fact that AI creates clear benefits obviously desired in predictive policing, including less invasive surveillance, more rapid data processing, and greater threat detection capabilities, its adoption is not without major complications. However, concerns around privacy, data security, algorithmic bias, and the risk of abuse require strong oversight, transparent governance, and ethical guidelines to ensure that the development and use of AI stays effective, equitable, and aligned with the principles of democracy [2]. The key issue related to the AI systems comes from the ability of AI to reflect historical systemic biases. These computerized systems over-target certain demographic groups, resulting in ethical issues that create distrust in communities. Despite these challenges, the future of AI predictive policing looks really bright. The academic approaches for countering terrorism evolve and cannon forward with the tide of technological progress. Recent advancements in artificial intelligence, through the development of deep learning and predictive analytics technology, enhance the accuracy and effectiveness of criminal predictive policing techniques. Technologists and law enforcement agents should coexist and work with civil rights groups to set moral guidelines to direct AI use in this complicated space [3].

1.1 Purpose and Goal of Chapter

The analysis in this chapter investigates the law enforcement-deployed predictive policing strategies for crime deterrence. Specifically, we explore the ethical and social risks of the implementation, as well as the technical performance and system discrimination. It is important to understand how AI technology may shape policing strategies, though as AI enforcement becomes more prevalent and begins to protect the public from potential excess of rights abuse. The focus will be on predictive policing and how such data-driven techniques might be moving the needle on law enforcement effectiveness in a way that prevents terrorism from occurring, so that readers can grasp the impact of crime prevention from an AI algorithmic angle.

AI integration within predictive policing enables law enforcement to make substantial progress in terrorist response efforts. Through data-driven analysis, security forces obtain better capabilities to stop crime while safeguarding public communities. Accepting predictive technologies demands proactive action to resolve their related moral and technical issues. Predictive policing strategies in counterterrorism will succeed if proper balance is established between AI capability utilization and civil rights protection. The AI-driven Predictive Policing Cycle illustrates how artificial intelligence is utilized to forecast and prevent criminal activities through data analysis and pattern recognition as mentioned in (Fig. 1). AI has the ability to improve public safety while building better relationships between law enforcement agencies and their communities through strategic deployment [4].

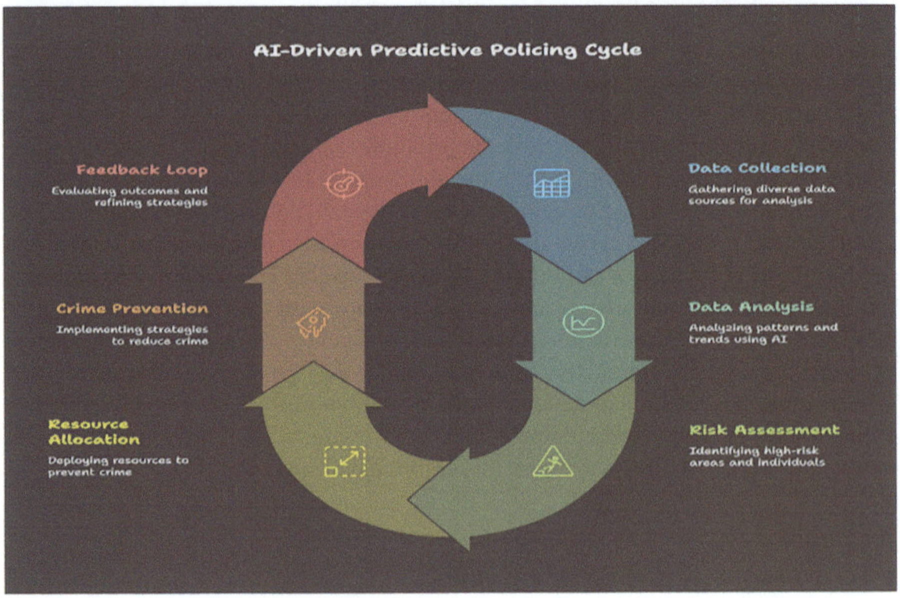

Fig. 1 AI-driven predictive policing cycle

2 An Understanding of Predictive Policing

Predictive policing is a new concept for law enforcement in the twenty-first century. Although it is still relatively new and unproven, predictive policing has the potential to revolutionize the way that law enforcement responds to crimes and victims. The definition and history of predictive policing, emerging ideas and models, its uses in law enforcement, and related concerns are all covered in this section. Using data and predictive analytics, predictive policing forecasts the location and timing of the next crime or sequence of crimes. In theory, predictive policing uses data and predictive analytics to determine the location and timing of the next crime or string of crimes. In law enforcement, the idea has led to the creation of new terms. Aspects of predictive policing are being described by chief executives, policy officials, and scholars using novel terms, including "predictive analytics," "data mining," "nonobvious relationships," and "predictive spatial analysis [5]." Predictive policing involves leveraging data analysis, machine learning, and artificial intelligence (AI) to forecast potential terrorist actions before they take place. Law enforcement agencies can use crime pattern analytics, regional trends, and behavioral data to help keep the public safe, deter crime, and allocate resources. It is based on the premise that crimes often follow predictable patterns and that statistical models can predict when and where crimes are likely to occur [6]. Predictive policing uses artificial intelligence (AI) methods—specifically, machine learning and predictive analytics—to forecast possible criminal behavior. This will be utilized to primarily prevent terrorism by identifying where criminals strike and focusing law enforcement activity where it is most effective. These AI-based models use past crime statistics and additional factors to infer where and when criminal activities may happen [4]. This may reduce crime rates and improve public safety by helping law enforcement agencies focus their resources on areas where terrorist activity is more likely to occur [7]. Utilizing advanced behavioral science algorithms as part of supervised machine learning frameworks, predictive policing predicts crime events in a more effective and efficient manner. From hotspot analysis to more complex models that can learn from larger datasets and include many variables, predicting accurately has now become a data-driven art. While this can improve operational efficiency and resource allocation for law enforcement, predictive policing possesses grave ethical concerns, especially in the area of algorithmic bias. But predictive models need to be sufficiently vetted and transparent, and equitable algorithms need to be used to mitigate the risks of over policing and the reinforcement of societal biases if they are built on erroneous and biased data [8].

To improve the effectiveness of crime prevention and investigative efforts, predictive policing uses cutting-edge technologies, such as machine learning algorithms, to evaluate digital data from crime scenes, including photos, emails, and videos. This strategy seeks to reduce the consequences of terrorism and prevent it from happening by strategically allocating law enforcement resources [9].

Through the use of data and analytics, predictive policing assists law enforcement in their mission to decrease terrorist activity by pinpointing problem areas and foreseeing when such instances will occur. Algorithms trained with machine learning may sift through crime statistics from entire cities or even entire neighborhoods to determine exactly where the police are needed most, making for more efficient enforcement. When used in predictive policing, machine learning and deep learning have the ability to revolutionize crime prediction by offering more precise and efficient ways to foretell criminal activities. If we want to see these technologies used for crime prediction to their full potential, we have to solve problems like making models that everyone can understand, getting trustworthy data, and dealing with ethical concerns [10].

Over the past 10 years, predictive policing systems have been implemented in several nations. They use modern technology to forecast criminal activity. These systems have evolved from simple heuristics and algorithms to more complex applications as technology has progressed [11].

Figure 2. involves data collection, processing, machine learning analysis, prediction, law enforcement response, and a feedback loop to refine crime forecasting and resource allocation.

3 How Predictive Policing Works

Predictive policing involves the collection and analysis of vast amounts of data, which can be broadly categorized into the following areas:

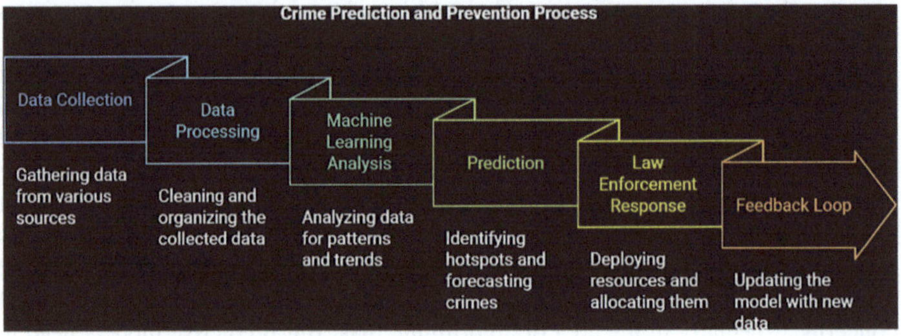

Fig. 2 Crime prediction and prevention process

1. **Crime data collection**: Law enforcement agencies gather historical arrest reports, crime logs, and incident data to produce a comprehensive dataset.
2. **Data processing and analysis**: Advanced AI and machine learning algorithms are used to process data in order to identify trends, correlations, and hotspots where crimes are more likely to occur.
3. **Predictive models and algorithms**: Algorithms such as decision trees, neural networks, and regression models examine crime patterns and produce risk evaluations for certain places, times, or people.
4. **Resource allocation and deployment**: Police departments can optimize patrol routes, assign officers to high-risk locations, and create preventive measures to discourage crime based on forecasts.
5. **Continuous learning and improvement**: By integrating fresh crime data and officer input, AI-powered predictive police systems get better over time [10].

4 AI Applications in Counterterrorism

This section describes how predictive AI role in fighting against terrorism has been recognized and applied in a limited capacity. A selection of methods and participants is shown. Automated data analytics, especially for data visualization, is key in boosting the utility of the intelligence and security services. Those who are suspects of terrorism are flagged by algorithms that routinely check the risk of a person getting on a plane. Also, data may be collected and archived by default to analyze for trends and links that would identify terrorist networks or suspicious activity. Machine learning techniques have made it possible to interpret and analyze patterns in large amounts of data that would otherwise be unthinkable. These methods could include filtering, entity relationship analysis, or more advanced image or voice recognition software [2]. The predictive potential of data is not only recognized and attempted to be realized by intelligence agencies and security services. Methods and capacities have been transferred to civilian authorities, such as the police, as a result. Examples of AI-supported predictive technologies that are already being used by law enforcement organizations and that are relevant to counterterrorism include social network analysis of urban gangs, citywide alert systems, crime-spot prediction, and custody decision-making aids. When it comes to counterterrorism, the intelligence and security services typically use investigative techniques before an attack occurs. Generally speaking, these methods concentrate on expanding from known suspects or partially uncovered plots to identify more persons engaged or connections that go deeper into terrorist organizations. Access to information about a specific person can only be granted if they are connected to one or more ongoing investigations [12].

5 Function of Prediction Policing in Counterterrorism

This section explains the function of prediction in counterterrorism and presents the predictive applications of specific AI types. It defines artificial intelligence (AI) and sets it apart from "big data" analytics in general. It contends that in order to implement a counterterrorism policy that effectively deters terrorism without unnecessarily violating the rights of citizens, accurate forecasting is essential. It also implies that predictive AI is probably going to help with this. In liberal democracies, terrorist attacks aim to weaken popular support for the governments they target. The illusion of a secure environment maintained by the nation state is disrupted when civilian targets are randomly struck [13]. It is always preferable to prevent an attack completely, even if the aftermath is well controlled. Therefore, the main goal of counterterrorism initiatives is frequently prevention. Terrorist attacks can be avoided in two ways. There is one strategy for countering terrorism—deterrence—which includes hardening critical infrastructure, implementing heavy security, and having associated penalties in place. The second one centers on the idea of "intercepting attacks before they are executed"—stopping recruitment and radicalization and limiting the mobility of people who can carry out these actions. The techniques should be focused on improving the actual predictive capacity in preventing behaviors and attacks related to terrorism, leaving the question of prevention for powers to be at its best. This means that effective prediction makes it possible to identify and treat the affected population beforehand in order to reduce the impact on the general population. Prediction can be used to better allocate resources to areas that are most likely to be targets in the case of physical protection deterrent [13].

6 Obstacles in the Present Application of Predictive AI in Counterterrorism

Based on publicly accessible data, including social media activity, travel patterns, financial transaction data, communications metadata, and internet surfing activity, artificial intelligence (AI) can forecast acts of terrorism. There may be a push to employ this technology more widely due to its ability to stop terrorist strikes. For instance, a UK Operational Improvement Review conducted in 2017 following four terrorist attacks recommended a step change in the capacity to "exploit data to detect activity of concern" with respect to both previously known and unknown subjects of interest to security services [14]. Regarding the application of predictive AI in counterterrorism, several issues have arisen or are about to arise. Two categories of issues should be addressed by its implementation: practical ramifications and human rights issues.

6.1 Absence of Remedies

It is challenging to invoke legal assurances of remedy due to the inherent opacity of predictive AI techniques used in counterterrorism or even in the usage of retained bulk data generally. One of the most comprehensive data protection laws in the world, the EU's General Data Protection Regulation (GDPR), aims to strike a balance by guaranteeing a right of recourse on any completely automated decision that is produced. It is uncertain, nevertheless, if choices involving an arbitrary degree of human control may satisfy this condition. It also includes an exemption for government organizations [15]. Systems like the UK's Investigatory Powers Tribunal (IPT) make an effort to hold government agencies accountable for their acts; however, they fall short in this regard, with some processes being carried out in secret. Despite the IPT's rulings against the government, which demonstrate its independence, the system has come under fire for providing little recourse, depending too heavily on public confidence in governmental institutions, and being challenging for the general public to use. However, the IPT reflects a compromise that many people believe to be fair because counterterrorism strategies generally need a trade-off between operational security and transparency. Maximizing transparency whenever possible is a crucial component of effective counterterrorism policy, notwithstanding the inherent limitations of transparency in the fight against terrorism. AI use is troublesome if it threatens this or is seen to do so [16].

6.2 Concerns About Privacy and Surveillance

As predictive policing advances, significant privacy and surveillance concerns have emerged, raising grave ethical questions regarding data collection practices and their impact on civil liberties. Thanks to the incorporation of cutting-edge technologies like machine learning and big data analytics, law enforcement agencies can now monitor individuals and communities in ways that were previously unheard of. This often makes it impossible to discriminate between public safety and individual rights [17].

6.3 Privacy Abuses

Privacy abuses, after all, are among the key issues with predictive policing. These systems have been found to utilize a wide range of input for their extensive data collection processes, including social media activity, location tracking, and historical criminal data. If such surveillance methods result in personal data being collected without the knowledge or consent of the individual, then this may be an infringement of the individual's right to privacy. However, critics contend that these activities turn normal citizens into suspected criminals, breeding an environment of mistrust and fear [18].

6.4 Problems with Mass Surveillance

Many predictive policing technologies use forms of mass surveillance not limited to the monitoring of specific individuals or even types of behavior, the latter of which is standard to the operations of traditional police forces. Apart from privacy concerns, this approach also risks creating a surveillance state. The more that law enforcement organizations are relying on technology for prediction and prevention of crime, the greater the likelihood of abuse and overreach. If people begin to shy away from open expression due to more prevalent mass surveillance, it could lead to an erosion of democracy [19].

6.5 Algorithmic Opacity

For predictive policing, the opacity of algorithms presents another obstacle to establishing accountability. The highly complex machine learning models used by many law enforcement agencies are often so deep that even their designers cannot fully explain how they work. This opacity may make it harder for stakeholders, including community and civil rights organizations and oversight agencies, to assess whether the systems are biased or are making errors. The inability to describe how decisions were made could erode public confidence and trigger moral debates in regard to whether predictive policing technologies produce just outcomes or not [20].

6.6 Legal and Regulatory Gaps

Predictive police algorithms: It is not at all clear how predictive police algorithms are to be accounted for under existing law. It seems likely that these ethical feedbacks are not reflected in existing legislative frameworks—which leaves law enforcement agencies wide latitude to carry it out anyway. This regulatory gap could lead to a range of results and a variety of strategies in these communities, as it denies them a remedy if they are falsely charged or over-policed. To ensure equitable law enforcement practices, we need to raise standards and have accountability measures for predictive policing technology [21].

6.7 Over-Policing

The practice of predictive policing faces a critical drawback because it risks intensifying police surveillance against minority racial or ethnic individuals. A record of past high crime reporting often triggers algorithm-recommended police deployments while using historical crime statistics. An increased number of marginalized individuals in particular neighborhoods could lead law enforcement to enhance their presence, thus generating increased stops searches and arrests within those neighborhoods. The pattern continues exponentially because increased police surveillance generates more crime reports, which just validates the initial algorithm predictions [22].

Predictive policing produces disastrous results for communities with limited economic opportunities, together with social and ethnic minority groups. The combination of deficient social programs and elevated jobless statistics, together with restricted educational opportunities, has proven to increase criminal activity within communities. Predictive algorithms might deepen the marginalization and stigma of population groups when they identify socioeconomic behavior as proof of crime. Inside the criminal justice system, members of these backgrounds risk higher vulnerability because they typically have restricted access to legal resources, which helps challenge discriminatory practices [23].

7 AI-Powered Counterterrorism

AI-powered counterterrorism applications work toward enhancing security performance by strengthening both processing speed and genuine-time risk discovery operations. The dual-use properties of AI exhibit two functions by delivering protective operations while also creating security dangers. The employment of artificial intelligence in counterterrorism practices brought substantial modifications to the methods that defend against jihadist and right-wing extremist organizations. The accuracy and operational efficiency of intelligence agencies enhance through AI technologies, making attacks on international terrorism networks more successful and effective. The counterterrorism operations heavily depend on AI systems for multiple functionalities. Artificial intelligence (AI) analyses extensive data to uncover hidden patterns that human intelligence analysts normally would not detect, thereby assisting conventional intelligence analysis. Military and security forces require better strategic and operational capabilities, which can be achieved through machine learning applications on both public databases and enemy captured documents. The defense against cyberterrorism strongly relies on artificial intelligence functionalities [24]. The UN Office of Counterterrorism acknowledges that artificial intelligence can detect extremist narratives along with online extremist propaganda, which it can then thwart effectively. AI systems with monitoring and analysis capabilities can identify extremist ideology transmission in order to stop its dissemination and break up dangerous online radicalization areas.

Counterterrorism capabilities will receive AI upgrades while the effectiveness of terrorist media campaign grows. Strong systems of AI governance with moral standards become vital because AI technologies can serve terrorism purposes as well as counterterrorism objectives. The need for technological firms to collaborate with governments and counterterrorism bodies grows more important in maintaining an elevated level of international security from harmful actor advances [25]. Technology can greatly improve security measures by instantly detecting known or suspected terrorists in a variety of locations, including train stations, airports, and public gathering places. Essentially, the technology identifies individuals in a crowd by scanning their faces and comparing them with images stored in databases of known persons. Additionally, AI-powered cameras that can identify even firearms are already commonplace due to recent advancements in the technology sector [26].

Algorithms can identify firearms or shotguns by utilizing the video networks that are already in place in expansive settings such as airports, schools, or business campuses. The technology first flags the gun as suspect in orange before rapidly raising the warning level to red in a matter of seconds. The software then displays a still image that identifies the suspect and provides information on the handgun after a security guard receives a notification on their cell phone. This makes it easier to decide whether to send out first responders or to write off the signal as a false alarm. The AI is able to differentiate between a sprinkler head and a pistol, for instance. However, as was already noted, this technology is highly dependent on enormous volumes of data in order to be improved. We may anticipate a steady increase in accuracy over time as it collects more video data and refines models and algorithms for improved item detection. Nevertheless, privacy issues, possible prejudice, and the precision of recognizing people across various demographics are raised by the use of image processing and facial recognition [27]. In liberal democracies, terrorist attacks aim to weaken popular support for the governments they target. The illusion of a secure environment maintained by the nation state is disrupted when civilian targets are randomly struck. It is always preferable to prevent an attack completely, even if the aftermath is well controlled. Therefore, the main goal of counterterrorism initiatives is frequently prevention. Terrorist attacks can be avoided in two ways [28]. One is deterrence, which is achieved by securing infrastructure, enforcing security measures, and threatening to punish. Another is the denial of the ability to carry out attacks: by stopping terrorists before their plans are carried out, preventing the recruitment and radicalization of potential terrorists, and imposing limitations on people's freedom of movement. Many of these techniques have traits in common. In particular, they impose demands on limited resources and, to a certain degree, violate the rights of the individuals to whom they are applied [29].

The ideals of liberal democracy are betrayed when rights are arbitrarily or excessively violated, giving the terrorists the upper hand. Effective counterterrorism can therefore be defined as an optimization problem that seeks to offer protection for the majority of individuals with the least amount of violation of their rights and freedoms, both pragmatically and philosophically. Effective terrorism prevention would benefit from techniques that enhance the forecasting of attacks or behaviors linked to them in order to achieve this ideal state [30, 31].

Even though the dangers of AI have already been discussed, there are a number of ways in which AI might be extremely beneficial to counterterrorism efforts [1].

Monitoring and surveillance are two uses for it. In order to help police react swiftly to possible threats, AI can analyze live videos to identify suspect behavior or objects in public. Artificial intelligence (AI) systems could automatically identify and eliminate extremist information from internet platforms, thereby reducing the transmission of terrorist propaganda in the areas of counter-propaganda and deradicalization [32]. By detecting at-risk individuals and analyzing their online behavior, it could assist deradicalization initiatives.

Another application of AI is in predictive policing. AI could forecast possible terrorist acts by examining trends in past data, social media activity, and other intelligence sources. It can evaluate a person's or a group's behavior to spot radicalization indicators and take action before an attack occurs. In order to deliver thorough insights, artificial intelligence (AI) combines massive datasets from sources such as internet platforms, surveillance footage, and financial transactions. It interprets and evaluates online material and communication intercepts for possible dangers using language processing. AI may also increase counterterrorism's operational effectiveness. It can optimize the allocation of resources for operations, guaranteeing the efficient deployment of both manpower and equipment. AI can improve the efficacy of counterterrorism tactics by giving decision-makers access to real-time data and recommendations. But it's important to keep in mind that any countermeasures must carefully balance protecting the general welfare with maintaining the free flow of ideas and creativity that characterize a democratic society [33].

Predictive AI's role in combating terrorism has previously been acknowledged and, to a limited degree, implemented. It presents a few of the methods and participants. The intelligence and security services' operations are supported by automated data analytics, especially when it comes to data visualization [34] Algorithms regularly evaluate the risk of individuals traveling by plane and give priority to terrorism suspects. By default, data may be gathered and saved for subsequent analysis in an effort to identify trends and connections that could reveal terrorist networks or questionable activity. Patterns in vast volumes of data that would normally be impossible to interpret and analyze can now be done thanks to machine learning techniques. These methods could include filtering, entity relationship analysis, or more advanced image or voice recognition software [35].

The usefulness, biases, and ethical dilemmas of predictive policing in law enforcement have all been examined in this study. The term "predictive policing" describes the application of AI and data-driven algorithms to anticipate criminal activity and effectively deploy law enforcement resources. Proponents contend that successful applications of predictive policing in a number of areas, where data analytics have been used to enhance patrol tactics and resource allocation, can result in notable drops in crime rates [36]. Nevertheless, recognizing their potential benefits, the chapter also highlights a variety of biases in the predictive police systems. The datasets used to train these algorithms are often corrupted by historical and cultural biases that lead to over-policing and over-surveillance of marginalized communities. This can then lead to over policing, cementing systemic inequalities, as well as a loss of trust in the police [4]. Predictive policing raises similarly concerning ethical questions. The construction and analysis of vast databases of personal information—frequently gathered without the subjects' voluntary participation—can be significantly more invasive than traditional methods like sniffer dogs, thereby generating a host of privacy and surveillance-related concerns, particularly regarding insider access and misuse. In addition, the lack of accountability and transparency surrounding algorithmic decision-making further raises issues about the fairness and reasonableness of the decisions made on the basis of these predictions. Therefore, while predictive policing offers opportunities for more efficient allocation of resources to reduce crime, it requires careful consideration of its ethical consequences and biases. These must be dealt with in order to create responsible policing tactics that enhance public safety while protecting civil liberties and promoting equity in communities [4].

8 Enhancing Predictive Policing with AI

Artificial Intelligence (AI) potential is also applied to the enhanced predictive policing by the psychological analysis of large datasets and predicting where a type of crime is likely to occur. AI can predict patterns and hot spots for crime using machine learning–based algorithms and many other hidden hot spots of spam, preventing a crime even before it occurs. By being able to allocate resources in such an efficient manner that it helps you deploy personnel on the streets, predictive policing deters crimes before they happen. Nevertheless, ethical issues like bias, lack of transparency and accountability, and privacy violations are still major obstacles for the future of AI in policing. It is imperative to balance technological innovations with protections to ensure law enforcement practices are performed in a fair and transparent manner [4].

Occurring overlays between new technologies and AI work together to increase both predictive policing accuracy and efficiency as we exist in the present [4].

9 Key Contributions of Predictive Policing

The application of advanced data analysis tools coupled with machine learning techniques enables predictive policing through better and more efficient forecasting of criminal activity for law enforcement agencies. Many law enforcement agencies experience improved prediction accuracy throughout time because their evolution away from hotspot analysis uses a progression to powerful algorithms that handle multiple variables and scale up from large datasets. Prediction services used in policing have transitioned from easy algorithms to elaborate applications because artificial intelligence technology continues advancing the efficiency of these systems for precise criminal activity forecasts. AI models use past crime statistics combined with traffic statistics and cycle crime patterns to generate correct predictions about future crime occurrences. Such analysis enables authorities to make informed decisions for resource distribution while using data-based crime prevention methods in law enforcement programs. Worldwide crime hotspots that may produce upcoming criminal events become visible through machine learning algorithms, which process representative geographic region crime data. Police departments enhance their budget effectiveness by identifying high-crime zones; thus, they can optimize their prevention programs across the board. Deep learning algorithms made from recurrent neural networks and convolutional neural networks successfully predict crime patterns through the evaluation of various data types, including time frames, location data, and criminal activity types [4]. These sophisticated models produce more precise crime predictions, which provide essential information about underlying factors that drive criminal actions because they detect multiple levels of correlations between many variables. The analysis of extensive datasets surpasses all other technologies since artificial intelligence (AI) demonstrates clear superiority in managing structured and unstructured information. Various criminal investigation materials, such as public reports, social media content, security video footage, and crime incident logs, represent this category. Machine learning algorithms discover hidden data patterns that escape the human eye since they spot relationships between income-based characteristics and criminal statistics. The placement of AI prediction systems provides constant analysis, which enables law enforcement personnel to detect upcoming dangers before taking proactive steps [4]. The deployment of staff and resources reaches its highest level, thanks to AI, which anticipates crime risk areas, allowing better coverage combined with rapid response times. The three functional elements of AI-powered predictive policing can be observed in Fig. 3: AI and machine learning, law enforcement practices, and ethical and legal considerations. Through the implementation of AI and machine learning technology, the identification of crime patterns becomes feasible, together with data analytical capabilities for predictions. Legislative agencies establish crime prevention strategies through resource allocation efforts. The ethical and legal framework requires law enforcement to handle three main concerns: eliminating bias, respecting privacy, and ensuring equal police treatment [4].

Benefits of AI in Predictive Policing Through predictive policing systems, the risk of crime decreases because they detect potential criminal operations beforehand.

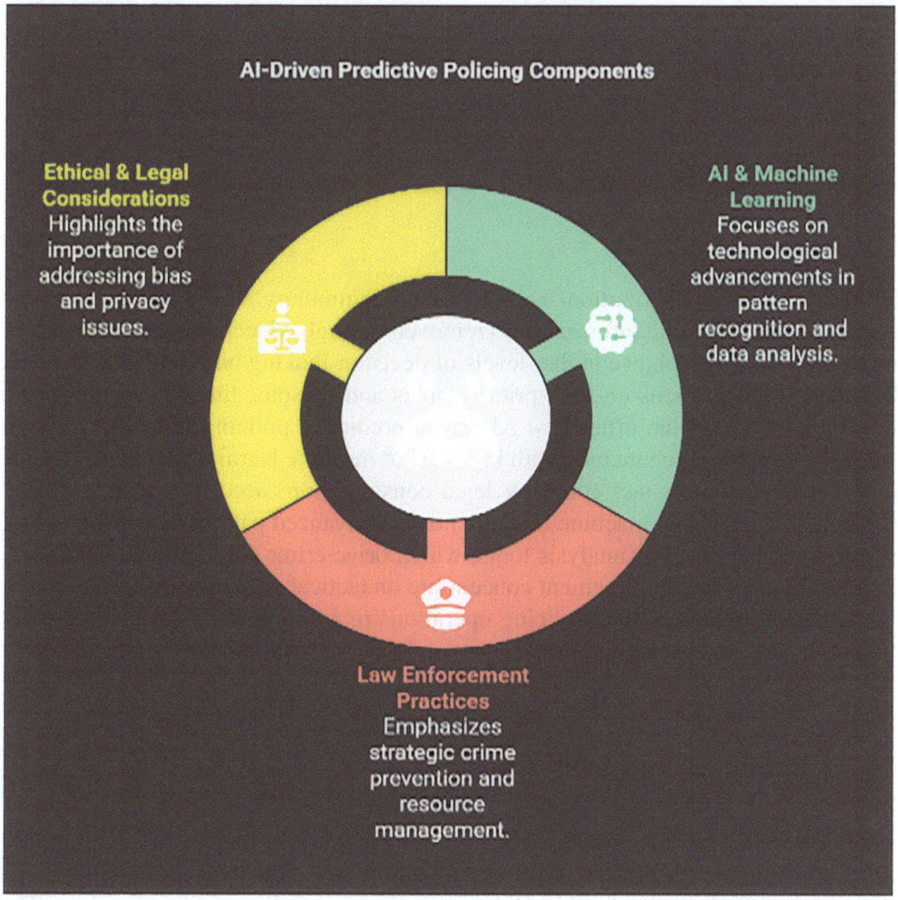

Fig. 3 AI-driven predictive policing components

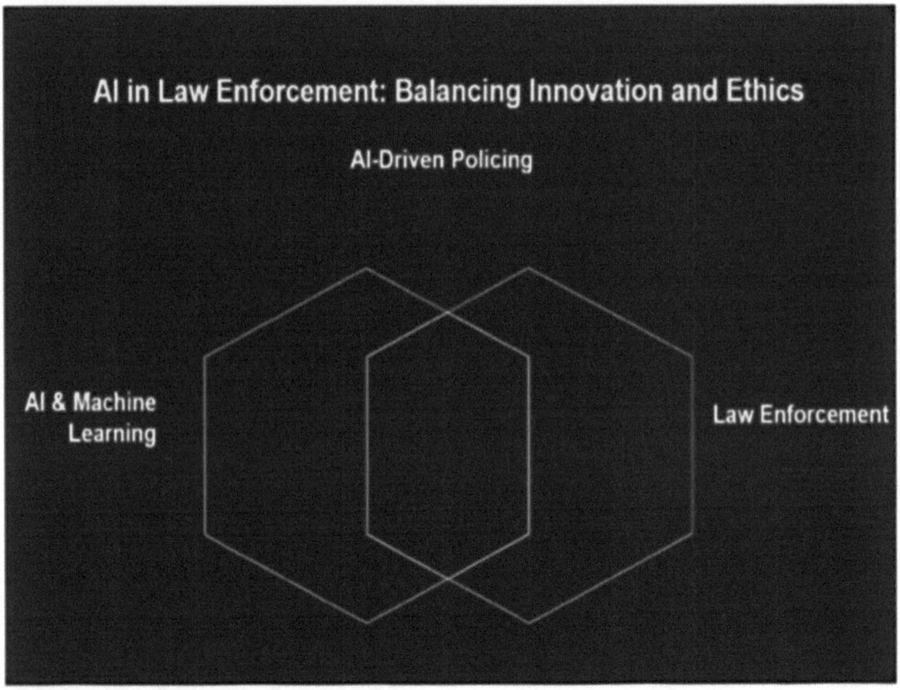

Fig. 4 AI in law enforcement

Effective resource distribution leads to better community safety as public safety improves. When certain information is removed through AI technology, law enforcement professionals achieve higher levels of decision-making based on proven facts. Through strategic focus on high-priority areas and persons, limited resources will operate with maximum efficiency. AI-driven predictive policing functions through three main parts, which include both Fig. 4 AI & machine learning elements and law enforcement practices and ethical & legal considerations according to Fig. 4. The combination of AI and machine learning powers advanced pattern recognition algorithms and superior data analysis tools, which drive crime forecasting capabilities. The practices of law enforcement concentrate on tactical crime prevention, together with resource management. Policing operations require ethical and legal examination to handle bias issues and privacy demands, along with fair treatment standards.

10 Challenges and Limitation

Predictive policing, which uses artificial intelligence (AI), has the potential to significantly increase the effectiveness of law enforcement and reduce crime. However, there are difficulties and ethical discussions surrounding its application. The interpretability of AI models, biased data entry, and poor prediction performance are only a few of the numerous problems that cast doubt on the accuracy and equity of technology. Additionally, the software tools for policing and crime prevention may intensify already-existing civil rights inequalities, leading to over policing of some areas. To ensure that the AI-driven policing models are equitable, effective, and accountable, it is critical to solve these issues [4].

1. AI-based predictive policing solutions often fall short with low predictive accuracy and garbage-in, garbage-out data inputs, leading to predictive policing solutions that claim scientific accuracy but in fact frequently result in police showing up at the door of wrongfully accused citizens. This inaccuracy has real-world repercussions that diminish the technology's usefulness and legitimacy.
2. To improve forecast accuracy, AI models must be continuously improved. In order to reduce the mistakes made when anticipating a particular phenomenon, sophisticated techniques and machine learning algorithms that can adapt to the nonstationary behavior of crime and take into account spatial-temporal relationships are used. Additionally, the model must be continuously assessed and modified to ensure that the predictions align with the real-time events.
3. Building data-driven, AI-based models that represent and capture nonlinear, dynamic spatial dependencies and temporal patterns in the crime behavior is a tough challenge. Another strategy is to integrate data from several sources, past criminal activity, and outside variables to preserve interpretability and shed light on anticipated occurrences. Artificial intelligence systems in predictive policing demonstrate an ability to improve law enforcement performance while cutting down crime statistics. Its implementation faces various challenges alongside ethical questions that must be solved. Various issues, such as the untraceable nature of AI models, along with biased data entry and poor prediction outcomes, prove challenging to the accuracy and equity reliability of technology systems. The software tools used in police work and crime prevention appear to worsen current civil rights imbalances, which result in excessive police presence in specific areas. AI-driven policing models require the successful resolution of current problems to achieve their goals of equity, along with effectiveness and accountability [4].
4. The combination of poor predictive precision techniques and flawed data entry patterns in AI-based predictive policing systems generates solutions that pretend to have a scientific basis yet prompt police to wrongfully visit innocent citizens at their residences. The technology becomes less valuable while losing its credibility through this systematic, flawed output.
5. Improving AI model forecasts requires unremitting enhancement work. Sophisticated techniques, along with machine learning algorithms, detect crime nonstationarity by adapting to it and incorporating spatial-temporal relationships to reduce errors in specific phenomenon predictions. A constant assessment of the model alongside modifications is necessary to guarantee that the prediction results match actual events.

6. The challenge of building AI-driven models from data that accurately represent non-linear transitions among geographically dispersed crime-event places, as well as the connected temporal behavioral links between such events, endures. We can combine several data sources, and with crimes, other variables can be analyzed in conjunction with the results and maintain interpretability while investigating future events.
7. When algorithms are trained on biased data, they can produce biased outcomes that reinforce systemic inequalities and disproportionately impact vulnerable demographic groups. To ensure fairness and uphold legal and human rights standards, predictive policing must prioritize the elimination of such biases. This requires a framework for developing AI systems that are transparent, accountable, and grounded in ethical principles—ensuring that discriminatory practices are prevented and civil liberties are safeguarded.
8. AI model hits an important limitation—it delivers results in a black box that does not provide any explanation to the human analyst. The predictive models must be explainable because the fact that they are noninterpretable will bring down trust, together with accountability, so that the consequences will be disastrous for the individuals or communities that get the wrong prediction.
9. To make predictive policing feasible, police organizations must maintain up-to-date crime data of high quality. This raises a wide range of strong challenges when it comes to having appropriate laws that protect personal data and guard against unethical information processing, while at the same time providing existing data privacy protection in place. AI policing tools are predictively targeting geographic areas and demographic groups, leading to increased police feet on the ground in communities, decreased community trust, and increased surveillance.
10. The public finds it challenging to believe in human algorithm systems because these systems remain inscrutable within their black-box nature. Detailed explanations of the forecast-making process enable more efficient tracing of errors and biases in predictions because of their clarity. Being responsible requires proper identification of those who need to answer for their actions.
11. The main problem with predictive policing systems comes from their need to use labelled data sets for machine learning operations. Real-world data scarcity impacts the predictive models, making it necessary to study methods of semi-supervised and unsupervised learning so they can operate effectively.
12. AI systems that operate with biased programming have a high potential to strengthen current biases and consequently impact underprivileged individuals the most severely. AI drivers should operate under open systems with extensive regulatory safeguards to ensure justice and fairness in law enforcement practices.
13. The use of artificial intelligence in surveillance demands the establishment of structured legislation regarding privacy rights to stop unauthorized data breach of citizens and misuse of AI systems.

11 Conclusion

As in today's time, to see more potential, there is a requirement for AI, which can transform predictive policing and offer crime prevention and public safety. To use this, there is a requirement to be accompanied by a commitment to ethical practices, transparency, and community involvement. By responsibly addressing the challenges and harnessing the benefits of artificial intelligence, law enforcement agencies can strengthen their capacity to protect citizens, while simultaneously building public trust and ensuring accountability.

Not surprisingly, the future of predictive policing will probably require ongoing iterations of our machine learning models to achieve both accuracy and fairness. The expansion of the field to include more and different types of data, beyond just the molecular data currently utilized, including socio-economic data, environmental data, and real-time data through Iota devices, will provide even more predictive power for these systems as they evolve. Finally, improving the transferability of predictive models in space and crime type will further guarantee that such technologies can be used in different contexts.

References

1. Berk, R. (2023). Artificial intelligence, predictive policing, and risk assessment for law enforcement. *Annual Review of Criminology, 4*. https://doi.org/10.1146/annurev-criminol-051520-012342
2. Stokes, S. (2023, July 27). *The AI revolution and its implications on domestic counterterrorism | Middlebury Institute of International Studies at Monterey*. https://www.middlebury.edu/institute/academics/centers-initiatives/ctec/ctec-publications/ai-revolution-and-its-implications-domestic.
3. Uchida, C. D. (2024). Predictive policing. In G. Bruinsma & D. Weisburd (Eds.), *Encyclopedia of criminology and criminal justice* (pp. 3871–3880). Springer. https://doi.org/10.1007/978-1-4614-5690-2_260
4. Author (n.d.)
5. Rayhan, Y. and Hashem, T. (2023) "AIST: An interpretable Attention-based deep learning model for crime prediction," ACM transactions on spatial algorithms and systems [Preprint]. Available at: https://doi.org/10.1145/3582274.
6. Van Puyvelde, D., Coulthart, S., & Hossain, M. S. (2024). Beyond the buzzword: Big data and national security decision-making. *International Affairs, 93*(6), 1397–1416. https://doi.org/10.1093/ia/iix184
7. Chuang, Y. -L., & D'Orsogna, M. R. (2023). *Mathematical models of radicalization and terrorism*. 10.48550/arXiv.1903.08485.
8. Stokes, S. (2021, July 27). *The AI revolution and its implications on domestic counterterrorism | Middlebury Institute of International Studies at Monterey*. https://www.middlebury.edu/institute/academics/centers-initiatives/ctec/ctec-publications/ai-revolution-and-its-implications-domestic.
9. Anderson, D. (2024). Attacks in London and Manchester March-June 2017. *SSRN Electronic Journal*. https://doi.org/10.2139/ssrn.4833522
10. Hung, T.-W., & Yen, C.-P. (2023). Predictive policing and algorithmic fairness. *Synthese, 201*(6), 206. https://doi.org/10.1007/s11229-023-04189-0

11. Fontes, C., Hohma, E., Corrigan, C. C., & Lütge, C. (2022). AI-powered public surveillance systems: Why we (might) need them and how we want them. *Technology in Society, 71*, 102137. https://doi.org/10.1016/j.techsoc.2022.102137
12. Bernd, L. (2024, May 3). AI-enabled deception: The new arena of counterterrorism. Georgetown Security Studies Review. https://georgetownsecuritystudiesreview.org/2024/05/03/ai-enabled-deception-the-new-arena-of-counterterrorism/.
13. Uddin, M. I., Zada, N., Aziz, F., Saeed, Y., Zeb, A., Ali Shah, S. A., Al-Khasawneh, M. A., & Mahmoud, M. (2023). Prediction of future terrorist activities using deep neural networks. *Complexity, 2020*, 1–16. https://doi.org/10.1155/2020/1373087
14. Raji, I., & Sholademi, D. (2024). Predictive policing: The role of AI in crime prevention. *International Journal of Computer Applications Technology and Research, 13*, 66–78. https://doi.org/10.7753/IJCATR1310.1006
15. Choubey, S. (2024). The role of artificial intelligence in crime prediction and prevention on a global scale.
16. Chandak, S. (2020). Artificial intelligence and policing: A human rights perspective. *NLUJ Law Review, 7*(1), 43–69.
17. India Today. (2023), "Literacy rate in India: Bihar lowest at 61.8%, Kerala highest at 94%", 14 March, available at: https://www.indiatoday.in/education-today/news/story/literacy-rate-in-india-bihar-lowest-at-618-kerala-highest-at-94-2346672-2023-03-14. Accessed 15 Mar 2025.
18. Janyala, S. (2023). Hyderabad-based startup launches smart robocop, named after 26/11 martyr Hemant Karkare. The Indian Express, 30 December, available at: https://indianexpress.com/article/technology/tech-news-technology/hyderabad-based-startup-launches-smart-robocop-named-after-26-11-martyr-hemant-karkare.
19. Jenkins, R., & Purves, D. (2024). Artificial Intelligence and predictive policing: A roadmap for research. Available at: http://aipolicing.org/year-1-report.pdf. Accessed 12 Apr 2023.
20. Koshy, J. (2024). India ranks third in research on Artificial Intelligence. The Hindu, 18 January. Available at: https://www.thehindu.com/sci-tech/science/india-ranks-third-in-research-on-artificial-intelligence/article26030596.ece.
21. Lifschitz, V. (2023). *Artificial intelligence and mathematical theory of computation: Papers in honor of John McCarthy*. Academic Press.
22. Mudaliar, S. (2023). Police-public ratio stands at 152.80 per lakh person: Govt informs parliament. Hindustan Times, 30 March, available at: https://www.hindustantimes.com/india-news/policepublic-ratio-stands-at-152-80-per-lakh-person-govt-informs-parliament-101680162971094.html.
23. NASSCOM (National Association of Software and Service Companies). (2023). AI patents—driving emergence of India as an AI Innovation hub. Available at: https://nasscom.in/knowledge-center/publications/ai-patents-driving-emergence-india-ai-innovation-hub. Accessed 16 May 2025.
24. News18 (2023). Telangana Police use facial recognition app to reunite families with lost children. 14 February, available at: https://www.news18.com/news/india/telangana-police-use-facial-recognition-app-to-reunite-families-with-lost-children-2501341.html. Accessed 3 May 2025.
25. Press Information Bureau. (2022). Artificial Intelligence. 30 March, available at: https://pib.gov.in/PressReleasePage.aspx?PRID=1811372. Accessed 12 Jan 2023.
26. Sachdev, G. (2023). India's AI market to reach USD 7.8 billion by 2025, says IDC's latest report on ai. INDIAai, 31 October, available at: https://indiaai.gov.in/article/india-s-ai-market-to-reach-usd-7-8-billion-by-2025-says-idc-s-latest-report-on-ai. Accessed 1 June 2023.
27. Singh, D. (2020). Two police officers suspended after Palghar mob lynching incident. India Today, 20 April, available at: https://timesofindia.indiatimes.com/city/thane/palghar-lynching-35-cops-from-kasa-police-station-transferred/articleshow/75436467.cms. Accessed 10 Mar 2025.
28. Supreme Court Observer. (2023). Judgment of the court in plain English (I). 24 August, available at: https://www.scobserver.in/reports/k-s-puttaswamy-right-to-privacy-judgment-of-the-court-in-plain-english-i/. Accessed 15 Mar 2025.

29. Suresh, N., & Ali, S. (2023). UP police detained 41 children during CAA protests, some were tortured, says citizens' report. Scroll.in, 13 February, available at: https://scroll.in/article/952964/up-police-detained-41-children-during-caa-protests-some-were-tortured-says-citizens-report. Accessed 22 May 2025.
30. The Indian Express. (2023). Manipur violence: 29 women officers in CBI's team of 53 to probe 11 cases, 17 August, available at: https://indianexpress.com/article/cities/delhi/cbi-mobilises-officers-women-probe-manipur-violence-cases-8895800/. Accessed 8 Oct 2023.
31. West, D. M. (2023). *Moving forward: Self-driving vehicles in China, Europe, Japan, Korea, and the United States*. Center for Technology Innovation at Brookings.
32. Brodowski, D., & Sprenger, J. (2023). Predictive policing in Germany. *RIDP*, 117. Retrieved from https://www.maklu-online.eu/en/tijdschrift/ridp/2023/artificial-intelligence-and-administration-crimina/predictive-policing-germany/maklu-online.eu.
33. Kumar, A., & Sharma, P. (2024). The role of artificial intelligence in predictive policing: Benefits, risks, and ethical considerations. *International of Law Enforcement, 1*(4), 21–25. Retrieved from https://international.appihi.or.id/index.php/ILE/article/view/273international.appihi.or.id.
34. Srinithi, T., & Revathi Sri, P. (2024). AI-driven crime prevention: Balancing predictive policing with individual rights. *International Journal of Legal Science and Innovation, 6*(6), 143–156. https://doi.org/10.10000/IJLSI.112278IJLSI
35. Yang, C. (2023). CrimeGAT: Leveraging graph attention networks for enhanced predictive policing in criminal networks. *arXiv*. https://arxiv.org/abs/2311.18641arXiv.
36. Zhang, X., & Li, Y. (2023). Artificial intelligence adoption in predictive policing to predict crime mitigation performance. *International Journal of Sustainable Construction Engineering and Technology, 14*(3), 289–298. Retrieved from https://publisher.uthm.edu.my/ojs/index.php/IJSCET/article/view/15323.

Exploring Facial Recognition Technology in Counterterrorism: AI in Surveillance and Monitoring

Bhupinder Singh and Saurabh Chandra

Abstract Facial recognition technology has become a cornerstone in the fight against terrorism because it has changed the way surveillance, identification and threat identification are done. Aided by the use of artificial intelligence (AI), facial recognition technology now has the ability to search through large databases, recognize people in real time, and predict whether a person might pose a potential threat based on his or her pattern of behavior. This chapter examines the dynamic deployment of AI-based facial recognition technology in national security systems in terms of tracking down terrorist suspects, protecting critical infrastructures, and supporting rapid response time. Through biometric recognition, deep learning algorithm, and big data analytics, the accuracy and efficiency of intelligence work are improved and traditional monitoring work becomes a forward-looking and defensive fight. The chapter also analyzes the deployment of facial recognition technology by airports, in public spaces, and within urban surveillance networks and demonstrates how AI enables automatic alerting and identity checks of vast groups of people at a scale and pace not possible before. However, the chapter discusses the legal, ethical, and privacy challenges around mass surveillance, including concerns about misidentification, fraud, and bias in the database. It recommends strong regulation, international cooperation, and transparent governance in order to ensure that the use of AI facial recognition technology is compatible with human rights and fundamental freedoms. This chapter also highlights the transformative nature of AI in counterterrorism but promotes responsible, accountable, and ethically anchored technological applications.

B. Singh (✉)
Sharda University, Greater Noida, Uttar Pradesh, India

S. Chandra
School of Law, Bennett University, Greater Noida, Uttar Pradesh, India

C. Kaunert et al. (eds.), *Artificial Intelligence for Global Counter-Terrorism*, Contributions to Security and Defence Studies,
https://doi.org/10.1007/978-3-031-99235-3_11

1 Introduction

While security threats are changing at an alarming rate, terrorism continues to be a global threat requiring advanced and dynamic responses. Sophistication of networks of terror, lone-wolf actors, and the use of digital and physical spaces for radicalization have altered the world of global security [1]. The incorporation of artificial intelligence (AI), in particular, face recognition technology (FRT), in surveillance and monitoring systems is a game changing strategy not only in counter terrorism but also as surveillance mechanism. Through AI-powered facial analytics, security and government authorities are increasingly able to pinpoint, chase, and apprehend offenders as never before with greater accuracy, speed, and effect. This chapter investigates the use of facial recognition technology (FRT) as a strategic mechanism to combat terrorism, its criticalness, process, ethical issues, application, and future outlook in the global fight against terrorism.

Facial recognition technology uses computer vision and deep learning algorithms to automatically identify and verify human faces from digital images or video frames to those stored in a database. Facial recognition technology is a potent tool that, combined with AI and big data analytics, can enable real-time surveillance, automated monitoring, predictive policing, and even behavior analysis. In the context of countering terrorism, such capabilities may also be used to identify known terrorists at airports, train stations, or at large public events to monitor suspect individuals across national borders, as well as detect imposture or identity fraud in official documentation. The integration of biometrics with machine learning increases the system's adaptability and accuracy and enables not only proactive but also reactive steps within national and international security systems [2].

The importance of facial recognition technology to the development of contemporary counterterrorism methods is evidenced by its use in high-risk areas and strategic installations. FRT has been increasingly used by governments and intelligence agencies to track entry points, secure public spaces, and react to terror threats. For example, countries such as the United States, United Kingdom, Israel, and China have integrated facial recognition in airport security checks, border control, and public surveillance systems. These systems have the potential to quickly identify potentially dangerous individuals, match their facial signatures against one or more watchlists, and send alerts to security officers in real time to conduct potential interdictions. AI-powered facial recognition can assist in forensics by examining video after an attack and piecing together timelines, cross-referencing collaborators, and retracing suspected perpetrators' escape routes.

Facial recognition software to monitor both online and offline behavior related to the radicalization and recruitment process. AI algorithms can read digital content, whether that is live streams or videos posted to social media, and isolate people linked to extremist networks. Facial detection has moved beyond simple surveillance and has been combined with cyber intelligence and used in counter-extremism operations. AI-based systems combine visual with behavioral data to ensure a multifaceted security apparatus that will pick up threats when in their infancy [3].

1.1 Background and Context

While the potential appears enormous, the application of facial recognition in counterterrorism introduces important ethical, legal, and social issues. Privacy concerns Critics of mass surveillance through facial recognition believe that these techniques could infringe upon personal freedoms, especially in democracies that hold civil liberties in high regard. There also loom worries about algorithmic bias, in which facial recognition systems display higher error rates for some demographics, which could result in false identifications or discrimination. These challenges also highlight the importance of effective regulatory, transparency, and accountability mechanisms to govern the use and deployment of FRT in security. The right balance between security and privacy is a tough nut to crack, and policymakers would have to tread carefully.

There's a geopolitical dimension to global facial recognition technology being the solution to the problem. FRT can be used by authoritarian regimes for political repression in the name of counterterrorism, and used for the purposes of surveillance toward political dissidence, to quash protests, and to manage populations [4]. This dual-use attribute of AI will require a nuanced discussion internationally concerning the ethical use of AI, international norms, and cooperative frameworks to minimize the misuse of AI and maximize legitimate counterterrorism gains.

The investigation of FRT in the counterterrorism context is pertinent and of significance. Because as the tactics of terrorists change and shift from the centralized to the decentralized, traditional surveillance alone cannot protect the public. Leveraging AI to empower facial recognition is as strong, scalable, and smart a solution as any to supplement current security frameworks. But its introduction should be informed by the rule of law, ethics, and public confidence that its use is consistent with democratic norms and human rights. This research is intended to support a complete framework of the appropriate and responsible use of facial recognition as a tool to safeguard society, prevent violence, and promote security, safety, and decision-making in our ever-changing world [5].

2 Understanding Facial Recognition Technology: Role of AI and Deep Learning

Facial recognition technology is a pivotal biometric identification technology that has been widely used for identifying and authenticating people in many real-world applications of public and private sectors in recent years. At the heart of facial recognition is the process of capturing, analyzing, and comparing a person's unique facial features to establish an identity. But the seemingly simple process is being driven by sophisticated algorithms based on AI and deep learning, which makes it highly accurate, scalable, and suitable for real-life use cases, particularly in the areas of surveillance, taps by law enforcement, and counterterrorism.

AI is a key factor in empowering facial recognition systems to efficiently understand and handle visual data. By using AI, systems can automatically identify human faces from images or live video streams; identify specific individuals within large, crowded scenes; and match photographs of faces to an even bigger database with incredible accuracy. This automation decreases the need for manual assistance and greatly speeds up the search process. Further, AI can learn and get better continuously and improves with each data processing as it becomes more accurate over time.

Facial recognition is greatly improving with the help of AI, particularly with the advent of deep learning—a subcategory of AI based on a group of neural networks roughly simulating the human brain. Deep learning algorithms are learnt from huge datasets that include a variety of facial images; therefore, they are able to learn fine-grained differences in face structure, texture, angle, and face light sensitivities in image [6]. Convolutional neural networks (CNNs), one branch of deep learning models, is especially good at capturing high-level representations of facial images, such as eye location, jawline shape, and skin texture. These features are then converted into mathematical vectors called face embeddings, which encode a person's identity as a string of numbers.

The integration of AI and deep learning allows facial recognition systems to carry out face detection, identification, and tracking in real time and with high precision, even in challenging environments, such as low light, occlusions, or partial face appearances. The technological cooperation and harmony are essential for high-risk scenarios in airports, border control, or any kind of public encounters where fast and accurate identification can neutralize possible threats. Facial recognition now works effectively across distributed networks to edge computing and cloud integration and thus is much more versatile and responsive.

AI and deep learning, in other words, have taken facial recognition from being simply a biometric mechanism with its restrictions and turned it into a dynamic and adaptive intelligent system. As the technology will keep progressing, its uses in security, identity, and counterterrorism will grow increasingly important, as long as it is used responsibly and within the legal framework [7].

2.1 Neural Networks in Facial Recognition

Facial recognition system is based on neural networks (NNs), and convolutional neural networks (CNNs) that allow systems to be highly accurate, fast, and robust. These networks are inspired by the activities that take place in the human brain and are matched perfectly to tasks such as image classification and recognition. CNNs are employed to learn a set of complex features inherent in the facial image, such as the spatial relationship between the eyes, nose, mouth, and jaw, in an automatic process without requiring manual feature extraction.

It starts from an input image of the face and passes through several layers of the CNN. Each layer is designed to detect different types of features, from simple edges and textures in the first few layers to more complex patterns such as a face in deeper layers. This is particularly essential in practical applications such as surveillance, border security, or mobile authentication, where perfect conditions cannot always be assured. Even better, advances in deep learning are paving the way for the capabilities used in facial recognition technology to grow even stronger. With even fewer errors on more data, the more data a machine can train on, the more accurate it will become [8]. Neural networks have transformed face recognition into an intelligent, efficient, and generalized process. With its disproportionate capacity to learn from massive data and succeed over time, this capability is invaluable in security and counterterrorism contexts, where accurate and near-immediate facial recognition can make the difference in averting threats and keeping the public safe.

2.2 Evolution of Face Recognition Technology in Security: From Static Biometric Systems to Dynamic AI-Enhanced Surveillance

The development of face recognition in security has come a long way from early static biometric systems to today's dynamic, AI-augmented security and surveillance solutions. At first, facial recognition was dependent on conventional biometric techniques where static images were used and features were extracted manually. Typically restricted in size and accuracy, these systems required the subject to be well illuminated, facing front-on, in a controlled environment; they were not suited for real-time, large-scale security systems [9]. Their dependence on finite models and limited computational capacities did not optimize flexibility and accuracy, especially in uncontrolled environments, such as in crowded public spaces.

The development of artificial intelligence and machine learning, and in particular deep learning, was a game changer for facial recognition. The combination of convolutional neural networks (CNNs) and large-scale datasets emphasized face recognition as a dynamic, automatic, and intelligent tool. Models can now watch, in real time, live video feeds, detecting and identifying faces and never-endingly learning from new data to increase accuracy and responsiveness. These steps have successfully ensured easy operation in different types of scenarios, such as airports, stadiums, border crossings, and surveillance of the urban environment.

Dynamic AI-driven monitoring systems also interweave facial recognition with behavioral analytics, motion detection, and predictive models, enabling security agencies to make proactive discovery of suspicious activities or potential threats. Also, edge-computing and cloud-based offerings now offer more scalability, enabling viewing over wide, geographically distributed surveillance networks without latency [10]. Today, facial recognition is more than just an identification tool; it's a "missing link" that connects older biometric systems with the newer generation of AI, making public safety infrastructure stronger and more efficient.

3 Applications of Face Recognition Technology in Counterterrorism

There's been a significant amount of attention and expenditure on facial recognition technology as one of a number of counterterrorism tools available, providing the intelligence and law enforcement communities with a sophisticated means to identify, monitor, and intercept the presence of individuals associated with, or suspected to be involved in, terrorist activity. Using artificial intelligence and biometric data, facial recognition technology offers real-time monitoring and forensic tools that are critical in deterrence and investigation after an attack. Border and airport security is one of the most sensitive areas of facial recognition technology for counterterrorism [11]. By marrying facial recognition systems and immigration and customs databases, officials can quickly match the faces of travelers to global watchlists, flagging high-risk individuals as they cross a border. This app is a key tool in the detection of identity fraud, preventing people from travelling on false documents, and also keeping known terrorists out of the country.

For urban surveillance, use of facial recognition has been growing for monitoring sensitive public locations, including transportation centers, government buildings, tourist attractions, and major events. Facial recognition–enabled cameras powered by AI will be able to analyze crowds and pick out potential targets in real time to be reported to security services. This provides not just increased situational awareness but responsive capability in the presence of a threat. It is also being deployed in counter-radicalization and cyber-intelligence investigations, where it is being used to analyze images and/or videos found on the internet and social media to recognize individuals in the act of conducting extremist propaganda, recruitment, or training. That ability is invaluable when breaking up online terror networks and tracking the digital print of suspects across platforms [12].

Facial recognition is also a great aid for postattack investigations. Video material from a crime scene or nearby locations can be fed through facial recognition technology to reconstruct suspects' activities, identify associates, and form a timeline of terror activities. Facial recognition technology has also proven useful in intelligence gathering in conflict areas, where images from, for example, drone surveillance and reconnaissance missions can be checked against databases of known militants. There is R&D work on advanced FRT technologies that incorporate behavior analytics and can read micro-expressions and suspicious facial reactions in relation to threats during screenings and interrogations. There are challenges, to be sure, particularly around privacy, data security, and algorithmic bias, but the efficacy of facial recognition in counterterrorism is indisputable [13]. As long as ethical and legal control are in place, it empowers the resources of national security agencies that need to offer surveillance precise enough, scalable enough, and quick enough to be effective. In response to this ever-evolving terrorism threat, the preemptive use of facial recognition technology represents a significant force multiplier in safeguarding our communities, preventing devastating attacks and enhancing global security, as shown in Fig. 1.

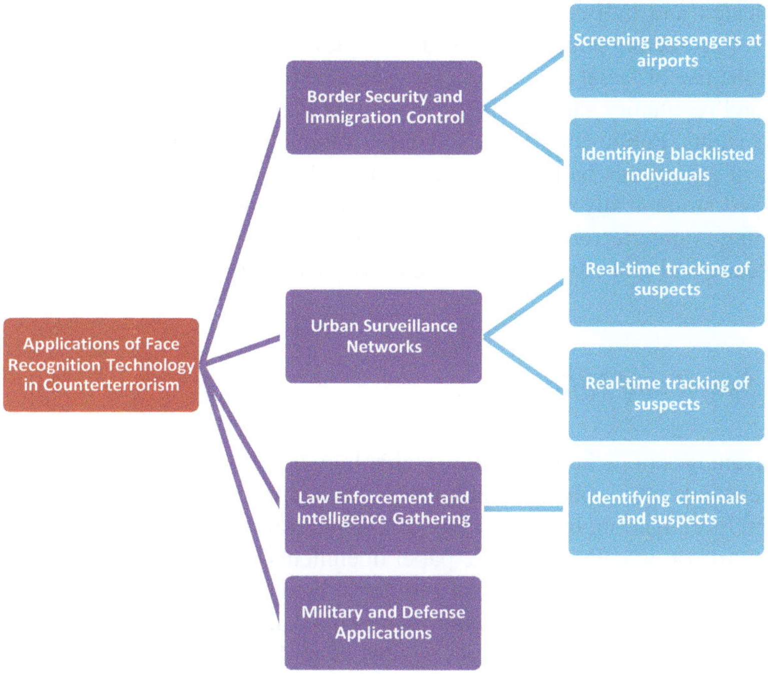

Fig. 1 Applications of face recognition technology in counterterrorism (Source: Self-prepared, Original)

4 Advantages and Opportunities in Counterterrorism

The fusion of facial recognition technology and artificial intelligence into counterterrorism efforts has significant advantages and potential for transformational impact on operational practices for law enforcement and national security. The use of these state-of-the-art tools will bring us speed, accuracy, and interconnectivity like never before to allow us to get out in front of the threats and make real-time decisions, as well as provide a new layer to global terrorism cooperation [14]. AI technology facial recognition is not just an extrapolation but the spearhead supplementing the old intelligence and surveillance systems and actively setting the direction of how counterterrorism is going to be developed. Benefits and opportunities: a discussion. The following section discusses the main advantages and opportunities in three key pillars: speed and efficiency, crime prevention and proactive threats identification, and inter-agency collaboration and intelligence sharing.

Using the AI-based facial recognition in counterterrorism has revolutionary benefits beyond surveillance. FRT is being touted as the future of security, from huge improvements in speed and accuracy in verifying identity, to predictive threat analysis, to real-time multiagency cooperation. With worldwide terrorism growing more complicated and indiscriminate, such systems provide essential high-tech intelligence for protecting public areas, vital facilities, and national borders.

But the use of facial recognition for good needs to be paired with strong ethical, legal, and regulatory safeguards to ensure that it does not violate civil liberties or privacy rights. Public confidence and democratic legitimacy require that the performance of algorithms be transparent, accountable and fair [15]. In the right hands, employed strategically and responsibly, facial recognition will be instrumental in redefining counterterrorism, shifting it from today's reactive posture into a proactive, aware, and globally interconnected force against modern threats.

4.1 Speed and Efficiency

The advantages of facial recognition technology for counterterrorism are numerous, but one stands out—speed and efficiency. The cumbersome old ways of identification and investigation, involving a lot of manual scrutiny of documents and eyewitness reports or perusing extensive paper documents, are being overtaken at a rapid pace by the automated systems of biometric technology with their instantaneous verification powers. Facial recognition systems can verify identities in seconds by searching through real-time images against large databases of known persons, suspected criminals, and self-proclaimed militants. This instantaneous identification is especially critical in high-risk situations such as airport security, border control and public events, in which immediate response may be the difference between eliminating a threat and a catastrophe [16].

The automation of time-consuming and labor-intensive manual investigative processes greatly facilitates the diminishing of error, load and lead times. Facial recognition, powered by AI, automatically sifts through video feeds around the clock, alerting authorities to any unusual activity or individuals without requiring human monitoring at all times. These systems allow investigators to review thousands of hours of materials much more quickly than they can manually, resulting in the ability to resolve cases much more quickly, as well as deploying law enforcement when an incident of concern is detected. This improved operational efficiency allows counterterrorism forces to concentrate on strategic planning and response rather than raw data, increasing operational efficiency in both domestic and international environments.

4.2 Crime Prevention and Proactive Threat Detection

Face recognition in counter terrorism also offers another important benefit in terms of crime prevention and threat detection in general. Contemporary face recognition technology systems are being tethered to behavioral analytics and predictive modeling instruments that predict menacing behavior by parsing human facial expressions, movements, and contextual body activities. By monitoring facial expressions such as stress, agitation, or evasion, these systems can flag security personnel to people who may be a security risk even if they are not yet registered as a criminal in police databases [17]. It can be instrumental in thwarting lone-wolf attacks, suicide attacks, or other forms of violence against crowds.

Real-time alarm systems can add to the preventative capability that face recognition technologies offer. AI-powered surveillance networks are able to instantly alert the appropriate parties in cases a match is made against a watchlist entry, or there are signs of behavior that deviate from the norm in secured premises. If, for instance, a known extremist is spotted walking into a transportation hub or an embassy, the system could quickly zip off alerts through law enforcement networks, prompting lockdowns or surveillance. With the instant notifications urgently needed for quick reaction and response to new dangers to minimize damage and potentially save countless lives.

AI-driven predictive modeling also allows for the prediction of terrorist activities based on historical data, known networks, and trajectories of behavior. Agencies can identify potential hot spots and interventions on the basis of social, geographical, and digital patterns of terrorists and terrorism. The movement from a defensive to proactive security posturing is a significant development in contemporary counterterrorism that conveys strategic advantage over diffuse and adaptive terrorist organizations [18].

4.3 Inter-Agency Coordination and Intelligence Sharing

Facial recognition also has huge potential for better interagency cooperation and collaboration, which is key to effective counterterrorism. Terrorist threats are more and more international in nature, leveraging global transportation, online cloak of anonymity, and local law enforcement's jurisdictional seams. For a comprehensive threat profile, it is therefore crucial to have access to and share such facial data and identification results across borders in real time. FRT systems augmented with AI can be linked to international databases of INTERPOL's facial recognition system, thereby facilitating the real-time verification and tracking of suspects across borders.

Cross-jurisdictional data integration allows for a global response to terrorism. With cross-participation and access to common biometric repositories, multiple nations and agencies can track suspects' movements, identify hidden networks, and coordinate interdiction tactics. With this common intelligence infrastructure, there are no silos among national security agencies, with real-time cooperation possible during crisis. For instance, if the terror suspect flagged in one country is seen boarding a flight in another country, information can be broadcast to border and airport security officials worldwide in seconds to take action.

Facial recognition can also be a tool to improve cooperation among the intelligence and military services, and law enforcement, within a country. Integral agencies like Homeland Security and Immigration, counterintelligence groups, and local PDs can utilize FRT-run synchronized databases designed to aid the coordination of high-profile investigative work or mass-scale missions [19]. This avoids duplication of effort, minimizes blind spots, and encourages evidence-based decision-making. The centralized nature of facial data also helps in evidence building and the judiciary system, where suspect identification and surveillance records need to be accessed across legal and investigation frameworks.

Facial recognition technology integration enables real-time messaging capabilities via smart command and control centers, enabling various agencies' officers to see live surveillance, get alerts, and take action in concert. In the event of joint anti-terror actions, such capabilities make it possible to coordinate their field execution for greater effectiveness and security. The capacity to bring diverse stakeholders together through technology is a strategic advantage in combating complex, networked terrorist threats.

5 Challenges and Limitations: Accuracy and Algorithmic Bias

The capability of facial recognition technology for counterterrorism also confronts a number of significant challenges and limitations that must be critically assessed if it is to be used in a responsible, effective, and equitable manner. Above all, doubts about accuracy and algorithmic bias persist and cast a shadow over the trustworthiness of biometric identification systems: Misidentification and false positives could not only obstruct investigations but also cause untold distress to innocent people, further reducing trust in security agencies.

Research has consistently demonstrated that facial recognition algorithms have higher error rates when analyzing the images of women, older people, and people from certain racial and ethnic groups, impacting those communities disproportionately and exacerbating existing systemic biased discrimination. This bias has been attributed to biased training data, a lack of diversity of those developing algorithms, and the technical challenge of quantifying facial features in diverse populations, which has ethical implications for justice fairness in surveillance technology use. Second, false negatives (a failure to identify actual persons of interest) can seriously hinder the overall effort to maximize the potential to identify threats.

5.1 Data Privacy and Civil Liberties: Mass Surveillance vs Individual Rights

The use of facial recognition also brings vast issues related to privacy and rights. Wide network camera coverage and AI-based analysis are starting to verge into mass surveillance, and there is a real risk of abuse of the fundamental rights of the individual to privacy, anonymity, and freedom of assembly. As its citizens are subject to constant surveillance, there may be a chilling effect on legitimate expression and movement, undermining the democratic principles that the counterterrorism policies are intended to safeguard [20]. The fact that the collection and retention of sensitive biometric information are not subject to sufficient safeguards only serves to compound these fears, especially when proper consent is not given and data retention policies are unclear, and there is no avenue for redress. The transparency principle, purpose limitation, and strict procedural regulation, notably through the requirement for prior authorization by a court or by an independent administrative body, for instance, in the form of independent auditing and clear avenues for individuals to challenge or correct erroneous matches, are necessary, but far from sufficient.

Adding to these ethical and privacy concerns is an inconsistent legal and regulatory landscape with regard to facial recognition from one jurisdiction to another. Some countries have adopted comprehensive laws that govern the use of biometric surveillance explicitly, but other nations have no such laws, leading to a patchwork of regulations that stand in the way of international cooperation and make it difficult to hold anyone accountable. Even in democratic states, data protection laws and human rights agreements were designed before AI surveillance, leaving room for loopholes that adversaries can have filled. With the speed of technological advancements leapfrogging the production of proper digital surveillance laws, the report highlights an urgent demand for modernized legislation that trims privacy abuses without sacrificing law enforcement needs, sets a standard of use, and sanctions abuses when they occur.

5.2 Legal and Regulatory Frameworks: Technological Limitations and Security Threats

There are technological constraints and security concerns that make it challenging to implement facial recognition in counterterrorism operations. Systems are susceptible to spoofing attacks by adversaries using photographs, video images, masks, or even 3D-printed replicas to trick cameras and to more advanced deepfake manipulations that produce realistic but false imagery [21]. These vulnerabilities exist in the integrity of the verification process and require multimodal biometrics, liveness detection, and strong anti-spoofing systems. Furthermore, the employee list of suspected facial templates and watch lists are stored in centralized databases, and they are attractive to cybercriminals as valuable sources of information; when lost to security breaches, the personal information is compromised, resulting in identity theft, illegal on-premises monitoring, and loss of trust in the public.

While facial recognition technology may be extremely valuable for strengthening counterterrorism, it also presents numerous obstacles relating to technical accuracy, fairness of algorithms, privacy protections, legal consistency, and cyber vulnerabilities. Tackling these challenges will require a cross-disciplinary effort in terms of algorithmic testing and validation, diverse data set generation, transparent governance models, strong legal protections, best-in-class anti-spoofing techniques, and encryption [22]. It is only through recognizing and addressing these barriers that politicians and the police can exploit the benefits of AI-driven facial recognition in a way that is effective against shaping terrorism while being respectful of the basic rights of humankind.

6 Policy Recommendations and Best Practices

For the responsible use of FRT for counterterrorism, ensuring the protection of civil rights, a set of best practices under a policy framework is critically needed. One, clear, transparent, and accountable governance structures should be established and implemented. Regulatory frameworks must require transparency in code design, deployment, and use, leading to public trust [22]. Agencies that utilize FRT need to specify why FRT is being deployed, including how and for what purpose, as well as the legal rationale for their use, accompanied by oversight by independent regulators or ethics review bodies. These oversight bodies need the power to inspect FRT systems at regular intervals, enforce compliance with legal standards, and respond to complaints from the public.

Secondly, there must be mandates for new or updated data protection laws to include biometric data, with rigorous regulations on its collection, use, access, and sharing. Positive consent procedures can be bolstered where feasible, especially for civilians. In sensitive counterterrorism situations where active consent may be impossible, strong justifications and judicial or legislative authorizations should be mandated to avoid abuse. Robust encryption, anonymization schemes, and role-based access mechanisms need to be standardized to secure facial information against breach and unauthorized surveillance.

Third, algorithmic transparency and bias reduction should be incorporated within system design and purchasing guidelines. This mandate included the requirement that diverse and representative training datasets be used, regular checks for accuracy of the algorithm on different sex and demographic categories, and metrics must be reported on performance. Governments must promote the co-creation between academics, civil society, and industry stakeholders to calibrate models, exchange best practices, and co-develop inclusive technologies.

The fourth key is context-specific deployment guidance. The use of facial recognition technology should not be used as a mass surveillance tool, but only to support targeted and authorized interventions for a specific legitimate aim. This could include surveillance of persons crossing an international border or persons that are subject to a potential threat. There needs to be a difference in usage principles between real-time surveillance and offline analysis, with the bar higher for real time [23].

Fifth, inter-agency and international interoperability arrangements would need to be strengthened to facilitate the sharing of data in a cross-border context, under consistent conditions of privacy and accountability. Secure conduits for intelligence need to be created, accompanied by shared ethical norms, developing trust and collaboration among jurisdictions. Finally, public involvement and education are key. There also needs to be a campaign to educate people on how FRT is being used, what rights people have, and how they can complain. The open discussion can help legitimize and reduce the fear of the government going too far. Consequently, facial recognition technology deployment tied to ethical principles, human rights standards, and security priorities demands proactive policy, institutional accountability, and continuous technology evolution [24].

7 Conclusion and Future Scope of AI-Facial Recognition Technology in Counterterrorism

The convergence of AI-fueled facial recognition technology with counterterrorism has ushered in an era of data-driven, proactive security; however, this technology takes off across the world certainly lies in balancing technology fast-pacing innovation with ethical stewardship and legal oversight. Indeed, real-time detection and automated threat detection can provide a quantum leap in our situational awareness, our ability to respond, and to take down terrorist networks before attacks are carried out. But the terrain in front of us will require ever more precision trimming false positives and algorithmic bias and durable protections for civil liberties. In the future, it should see advancement toward multimodal biometrics that concatenate facial data together with gait, voice, and behavioral biometrics to form robust and spoof-resistant systems.

New tools, such as explainable AI, will help to clarify the thought processes that result in matches. Simultaneously, global norms and treaties will emerge that will define common norms for data protection, cross-border sharing of intelligence, and accountability enablers. We need regulatory environments that can adapt to change but provide clear legal guidance on deployment, requiring regular assessments and providing recourse to individuals wrongfully identified. Public–private partnerships are vital to nurturing diverse, representative training datasets and to co-producing open-source tools that advance innovation and confidence. As terrorist adversaries develop ever more advanced evasion methods, from adversarial deepfakes to the employment of physical disguise, counterterrorism organizations will have to forge a constant stream of research partnerships with academia and industry in order to keep up with the long and winding threat curve. By embedding it with ethical safeguards, effective legal frameworks, and technological standards from the get-go, it can ensure it reaches its full promise of securing society without sacrificing the democratic values that underpin it.

References

1. Montasari, R. (2024). Analysing ethical, legal, technical and operational challenges of the application of machine learning in countering cyber terrorism. In *Cyberspace, cyberterrorism and the international security in the fourth industrial revolution: Threats, assessment and responses* (pp. 159–197). Springer.
2. Ige, T., Kolade, A., & Kolade, O. (2022). Enhancing border security and countering terrorism through computer vision: A field of artificial intelligence. In *Proceedings of the computational methods in systems and software* (pp. 656–666). Springer.
3. Bondarenko, Y., Svoboda, I., Tkachov, I., Kozenko, O., & Vislovukh, V. (2025). The impact of biometric technologies on the efficiency of terrorist crime investigation. *Salud, Ciencia y Tecnología-Serie de Conferencias, 4*, 1530.
4. Choung, H., David, P., & Ling, T. W. (2024). Acceptance of AI-powered facial recognition technology in surveillance scenarios: Role of trust, security, and privacy perceptions. *Technology in Society, 79*, 102721.
5. Gabrielli, G. (2025). The use of facial recognition technologies in the context of peaceful protest: The risk of mass surveillance practices and the implications for the protection of human rights. *European Journal of Risk Regulation*, 1–28.
6. Vavoula, N. (2021). Artificial intelligence (AI) at schengen borders: Automated processing, algorithmic profiling and facial recognition in the era of techno-solutionism. *European Journal of Migration and Law, 23*(4), 457–484.
7. Smith, M., & Miller, S. (2022). The ethical application of biometric facial recognition technology. *Ai & Society, 37*(1), 167–175.
8. Wall, C. (2025). The ghost in the machine: Counterterrorism in the age of artificial intelligence. *Studies in Conflict & Terrorism*, 1–27.
9. Singh, V. R. Navigating the complexities: AI, security, and liberty at the border. In *Artificial intelligence for cyber security and industry 4.0* (pp. 250–272). CRC Press.
10. Tuteja, V., & Marwaha, S. S. (2023). Artificial intelligence: Threat of terrorism and need for better counter-terrorism efforts. *International Journal of Creative Computing, 2*(1), 87–100.
11. Baig, M. A. A. (2024). Artificial intelligence, emerging technologies and National Security of Pakistan. *CISS Insight Journal, 12*(1), P90–P114.
12. Fussey, P., Davies, B., & Innes, M. (2021). 'Assisted'facial recognition and the reinvention of suspicion and discretion in digital policing. *The British Journal of Criminology, 61*(2), 325–344.
13. Yu, S., & Carroll, F. (2022). Implications of AI in national security: Understanding the security issues and ethical challenges. In *Artificial intelligence in cyber security: Impact and implications: Security challenges, technical and ethical issues, forensic investigative challenges* (pp. 157–175). Springer.
14. Ahmed, S. (2024). The evolution of terrorism: New trends and counterterrorism strategies. *Fari Journal of Global Affairs and Security Studies, 1*(02), 163–174.
15. Dhakal, S., Parvez, A., Das, P., Saxena, S., & Memoria, M. (2024). An analysis of AI-driven technologies for enhancing security along the India-Nepal border. In *2024 International conference on computing, sciences and communications (ICCSC)* (pp. 1–6). IEEE.
16. Kanellopoulos, A. N., & Stavropoulos, D. (2024). Travel intelligence: Enhancing counterterrorism and National Security. *Bulletin of "CAROL I" National Defence University, 13*(1), 80–93.
17. Ritter, A., & Harbecke, J. (2024). Counter-terrorism: The risk of performativity in big data-based mass surveillance. *Studies in Conflict & Terrorism*, 1–18.
18. Matthew, U. O., Kazaure, J. S., Onyebuchi, A., Daniel, O. O., Muhammed, I. H., & Okafor, N. U. (2021). Artificial intelligence autonomous unmanned aerial vehicle (UAV) system for remote sensing in security surveillance. In *2020 IEEE 2nd international conference on Cyberspac (CYBER Nigeria)* (pp. 1–10). IEEE.
19. Saheb, T. (2023). Ethically contentious aspects of artificial intelligence surveillance: A social science perspective. *AI and Ethics, 3*(2), 369–379.

20. Utkina, M. (2023). Digital identification and financial monitoring: New technologies in the fight against crime. *Scientific Journal of Polonia University, 58*(3), 303–308.
21. Machado, H., & Silva, S. (2025). Navigating the complex landscape of facial recognition technologies. In *Ethical assemblages of artificial intelligence: Controversies, uncertainties, and networks* (pp. 15–72). Springer Nature.
22. Lubin, K. L., & Fan, L. T. (2025). Rethinking the rhetoric of surveillance in public safety: A critical discourse analysis. In *Future of information and communication conference* (pp. 657–677). Springer Nature.
23. Fletcher, A. (2023). Government surveillance and facial recognition in Australia: A human rights analysis of recent developments. *Griffith Law Review, 32*(1), 30–61.
24. Schuetz, P. N. (2021). Fly in the face of bias: Algorithmic bias in law enforcement's facial recognition technology and the need for an adaptive legal framework. *Minnesota Journal of Law & Inequality, 39*, 221.

AI-Driven Predictive Analytics for Threat Assessment

Hemant Singh, Abhishek Bishnoi, and Saurabh Chandra

Abstract The threats to national as well as international security have changed in the quickly changing digital landscape of today and have become more dispersed, unpredictable, and technologically sophisticated. Even though they are still useful, the traditional intelligence techniques are frequently too slow or have a narrow focus to handle contemporary issues such as terrorism and radicalization. Artificial intelligence, particularly in the form of predictive analytics, becomes a potent instrument for proactive measures. This chapter elaborates on how AI-powered predictive analytics is changing and how security and law enforcement organizations recognize, evaluate, and address crucial threats before they become violent or terrorist acts. Predictive analytics is the process of forecasting future events using both historical and current data. This method enables the analysis of enormous datasets from a variety of sources, including financial transactions, communication logs, social media activity, and travel history, when paired with AI's enormous capabilities. The algorithms for machine learning are taught to spot trends, abnormalities, and possible warning signs of dangerous behavior. The authorities can use these insights to make well-informed decisions about resource allocation, who to keep a closer eye on, and proactive threat response. This chapter provides a very comprehensive overview of the technical base of predictive analytics, which includes data collection, data preprocessing, feature engineering, modeling, and deployment. As it mainly explains the commonly used machine learning algorithms, like the support vector machines, decision trees, and neural networks, both technical and nontechnical readers will find it convenient to understand.

H. Singh (✉) · A. Bishnoi
Amity Law School, Amity University, Gwalior, Madhya Pradesh, India

S. Chandra
School of Law, Bennett University, Greater Noida, Uttar Pradesh, India

C. Kaunert et al. (eds.), *Artificial Intelligence for Global Counter-Terrorism*, Contributions to Security and Defence Studies,
https://doi.org/10.1007/978-3-031-99235-3_12

1 Introduction

Adaptive, dynamic, and intelligence-led tactics have always been necessary in the global fight against terrorism. Terrorist threats have changed significantly in recent years, becoming more complex, dispersed, and integrated with technology. Artificial intelligence (AI) has become a game-changer in response to this changing threat landscape, revolutionizing how national and international security frameworks detect, track, and eliminate threats before they become serious crises. The actual case studies from countries such as the United States and the United Kingdom are included to show how these tools have already been used with measurable success.

One of the fundamental topics of this chapter is the integration of predictive analytics with other AI technologies, including computer vision, facial recognition, and natural language processing (NLP). The moment it is combined, these systems can recognize dangers and also understand communication patterns and the behavioral indicators that may indicate radicalization or the planning of serious crimes. However, using such powerful tools raises significant ethical and legal concerns. The issues of algorithmic bias, data security, privacy, and government accountability are critically examined. The chapter also lays emphasis on the comprehensive approach that combines technological innovation, robust oversight, and democratic ideals.

It also discusses new developments in this field, including federated learning, explainable AI, and the use of blockchain technology for safe data sharing. The chapter ends by highlighting the fact that although AI will never completely replace human judgment, it can be an essential collaborator in creating security frameworks that are more intelligent and responsive. The ultimate goal of this chapter is to demystify predictive analytics powered by AI in relation to counterterrorism. In order to make our world a safer place, without sacrificing the civil liberties that characterize democratic societies, it aims to educate academics, decision-makers, and practitioners about the potential, constraints, and responsible application of AI.

Artificial intelligence is the imitation of human intelligence in machines that can think, learn, and adapt on their own or with some degree of autonomy. Predictive analytics—a field that uses historical and current data, statistical methods, and machine learning algorithms to reasonably predict future events—is one of the most promising areas of artificial intelligence in the security space [1]. Predictive analytics is more than just a tool for calculating numbers when it comes to counterterrorism; it is a proactive tool that helps security agencies foresee possible threats and take preventative rather than reactive action. Traditional threat analysis techniques are severely challenged by the massive amount of data generated every second in the digital age, whether from social media, surveillance footage, financial transactions, GPS records, or telecommunications. Regardless of their level of expertise, human analysts face time constraints, cognitive limitations, and the ever-increasing complexity of data environments. The AI, however, thrives on this kind of complexity. Its actual processing and the analysis of large datasets provide it a significant edge for spotting correlations, patterns, and the anomalies which might otherwise go overlooked [2].

The ability of AI-driven predictive analytics to reveal and predict possible terrorist activity based on the observable precursors and behavioral signals makes it very important. For instance, AI can track financial transactions that may point to the funding of illegal activities, monitor the travel habits of suspected individuals, and also analyze communication patterns to identify radicalization processes [3]. By this thing, it will enable governments and the intelligence to prioritize high-risk matters, reduce false alarms, and also deploy resources timely and properly.

An in-depth examination of the relationship between AI, predictive analytics, and counterterrorism is the goal of this chapter. It starts by outlining the fundamentals of predictive analytics, including how data is gathered, preprocessed, and modeled for threat assessment. The importance of big data in enabling AI systems to operate at scale is then emphasized, especially in high-stakes settings such as national security. This chapter also explores the numerous machine learning methods, including support vector machines, decision trees, and neural networks, including how they are used in actual counterterrorism operations. To illustrate the concrete effects of the above-mentioned technologies, real-world incidents from the general public and the commercial intelligence domains are analyzed. However, there are certain serious ethical, legal, and human rights issues with using AI in counterterrorism, just like with any other super powerful tool. It is even necessary to critically assess the concerns about algorithmic bias, data privacy, surveillance overreach, and the opaque AI decision-making processes. To address these issues, this chapter highlights the keen necessity of transparent policy frameworks, accountability systems, and public oversight.

Governments can transition from reactive policing to preventive intelligence tactics by incorporating AI into their current threat assessment architectures. In a world where missed signals can have disastrous consequences, this change is essential. However, it is equally important to make sure that this technological revolution upholds democratic principles and doesn't jeopardize the very liberties it is meant to defend. This chapter concludes by making the case that AI-driven predictive analytics presents a game-changing chance to improve the precision, velocity, and strategic importance of counterterrorism operations. However, a well-balanced synergy between innovation, regulation, and human judgment is necessary for the successful and moral application of these technologies. In addition to being academically necessary, this interdisciplinary approach is morally required to protect civil liberties and national security.

1.1 Foundations of Predictive Analytics

The ability to look beyond the present and to make educated assumptions about the future is invaluable in a world where digital information is shaping things more and more. This is very true when it comes to matters that are important as national and international security. This is exactly what predictive analytics, a subfield of data science and artificial intelligence, is for. It is used to help a lot of organizations, especially those in the intelligence and security sectors, to shift from reactive to proactive decision-making after analyzing a huge amount of historical and real-time data.

Predictive analytics is the process of analyzing current and historical trends in order to forecast certain future outcomes by using statistical methods, machine learning models, and data mining techniques [4]. This method is successful, particularly in the areas of counterterrorism, where understanding the subtle patterns that precede certain violent events and can also make the difference between tragedy and prevention. The security agencies can now use the predictive tools to spot suspicious associations or risky behavior before any actual harm occurs, instead of waiting for threats to materialize. There are certain possible practical uses for predictive analytics in counterterrorism. These tools are now started to be used by governments across the world as main part of their intelligence operations. For example, based on a person's travel habits, online communications, or ties to known terrorist networks, predictive models can be used to determine the likelihood that they will participate in extremist activities [5].

1.2 Key Components

A multistep process is necessary for predictive analytics to be effective, with each step adding to the final predictive model's accuracy and dependability. The following are the steps:

Data collection: Raw data is collected from various sources at this foundational stage. This information can be unstructured (such as tweets, emails, voice recordings, or surveillance footage) or structured (such as official travel documents or financial transactions) when it comes to counterterrorism. This wealth of data is frequently gathered using social media scraping tools, satellite imagery, intercepted communications, and open-source intelligence [6].

It frequently includes irrelevant information, missing values, or inconsistencies. Cleaning this data, transforming it into a format that can be used, and making sure it follows a standard structure that makes additional analysis easier are all part of preprocessing. This phase is critical since the accuracy of predictive results is directly impacted by the quality of the data.

Feature engineering: Data science and domain expertise meet at this stage. In order for the predictive model to make decisions, analysts choose or produce particular variables, also referred to as features. Features could include, for instance, frequent trips to high-risk areas, the use of encrypted messaging services, or abrupt shifts in financial behavior in a context involving terrorism.

Modeling: Machine learning algorithms are trained on the data after features have been chosen in order to identify trends and produce predictions. The type of data, the performance objectives, and the nature of the problem all influence the algorithm selection.

Validation and deployment: A model needs to be thoroughly validated using different data sets before it can be used with confidence in real-world operations. This aids in confirming the accuracy and dependability of the model's predictions.

Following successful testing, the model is put into use; it is frequently incorporated into larger operational systems that are utilized by military intelligence or law enforcement agencies [7].

All of these elements work together to create a continuous feedback loop in which models are updated and improved on a regular basis in response to fresh information and changing threat patterns.

1.3 Algorithms Commonly Used

The algorithms at the heart of analytics are what give it its predictive power. The correct algorithm can make all the difference in counterterrorism, where data may be noisy, lacking, or extremely sensitive. In this field, the following algorithms are frequently used:

Decision trees: These straightforward but effective models divide data into branches according to predetermined criteria. They are helpful for fast classification tasks and are simple to understand.

Random forests: To increase accuracy and avoid overfitting, this ensemble learning technique constructs several decision trees and aggregates their outputs, especially efficient with high-dimensional data.

Support vector machines (SVM): These models are perfect for classification tasks, particularly when there is a small difference between two categories (such as threat and nonthreat). They need to be carefully adjusted, but they work well in high-dimensional spaces.

Neural networks: These models, which draw inspiration from the human brain, can recognize intricate, nonlinear patterns. When it comes to image recognition and natural language processing tasks, like identifying radical speech online or evaluating surveillance footage, deep neural networks are especially helpful.

Gradient boosting machines (GBMs): A technique that builds models one after the other, fixing the mistakes of the earlier models. Although these models frequently attain high accuracy, handling them carefully is necessary to prevent overfitting.

The algorithm selection is not universal. Data volume, label availability, processing power, and the output's necessary interpretability are some of the variables that affect it. Since analysts and decision-makers must comprehend why a model identified a specific person or activity as a threat, interpretability is frequently just as crucial as accuracy in intelligence settings [8].

2 The Role of Big Data in Counterterrorism

The battle against terrorism is no longer fought only on actual battlefields in the digital age. It increasingly occurs in the virtual world, where enormous volumes of data are constantly being created, gathered, and examined. Big data's emergence has transformed counterterrorism tactics by making it possible to glean valuable insights from vast amounts of intricate data. Artificial intelligence (AI) and machine learning (ML) systems, especially those that use predictive analytics to detect and lessen terrorist threats, rely on big data as their fundamental fuel.

Big data is not just about having "a lot" of data; it's also about managing data that has distinctive qualities, or what are known as the 5Vs: volume, velocity, variety, veracity, and value [9]. These components work together to define the opportunities and difficulties associated with using big data in national security operations.

Volume represents the vast amount of data produced every second, including biometric logs, surveillance footage, satellite photos, and internet activity.

Velocity emphasizes how quickly new data is generated and needs to be processed; in many cases, real-time analysis is crucial to averting impending dangers.

Variety encompasses a range of data formats, including voice recordings, videos, images, unstructured text, and structured databases.

Data accuracy and trustworthiness are addressed by veracity; inaccurate or misleading data can undermine intelligence operations.

Value highlights how crucial it is to glean useful insights from otherwise useless bulk data.

By using big data strategically, counterterrorism agencies can move from passive monitoring to active threat anticipation. Authorities can identify hidden relationships, odd behavioral patterns, or geographic movements that indicate terrorist activity by connecting disparate data points across systems and domains.

2.1 Data Sources in Counterterrorism

As varied as the threats themselves are the kinds of information that are pertinent to counterterrorism initiatives. Agencies use a variety of data sources to present a complete picture. Among the most important sources are:

Intelligence reports: These comprise global counterterrorism databases, informant reports, field intelligence, and declassified data. These reports serve as the foundation for strategic threat assessment and are frequently improved by text analytics powered by AI.

Financial transactions: Tracking questionable financial practices, like regular cash deposits, money transfers to high-risk jurisdictions, or the use of cryptocurrencies, frequently aids in the identification of terrorist financing networks [10].

Travel records: When compared to known watchlists or unusual travel patterns, passenger name records (PNR), visa logs, and customs databases aid in tracking down suspects' movements across international borders.

Mobile communications: Networks of interaction can be uncovered through call logs, SMS data, and encrypted messaging app usage. Even though these communications' content is frequently protected, metadata by itself can yield a lot of intelligence [6].

Posts on social media: Propaganda and radicalization have flourished on social networking sites. To identify extremist content or recruitment attempts, AI models examine text, photos, videos, and network connections [11].

Biometric information: For real-time identity verification and border security, fingerprints, voice prints, iris scans, and facial recognition information are being utilized more and more. By connecting aliases, biometric data integration helps stop terrorists from using false identities.

When combined, these data sources provide a thorough picture of possible risks. Before an act of violence takes place, predictive analytics systems trained on such data can identify subtle abnormalities, such as a person whose social, travel, and financial behaviors deviate from the norm.

2.2 *Challenges in Big Data Management*

Big data in counterterrorism poses a number of operational and moral difficulties despite its revolutionary potential. If data-driven threat prediction is to be precise, compliant with the law, and deemed acceptable by society, these issues need to be resolved.

Agencies' data silos: The fragmentation of data across different law enforcement and intelligence agencies is one of the biggest obstacles. Different agencies frequently possess complementary pieces of the puzzle, but they lack the necessary infrastructure or legal authorizations to effectively share information. Missed opportunities and real-time threat detection are hampered by this lack of interoperability [12].

Privacy and legal restrictions: Civil liberties and the vigorous pursuit of terrorist threats frequently collide. Concerns regarding privacy rights and possible data misuse have been raised by intrusive surveillance, illegal data collection, and the use of facial recognition in public areas. Agencies must carefully navigate the stringent boundaries imposed by legal frameworks such as the General Data Protection Regulation (GDPR) in the European Union [13].

Noise and data quality: Not all data has any value. A sizable amount of big data might be purposefully misleading, out-of-date, or irrelevant. Analytical models may be distorted and false positives or missed threats may result from poor data quality, which can be caused by incomplete records, duplication, or misinformation. Thus, maintaining data integrity is crucial.

Combining diverse data formats: Structured databases, PDFs, handwritten notes, and video files are just a few examples of the incompatible formats in which data gathered from various systems frequently exists. It takes a large technological investment in data fusion methods and interoperable platforms to integrate these into a single framework [14].

Big data is now a vital component of contemporary counterterrorism tactics. Although it promises data-driven, pre-emptive security, its full potential requires careful handling, moral protections, and a strong infrastructure.

3 Applications in Threat Assessment

When incorporated into predictive analytics frameworks, artificial intelligence (AI) has greatly improved the accuracy and promptness of counterterrorism operations. Threat assessments have historically mainly depended on human intuition and intelligence analysis conducted after the fact. These techniques, however, are reactive and frequently too sluggish to anticipate attacks. This paradigm is currently being altered by AI-powered predictive models, which make it possible to take a more proactive and data-driven approach to detecting and eliminating terrorist threats before they become real [1].

Predictive analytics is used in threat assessment to examine big, complex datasets, such as social media posts, travel logs, financial transactions, and behavioral patterns. The algorithms, by using artificial intelligence (AI), have been trained to recognize warning signs or subtle clues that may be imperceptible to human analysts but indicate hostile activity. Instead of focusing on identifying individual anomalies, these models connect the dots all across the data sources to predict where, when, and how a terrorist act may occur.

By merging historical attack data with real-time intelligence inputs, AI systems are able to identify patterns between past incidents and current warning indicators. This would help the law enforcement agencies to better allocate resources, concentrate surveillance, and promptly implement the preventative measures, apart from improving the accuracy of threat assessments.

3.1 Case Studies

The practical application of AI in threat forecasting is made clearer by a number of real-world examples that shed light on the tools, strategies, and successes of predictive analytics in national security.

Department of Homeland Security (DHS) at the United States.

The US Department of Homeland Security (DHS) has taken the lead in applying AI and machine learning tools to prevent the domestic infrastructure, especially public transportation setups. The use of the predictive modeling system for assessing the risks to airports, subway systems, and other mass transit hubs is one of its primary initiatives. These technologies look at the past terrorist activity, online chatter, crowd density, and seasonal trends to predict the potential attack scenarios [15]. To prevent or intercept any kind of threats, a huge number of security guards, and surveillance gear are made available in case the system detects a high-risk zone.

UK's MI5 and GCHQ

MI5 and the Government Communications Headquarters (GCHQ) of the United Kingdom use the AI tools to detect radicalization trends and to prevent domestic extremism. These systems work on sentiment analysis and natural language processing (NLP) to search digital communications, such as emails, forum posts, and social media feeds, for signs of ideological shift or extremist intent [16]. One of the famous illustrations was thwarting a bombing attempt in Manchester after the machine identified the crucial and abnormal changes in a suspect's online activity while they were being surreptitiously watched. The AI integration made the key authorities to intervene in the plan. These examples highlight the increasing importance of machine-driven threat forecasting in national security and demonstrate how predictive analytics can convert scattered intelligence into useful foresight.

3.2 Techniques Applied

The accuracy and efficacy of AI-driven threat assessments rely on the specific analytical techniques employed. These methods are chosen based on the threat type, data availability, and the intelligence operation's goals. Some of the most widely used techniques are:

Temporal Analysis

This approach is centered on predicting the possible times of terrorist attacks. By examining the temporal patterns of past attacks, such as spikes in activity around significant anniversaries, elections, or religious events, AI models can forecast likely times of increased threat. Time-series data forecasting, seasonal analysis, and clustering techniques are used for determining when vigilance should be raised [17].

Spatial Analysis

Spatial analysis assists in discovering geographic hotspots that are more vulnerable to attacks. To identify regions with higher risk profiles, AI systems are fed geolocation data, demographic data, crime statistics, and infrastructure mapping. In many cases, predictive models even pinpoint particular government buildings, transit routes, or urban areas to be probable targets [18].

Behavioral Profiling

One of the most sophisticated and controversial applications of AI in threat assessment is behavioral profiling. This means creating baseline profiles of individuals or groups and emphasizing any changes that could indicate imminent radicalization or malevolence. Examples of behavioral data include travel and purchasing patterns, online activity, and even subtle psychological indicators that manifest in language use. Without precise definitions of what constitutes a "threat," unsupervised learning algorithms allow systems to recognize unusual activity, enabling dynamic adaptation as terrorist tactics evolve [19].

AI-driven threat assessment is no longer just a theoretical concept; it is actively influencing how nations protect their citizens. From identifying the probable time and location of attacks to identifying radicalization trends before they escalate into violence, AI applications are expanding the breadth and depth of intelligence operations. However, these powerful tools also raise ethical issues, particularly with regard to openness, privacy, and bias. The potential of AI to anticipate and stop terrorism is one of the most intriguing aspects of modern security strategy, despite the fact that these problems still need to be fixed.

4 Integration with Other Technologies

Even though predictive analytics has a lot of power on its own, it can accomplish much more when combined with other state-of-the-art artificial intelligence (AI) technologies. In the complex and extremely competitive field of counterterrorism, no single tool can offer any effective solution. The integration allows the predictive systems to access the richest, most diverse data sources and also to conduct multi-dimensional analyses, which is way more useful than standalone predictive models. Even after the complexity and the adaptability of contemporary terrorism, these collaborative functionings are especially more significant. To evade detection, extremists usually use coded language or alter their tactics or uses new technologies. By integrating predictive analytics with computer vision, the recognition of faces and natural language processing (NLP), safety measures may raise the situational awareness in the real-time environments, which can also lower the gaps in data interpretation and expedite response times [1].

4.1 Natural Language Processing (NLP)

The modern counterterrorism initiatives must include natural language processing (NLP), especially when it is incorporated in the predictive analytics engines. After converting the unstructured text into a structured format, it is then appropriate for algorithmic analysis. Natural language processing (NLP) enables the machines to process, comprehend, and provide human-like language. This entails searching via vast amounts of textual data, like private messages, extremist manifestos, online posts, and also the deep web, for trends in radicalization recruitment and also threat indicators in the context of counterterrorism [20].

One of the keen features of NLP is its ability to realize coded words, euphemisms, and metaphors that terrorist organizations commonly use to conceal their communications. NLP tools can be trained to identify new symbols that are associated with the development of terrorist jargon or violent extremism. Sentiment analysis, which is a subfield of natural language processing, is also commonly used to detect instances of conflict or incitement of violence, as well as to assess the psychological climate of online discourse.

Governments and intelligence agencies use NLP-driven technologies such as entity recognition and topic modeling for sifting through hundreds of millions of posts on platforms such as Twitter, Telegram, and Reddit. These tools are used to promote faster identification of threats by flagging potentially harmful content for review. Also, when it is combined with the geolocation tagging, NLP becomes a powerful tool for anticipating circumstances where violent rhetoric could turn into a violent action.

4.2 Computer Vision

The computer vision, which enables the machines to understand and assess visual data from the real world is another state-of-the-art technology in counterterrorism analytics. When it is combined with surveillance systems, this technology will particularly be useful for keeping an eye on key public areas, for identifying odd activity, and for following movement patterns that may point to terrorists' preoperational planning [21].

Convolutional neural networks, also known as CNNs, along with other deep learning architectures, are used by computer vision systems to extract pertinent features from live camera feeds, video, and images. These systems are enabled to detect actions such as loitering, excessive pacing, leaving luggage unattended, or gaining unauthorized access that may lead to any attack. When such particular behavior is detected, the system may use predictive analytics models to decide if it needs to be looked into further or be addressed immediately.

The speed and scale of computer vision are its true advantages. Artificial intelligence (AI)-powered surveillance systems can simultaneously monitor thousands of video feeds and have the ability to replace human operators, as they may miss any important details because of fatigue or blind spots, which will ensure continuous vigilance throughout entire cities or high-risk areas. Dynamic risk scoring, which is used to rate people according to their behavior in real time and in the context of their surroundings, is only made possible by the combination of computer vision and predictive analytics. This data-driven approach will improve threat detection objectivity and also lessen dependency on racial profiling [22].

4.3 Facial Recognition

One of the most contentious but unquestionably effective weapons in the fight against terrorism is facial recognition technology. Real-time identity verification is possible when combined with predictive analytics, particularly in busy places like airports, government buildings, and sizable public gatherings. The system can immediately notify authorities of the presence of high-risk individuals by scanning facial features and comparing them with centralized databases, such as immigration databases, criminal records, and watchlists [23]. Facial recognition adds an extra degree of security without requiring direct interaction, in contrast to traditional identity checks that depend on paperwork or physical presence. For instance, facial recognition technology is now used by many nations at airport entry points to identify people who are on international no-fly lists or who are using false identities.

Apart from identifying the preknown threats, predictive analytics enabled facial recognition systems that can also dynamically update risk profiles. The facial recognition system will be more sensitive to the appearance of an unflagged individual in various locations, if he begins to travel suspiciously, tries to associate with known extremists, or if he frequently appears in high-risk areas. With assurance of this, the system will adapt to new data, and by this feedback loop, the predictive engine will be strengthened. To guarantee such responsible deployment, a strict oversight procedure and the open use guidelines must strictly be put in place. Predictive analytics, combined with computer vision, facial recognition, and natural language processing, forms a potent technological triad in the fight against terrorism. Such synergy greatly speeds up our reaction times, also enhances situational awareness, and will definitely enable real-time threat detection. As terrorist threats increase, simultaneously so do the sophistication and flexibility of the instruments employed to counter the same.

5 Ethical and Legal Considerations

Artificial intelligence (AI) and predictive analytics have revolutionary potential in countering terrorism, but their use is plagued with moral dilemmas and legal issues. Such concerns are not just theoretical, but they also have a direct bearing on the civil liberties, human rights, and foundations of democratic accountability. While assessing the effectiveness or the importance of AI-based systems, it is even more important to take into account the risks of prejudice, excessive surveillance, and unrestricted technological power. Nowadays, personal data is routinely mined and profited from "without informed consent" because of the "surveillance capitalism" [24]. These tensions have become even more evident in national security contexts as the delicate balance between safety and liberty has become shakier. The three main moral dilemmas discussed in this section, that is, privacy, algorithmic bias, and accountability, need to be given immediate focus by policymakers, technologists, and the civil society.

5.1 Privacy Concerns

Predictive analytics commonly uses data collected from multiple sources, including emails, phone metadata, biometric identifiers, GPS tracking, online activity, and posts on social media. When these technologies are used without adequate safeguards, it could amount to mass surveillance and jeopardize the right to privacy guaranteed by national constitutions and international human rights frameworks (Warren & Brandeis, 1890; UN Human Rights Council, 2014) [25].

One major issue is that people frequently don't realize they are being watched or how their information is being used. Even if a person has not revealed sensitive personal information, AI systems may still be able to deduce it, including sexual orientation, political views, and religious affiliation. Concerns about data misuse, power abuse, and lack of informed consent are brought up by this "invisible profiling."

Comprehensive data governance frameworks are required to mitigate these risks. These frameworks ought to specify in detail what kinds of information can be gathered and in what situations, who can access the information, how long it can be kept on file, and what oversight procedures are in place. Additionally, whenever feasible, personal data should be encrypted and anonymized, and people should have control over how their data is used [26].

5.2 Algorithmic Bias

Algorithmic bias is another serious ethical concern that, if left unchecked, can result in discriminatory actions. The quality of the data that predictive models are trained on determines how well they perform. The resulting AI system will probably reinforce or even magnify historical biases, institutional prejudices, or underrepresented demographics reflected in the training datasets. For example, if historical police data indicates that a specific ethnic group has been disproportionately arrested, the AI model might interpret that pattern as a predictor of future criminal activity, which could result in unwarranted surveillance or incorrect profiling of innocent people [27].

Such biases have operational as well as ethical repercussions. False positives that waste investigative resources can arise from misidentifying or over policing marginalized communities, which can also damage public confidence and undermine security efforts.

A multifaceted strategy is needed to address bias:

Transparency in model development: Developers are required to record the data sources they used, the presumptions they made when choosing features, and any known model limitations.

Fairness audits: To check for unequal effects across gender, race, religion, and other protected categories, independent audits ought to be carried out on a regular basis.

Inclusive datasets: Information must be curated to address known imbalances and represent the population's diversity.

5.3 Accountability and Oversight

The issue of accountability is among the most important legal issues in AI-driven decision-making. If a law enforcement response, like an arrest, a no-fly listing, or an immigration denial, is triggered by a predictive model that flags a potential threat, who bears the responsibility if the prediction proves to be incorrect? Who carried out the action: the algorithm creator, the data scientist, the government organization, or the end user? Serious repercussions could happen without anyone being held accountable if there are unclear lines of accountability.

Several legal measures are required to guarantee the responsible use of predictive analytics:

Regulatory frameworks that establish guidelines for risk assessments, specify acceptable applications of AI in security contexts, and forbid the application of inexplicable models in high-stakes situations.

Requirements for transparency, such as people's right to know when decisions involving AI have an impact on them (as in the EU's General Data Protection Regulation Article 22) [28].

Independent oversight organizations charged with examining the use and results of AI systems in national security, such as parliamentary or judicial committees.

These organizations ought to have the authority to look into complaints, carry out impact analyses, and suggest changes that would safeguard civil liberties without jeopardizing justifiable security concerns. The ethical legal concerns regarding AI in countering terrorism are not merely incidental but are also essential to the legitimacy and effectiveness of these concerned technologies. If these technologies are not controlled, then it has the potential to violate basic fundamental rights, also can marginalize vulnerable groups, and even erode public trust. Although if the proactive measures take place, then the AI can be created and applied in ways that can surely uphold the democratic principles while improving the national security.

6 Policy and Strategic Implications

There are certain significant policy opportunities and challenges that are associated with the integration of artificial intelligence (AI) and predictive analytics in countering terrorism strategies. The government has to manage a very complicated environment, where the technological advancements coexist parallel to human rights, national security, and international cooperation. To realize AI's full potential and to make sure that it aligns with the democratic values, legal requirements, and ethical standards, as desired, then a robust and progressive policy framework shall definitely be needed. If we want to assist policymakers in using AI in a responsible manner in countering terrorism, then this section will provide a summary of some of the important legal frameworks and the strategic recommendations.

6.1 Legal Frameworks

A very clear legal framework founded on domestic as well as global commitments, which is necessary for AI security and for its functioning. The international human rights law and the national cybersecurity and data protection regulations are two of the major legal considerations that apply to this particular situation.

International Human Rights Law

International instruments such as the International Covenant on Civil and Political Rights (ICCPR) and the regional human rights treaties also place a high priority on nondiscrimination, freedom of expression, and privacy protection. Article 17 of the ICCPR protects the "right to be protected from willful or illegal invasions of privacy" [29]. Any such state surveillance or data processing, especially via AI-driven methods, has to meet the tests of legality, necessity, and proportionality (UN Human Rights Committee, 2014) [30]. Additionally, private sector actors (such as AI developers and contractors) are required by the UN Guiding Principles on Business and Human Rights to refrain from violating human rights and to offer remedies when harm is caused [31].

National Cybersecurity and Data Protection Laws

Domestic laws that specify the collection, processing, and storage of personal data include the General Data Protection Regulation (GDPR) of the European Union, the CLOUD Act of the United States, and the Digital Personal Data Protection Act of 2023 of India. Any counterterrorism AI strategy must include consent, transparency, accountability, and redress mechanisms, as these laws highlight.

Without comprehensive data protection laws, nations run the risk of unrestricted surveillance and excessive algorithmic influence, especially when using predictive systems to target or profile individuals.

6.2 Strategic Recommendations

The following strategic policy directions are advised in order to guarantee the ethical and successful application of AI in counterterrorism:

Foster Cross-Agency Data Sharing Under Strict Protocols

For predictive analytics to be effective, security, intelligence, immigration, financial, and law enforcement agencies must share accurate and timely data. To avoid data misuse or unauthorized access, however, such interoperability needs to be controlled by stringent legal procedures, role-based access controls, and interagency memoranda of understanding (MOUs) [32].

Only the data required for particular analytical tasks should be shared, so privacy-by-design guidelines and data minimization techniques should be used.

Invest in AI Literacy and Training for Law Enforcement

A commensurate investment in human capacity building is necessary for the ethical and successful deployment of AI systems.

This entails educating law enforcement officers on:

Recognizing AI's limitations (such as bias risks and false positives).

Responsibly interpreting model outputs.

Dealing with moral conundrums when using predictive surveillance.

To create cross-disciplinary knowledge bases, policing agencies must also collaborate closely with data scientists, legal professionals, and civil society organizations [33].

Promote International Cooperation for Transnational Threats

As a transnational threat, terrorism frequently cuts across national boundaries, legal systems, and jurisdictions. In areas like standardizing data formats and threat typologies, exchanging best practices in AI governance, and creating multilateral frameworks for accountability in cross-border AI deployments, international cooperation is essential. Emerging international standards in this area are exemplified by initiatives such as the Council of Europe's Convention 108+ on data protection and INTERPOL's AI-driven threat intelligence programs [34]. The Global Counterterrorism Forum (GCTF) and the United Nations Office of Counter-Terrorism (UNOCT) are two multilateral forums that ought to make AI governance a top priority in order to find a balance between security innovation and human rights compliance.

More than just modern technology is required for the subsequent years; ethical consciousness, precise legal guidance, and deliberate policy foresight are also necessary. Only in a framework that respects fundamental liberties, boosts public confidence, and fosters global brotherhood can AI realize its revolutionary potential in counterterrorism. The ability of states to maintain equal levels of security and liberty will be the ultimate test of success for those deploying AI-based solutions.

7 Future Directions

As AI advances, it has the potential to completely alter counterterrorism initiatives. As predictive analytics, already a key element of threat assessment, becomes more transparent, decentralized, and secure, a new era of accountable and responsible intelligence operations is expected to dawn. But realizing this promise requires the careful use of state-of-the-art AI methods supported by strict moral and legal standards.

This section outlines three key technological trends that will likely influence the advancement of predictive analytics in counterterrorism.

7.1 Explainable AI (XAI)

One of the most pressing problems with the application of AI in national security contexts is the "black box" problem, which is the inability to understand or explain how AI models render their predictions. The absence of interpretability could undermine legal compliance, accountability, and public trust, especially when AI outputs influence crucial choices like pre-emptive surveillance or arrests. Explainable AI (XAI) asks for to address this challenge by developing algorithms that provide easy-to-understand explanations for their output. (Gunning, 2017) [35]. In the counterterrorism domain, XAI can help ensure that: Judicial oversight bodies are able to audit AI-based decisions; operators comprehend the reasoning behind threat scores or behavioral flags; and impacted parties have a channel for challenge and redress. XAI facilitates human-in-the-loop systems, which reduce the possibility of false positives or incorrect profiling by combining human judgment with machine reasoning.

7.2 Federated Learning

In counterterrorism, data centralization presents serious risks because it not only makes sensitive data more susceptible to breaches but also leads to ethical and legal snags, especially when cross-border data sharing is involved. Federated learning presents a strong substitute. Without moving raw data to a central server, this machine learning technique enables algorithms to be trained across several decentralized data sources (such as various intelligence agencies or jurisdictions) [36]. Sharing only model updates rather than the actual data allows for collaborative intelligence building while protecting privacy.

In counterterrorism, federated learning allows for:

Multiagency collaboration while adhering to local data protection regulations.

Quicker model adaptation to local threats without jeopardizing national security data.

Lessor chance of widespread surveillance by controlling unnecessary data exposure.

7.3 Integration with Blockchain Technology

The application of blockchain technology is another development in predictive analytics. The blockchain technology is well-known for its decentralization, transparency, and immutability; it can improve the auditability and integrity of the data transactions in any deliciated situations. The verifiable and tamper-proof international data sharing is also made possible only by blockchain technology, particularly through the smart contracts and the zero-knowledge proofs. It also guarantees that only those authorized have access to critical records as it will track the main source of data inputs, which are used in predictive models, and which aid in identifying and also correcting bias. By providing an automated, thrustless layer of accountability, blockchain integration can reduce bureaucratic friction and contribute to developing international trust in collaborative counterterrorism efforts.

Increasing technological complexity is just one component of the future of AI-powered predictive analytics in counterterrorism; another is incorporating these advancements into an open, safe, and ethically sound ecosystem. The next 10 years will be an important opportunity for policymakers, technologists, and legal scholars to work together in creating the frameworks that will define AI's legacy in the area of international security.

8 Conclusion

Predictive analytics powered by artificial intelligence (AI) represents a revolutionary change in the way that counterterrorism is approached globally. Security and intelligence organizations are no longer limited to reactive tactics because they can now use enormous amounts of structured and unstructured data, such as travel logs, biometric databases, online communications, and financial transactions, to proactively detect, evaluate, and neutralize possible threats before they become real [1].

This change is strategic rather than just technological. With the help of machine learning, deep learning, and natural language processing, predictive models can analyze patterns that human analysts would otherwise be unable to see. The effectiveness of these tools in identifying early indicators of radicalization and impending plots has already been shown by organizations such as the US Department of Homeland Security and MI5 [37]. Preparation and resource allocation have been significantly improved by the ability to predict the when, where, and how of a potential terrorist act. This evolution does, however, come with risks and complications. If left unchecked, the very qualities that make AI so potent, its ability to analyze data quickly, automate tasks, and make decisions in real time, can also raise serious ethical, legal, and societal issues. These include concerns about algorithmic bias, discriminatory profiling, privacy erosion, and the opaqueness of automated decision-making [24].

Here also exists an issue of legitimacy and accountability. Apart from the national laws, the intelligence operations in the democratic nations should give respect to the international human rights frameworks, which are used to protect the civil liberties of common people even at the time of incidents. If the decision made by any AI is ambiguous or if not verified, then it may undermine public trust and democratic accountability. Such advanced technologies are required to be kept under the straightforward regulatory frameworks, regularly tracked by efficient judges, and continually reviewed for its fairness and accuracy. The combination of explainable AI (XAI), federated learning, and blockchain computing creates a future where predictive analytics is ethically sound and effective. A number of the issues that currently hinder the use of AI in national security contexts have been solved by these new trends, which also focus on transparency, privacy-preserving collaboration, and auditability [35, 38].

As AI systems are increasingly incorporated into intelligence and law enforcement operations, human values, constitutional principles, and international norms must be taken into consideration during the development and execution of them. Only by taking this balanced approach will societies be able to fully utilize AI's potential to combat terrorism while adhering to the core values of justice, privacy, and human dignity.

References

1. Russell, S., & Norvig, P. (2021). *Artificial intelligence: A modern approach* (4th ed.). Pearson Education.
2. Jordan, M. I., & Mitchell, T. M. (2015). Machine learning: Trends, perspectives, and prospects. *Science, 349*(6245), 255–260. https://doi.org/10.1126/science.aaa8415
3. Kumar, A., Gupta, H., & Dubey, R. (2020). Predictive analytics in counterterrorism: A review of current tools and future prospects. *Journal of Intelligence Studies, 12*(3), 45–62.
4. Shmueli, G., & Koppius, O. R. (2011). Predictive analytics in information systems research. *MIS Quarterly, 35*(3), 553–572. https://doi.org/10.2307/23042796
5. Bakker, E., & de Graaf, B. (2011). Preventing lone wolf terrorism: Some CT approaches addressed. *Perspectives on Terrorism, 5*(5–6), 43–50.
6. Zegart, A. B. (2022). *Spies, lies, and algorithms: The history and future of American intelligence*. Princeton University Press.

7. Provost, F., & Fawcett, T. (2013). *Data science for business: What you need to know about data mining and data-analytic thinking*. O'Reilly Media.
8. Doshi-Velez, F., & Kim, B. (2017). Towards a rigorous science of interpretable machine learning. *arXiv preprint arXiv:1702.08608*. https://doi.org/10.48550/arXiv.1702.08608
9. Mayer-Schönberger, V., & Cukier, K. (2013). *Big data: A revolution that will transform how we live, work, and think*. Houghton Mifflin Harcourt.
10. Financial Action Task Force (FATF). (2019). *Terrorist financing risk assessment guidance*. Retrieved from https://www.fatf-gafi.org.
11. Weimann, G. (2016). *Terrorism in cyberspace: The next generation*. Columbia University Press.
12. Wirtz, B. W., & Müller, W. M. (2019). An integrated artificial intelligence framework for public management. *Public Management Review, 21*(7), 1076–1100. https://doi.org/10.1080/14719037.2018.1549268
13. Tzanou, M. (2017). *The fundamental right to data protection: Normative value in the context of counter-terrorism surveillance*. Hart Publishing.
14. Chen, H., Chiang, R. H., & Storey, V. C. (2012). Business intelligence and analytics: From big data to big impact. *MIS Quarterly, 36*(4), 1165–1188. https://doi.org/10.2307/41703503
15. U.S. Department of Homeland Security. (2020). *Science and technology strategic plan 2020–2024*. Retrieved from https://www.dhs.gov/science-and-technology.
16. Williams, R. (2019). Predictive policing and the ethical implications of AI surveillance. *Journal of Intelligence and National Security, 34*(6), 853–872. https://doi.org/10.1080/02684527.2019.1582323
17. Bakker, E., & de Graaf, B. A. (2014). Preventing lone wolf terrorism: Some CT approaches addressed. *Perspectives on Terrorism, 8*(3), 43–50.
18. Chien, S.-Y., Ding, Y., Liu, W., & Jin, X. (2018). Predictive analytics in homeland security: Mapping urban vulnerabilities. *Computers, Environment and Urban Systems, 72*, 221–231. https://doi.org/10.1016/j.compenvurbsys.2018.06.001
19. Taddeo, M., & Floridi, L. (2018). How AI can be a force for good. *Science, 361*(6404), 751–752. https://doi.org/10.1126/science.aat5991
20. Cambria, E., & White, B. (2014). Jumping NLP curves: A review of natural language processing research. *IEEE Computational Intelligence Magazine, 9*(2), 48–57. https://doi.org/10.1109/MCI.2014.2307227
21. Redmon, J., Divvala, S., Girshick, R., & Farhadi, A. (2016). You only look once: Unified, real-time object detection. Proceedings of the IEEE conference on computer vision and pattern recognition. (pp. 779–788). https://doi.org/10.1109/CVPR.2016.91.
22. Kumar, A. (2020). AI-enabled video surveillance for smart cities: Issues, challenges, and research opportunities. *ACM Computing Surveys, 53*(4), 1–36. https://doi.org/10.1145/3397181
23. Garvie, C., Bedoya, A. M., & Frankle, J. (2016). The perpetual line-up: Unregulated police face recognition in America. *Georgetown Law, Center on Privacy & Technology*. Retrieved from https://www.perpetuallineup.org.
24. Zuboff, S. (2019). The age of surveillance capitalism: The fight for a human future at the new frontier of power. PublicAffairs.
25. Warren, S. D., & Brandeis, L. D. (1890). The right to privacy. *Harvard Law Review, 4*(5), 193–220.
26. Gonzalez Fuster, G. (2014). *The emergence of personal data protection as a fundamental right of the EU*. Springer.
27. Angwin, J., Larson, J., Mattu, S., & Kirchner, L. (2016). Machine bias. ProPublica. Retrieved from https://www.propublica.org/article/machine-bias-risk-assessments-in-criminal-sentencing.
28. Union, E. (2016). Regulation (EU) 2016/679 of the European Parliament and of the Council (general data protection regulation). *Official Journal of the European Union*.
29. United Nations. (1966). International covenant on civil and political rights. Retrieved from https://www.ohchr.org.

30. UN Human Rights Committee. (2014). General Comment No. 34 on Freedoms of Opinion and Expression.
31. United Nations. (2011). Guiding Principles on Business and Human Rights.
32. Theohary, C. A., & Rollins, J. (2011). Terrorist use of the internet: Information operations in cyberspace. Congressional Research Service.
33. Cummings, M. L., Roff, H. M., Cukier, K. N., & Taddeo, M. (2021). *Artificial intelligence and ethics: An urgent Frontier*. Brookings Institution.
34. Council of Europe. (2018). Protocol Amending the Convention for the Protection of Individuals with regard to automatic processing of personal data (Convention 108+). Retrieved from https://www.coe.int.
35. Gunning, D. (2017). Explainable Artificial Intelligence (XAI). Defense Advanced Research Projects Agency (DARPA). Retrieved from https://www.darpa.mil/program/explainable-artificial-intelligence.
36. Kairouz, P., McMahan, H. B., Avent, B., et al. (2019). *Advances and open problems in federated learning*. arXiv preprint arXiv:1912.04977. Retrieved from https://arxiv.org/abs/1912.04977.
37. Williams, M. (2019). Digital counterterrorism: The use of artificial intelligence in the UK's security apparatus. *Security Journal, 32*(4), 329–345. https://doi.org/10.1057/s41284-019-00164-7
38. Kairouz, P., McMahan, H. B., et al. (2019). *Advances and open problems in federated learning*. arXiv preprint arXiv:1912.04977. https://arxiv.org/abs/1912.04977.

MIX
Papier aus verantwortungsvollen Quellen
Paper from responsible sources
FSC® C105338

If you have any concerns about our products,
you can contact us on
ProductSafety@springernature.com

In case Publisher is established outside the EU,
the EU authorized representative is:
Springer Nature Customer Service Center GmbH
Europaplatz 3, 69115 Heidelberg, Germany

Printed by Libri Plureos GmbH
in Hamburg, Germany